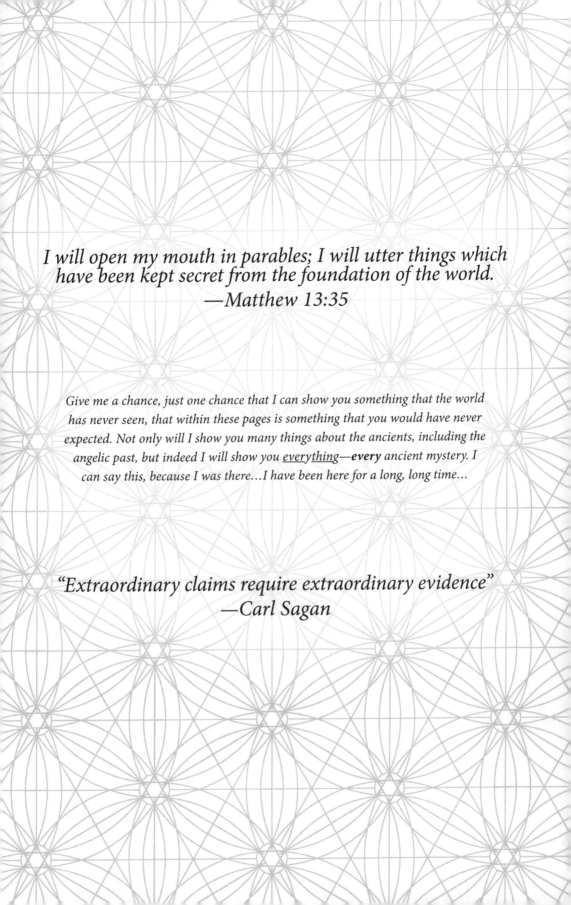

*I will open my mouth in parables; I will utter things which
have been kept secret from the foundation of the world.*
—*Matthew 13:35*

Give me a chance, just one chance that I can show you something that the world
has never seen, that within these pages is something that you would have never
expected. Not only will I show you many things about the ancients, including the
angelic past, but indeed I will show you <u>everything</u>—**every** ancient mystery. I
can say this, because I was there…I have been here for a long, long time…

"*Extraordinary claims require extraordinary evidence*"
—*Carl Sagan*

The Book of Daniel
And the Mystery of the Resurrection Machine
Day of the Fallen

Copyright 2019 /Daniel

Cover Design by H&R Productions LLC

Interior Design by H&R Productions LLC

Produced by H&R Productions LLC

Website: TheBookofDanielNovel.com

ISBN: 978-1-949709-53-7

Printed in the United States.

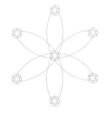

TABLE OF CONTENTS

GLOSSARY OF TERMS

ASTROLABE: an elaborate inclinometer, historically used by astronomers, navigators, and astrologers. Its many uses include locating and predicting the positions of the Sun, Moon, planets, and stars, determining local time given local latitude and vice versa, surveying, and triangulation.

ATOMOS: AKA; the God Element, God Particle, angelic-element or Faith-Element. The molecular structure of the higher string or dimension. It is an irradiant of the mind that is presently beyond the measures of modern science. The Atomos stores the God consciousness and can also super-charge the gas-layers of stratosphere which in turn produce a powerful aurora.

CELESTIAL EQUATOR: a great circle on the imaginary celestial sphere, in the same plane as the Earth's equator. In other words, it is a projection of the terrestrial equator out into space. As a result of the Earth's axial tilt, the celestial equator is inclined by 23.4° with respect to the ecliptic plane. In practice it tracks the Earth's rotation or spin.

DARK ELEMENT: AKA; Satanic-element. That quantum of God Element that changed mental polarity and realization that in turn would destroy the portal and become master of the Earth. It melded into what would become the high-primates and, eventually, cohabitate within the human.

ECLIPTIC: great circle on the celestial sphere representing the sun's apparent path during the year, so called because lunar and solar eclipses can occur only when the moon crosses it. In practice it tracks both the Earth's tilt and wobble.

GRID: a circular half, either northern or southern, of the celestial globe. The view of any grid is from either the top or bottom of the celestial globe's axis. Likewise its outer ring can represent the zodiac upon which the Sun, moon, planets and 12 constellation appear to travel.

GRID SYSTEM: AKA; *Wisdom Wheel or Firmament*. A collection of many grids that are arranged in a logical order so as to track the movement of the Sun, Moon, planets or stars.

IONS: An atom or a group of atoms that has acquired a net electric charge by gaining or losing one or more electrons, thus forming either positive or negative ions.

MAGNETOSPHERE: A region surrounding a planet, star, or other body, in which the body's magnetic field traps charged particles and dominates their behavior.

TACHYONIC PARTICLE: A hypothetical particle that always travels faster than light.

THE UNGRUND: Or the *"Ungrounded"* reality. Coined by Jakob Böhme in the early 1600s. In essence the ungrund describes a mental state that existed before the formation of the physical universe. In concept it explains the big-bang theory, showing how all things came from nothing.

WISDOM WHEEL: AKA; the *Firmament or Grid System*. The advanced, multi-layered grid-system used by the magistrates of several ancient priesthoods by which to write sacred Word. It included a map-layer, a colored aurora-layer, grid-layer and a Word-layer

This book was printed for your reading and travel convenience though it is highly recommended that the images are viewed on a digital-format. As such the details can be expanded and better appreciated.

Introduction

GOSPEL: OF ANCIENT ORIGIN MEANING, *GOD-SPELL*.

"And he said: Go thy way Daniel, for the words are closed up and sealed till the time of the end."

The ruins of the megaliths and pyramids are but faint reminders from a forgotten age. They are battered remnants now, yet they still allude to something profound, a long lost wisdom of which we know very little. There are few details of who built them or why, but what we do know is that early man witnessed something; they scribed as best they could the lore and images of something miraculous.

But the ancient past is so often shrouded in mystery; the voices that could tell us everything are long gone. Somewhere along the way something happened—a curse perhaps, some sort of decline. They fell, and with them their world collapsed into darkness. But that was long, long ago…

Now, everyone loves tales of magic—great mystical stories set within the outer limits of our imagination. But all magic isn't the same. There was a time when magic was real, and in this case the *truth* is more fantastic than fiction—to find in the end that what we thought was myth was, in fact, more credible than any movie, or even science could ever explain, -*is about to happen.*

Daniel was the last of the illuminated-ones and it was he who kept the ancient secrets. He also wrote the spell that would one day resurrect an ancient bloodline that came from another dimension. Remarkably, his work survived in an unlikely time capsule. It was in plain sight all along, right in front of us the whole time, yet hidden with a most ingenious cloak—a code that was truly *unbreakable.*

But even the Bible says that Daniel would one day return and that with him the seals would be opened, and the mysteries which separate us from the past would be revealed. Now, no one ever knows where fate will lead us: the intersection of two worlds, the past and the present, the then and the now. But I can tell you this: something miraculous is coming back and it will change the world forever.

Not every magician pulls a rabbit out of a hat, but there is one who can open a gateway to another dimension...Make no mistake; the God-Spell Prophet, isn't coming back. No, *he's already here, and he's come to finish what he's begun. Now, we are all under his spell...*

This never-before-seen anomaly occurred in the aurora over Siberia on the night of October 25, 2017, still leaving scientists puzzled...Daniel knew what it was and what it is.

It's happening and *this* magic is **_real_** . . .

PREFACE

O Daniel, whose name was Belteshazzar, master of the magicians,
because I know that the spirit of the holy gods is in thee, and no se-
cret troubles thee, tell me the visions of my dream; the beginning and
the end of all things.

These are the memoirs of a magi-priest: And though he lived long ago, his connection to the past directly affects all of us today. *Understanding*, it seems, changes
things: how we act and perceive the world in which we live. That is the point: that you
should finally comprehend the secret that lies beyond the veil of what we presently
think and believe.

There is more than we know, more than most would dare to imagine about the
history of our world. Certainly the amount of missing data about ancient cultures, their
ideals and knowledge, is incomplete at best. What's more, there has been a grand miscal-
culation about their level of intellect. We made the assumption that because early man
lacked electronics and computers, somehow they must have been poor scientists as well.

Yet I will tell you, and you will see, *I promise*, that we have pitifully underestimated the ancients' ability to comprehend the world in which we live, to articulate
information that modern experts, with all their gadgetry still haven't rediscovered.

The famous inventor Nikola Tesla once said,

"The day science begins to study non-physical phenomena, it will
make more progress in one decade than in all the previous centuries
of its existence."

Indeed there is another form of science, one that we missed entirely, *that the an-*
cients didn't. To say that it was profound in nature would be an understatement. Though
the knowledge of this study was eradicated by time and purpose, it stands in scope

and magnitude with any of today's theories on energy transfer or dimensional physics. Far from being a scientific daydream on a chalkboard however, it was fully developed, articulated and employed among those who knew. It doesn't border on super-science; *it is* super-science.

If anything, it seems more akin to magic in that it has and will accomplish things that seem impossible to the rational human mind, something that modern science can never accomplish or even approach. But the fact is, this *"magic"* is still affecting your life today. It is, without a doubt, the single most powerful manipulation of physics in the universe—more powerful than the atom bomb, yet more unassuming than you would ever expect.

Fortunately, we now live in the age of information in which our cultures can grasp concepts that even a few decades ago would have been impossible. That is why this wisdom is being released today instead of any other time in human history. Truly the veil that has hidden the *"mystery of God"* will finally be removed and the words comprehended to their fullest extent. To that end you are lucky.

But it is more than just learning new information about the past. *Now* is actually the *time* to understand—the *end times,* in which all things will be revealed: the *how,* the *when,* and the *why.* It is not the end of everything, but certainly the end of life as we have thus far known it. Until now the words were sealed and the science was protected.

You will learn not only of a formerly undisclosed ancient technology but of a well-hidden capacity buried deep within your very being. And with this we can go from where we are to where we were always destined to be. We live in a time of the great transition, an epic in which there is just enough education worldwide to allow this information to be understood.

Yet education also brings its own assumptions. Therein we often suppose our own superiority based solely upon what we presently know, never believing that there may be more. Worse yet, much of what we believe is based upon what we were told instead of what we have found to be true in ourselves. We seek proof yet fail to realize that our standards were indeed the proof of others, with no more value than our own.

I have endeavored for the sake of all readers to give them what they desire. There is a story, *a true story*, and *a true science*. Both are guaranteed to blow your mind, thus I have given the balance of both. No doubt there is far more science than what is provided, but I suppose this too will be revealed in its totality soon after this book is released. The story in itself however is enough to impress even the unimpressionable. Likewise the intellect of the ancients would have likely left Einstein scratching his head.

With the information herein I will take you to a place in both **_faith and science_** that you have never been. Not only does it reconcile these seemingly polar opposite studies, but also it actually marries them into a cohesive and functioning union as they were always intended to be. It is the unbelievable story of one man's journey through time and the formerly untold secrets from the ancient past he was given.

Since the beginning of human civilization until now, there has never been a book written like the one you are getting ready to read. This collection was designed to be pictorially rich. Pictures speak a thousand words, and will help you grasp the science, -the *magic*, of which I speak. From this point forward, however, you will begin find yourself in another world, the world of an ancient magician. *Your life is about to change.*

> *This information was first revealed in the summer of 1989. Since then the divine path has built and matured my life to the end that you might also understand. I will show you for the first time since the beginning, the real secret of the ancients.*

And the angel that talked with me came again, and waked me, as a man that is wakened out of his sleep. Zechariah 4:1

As I neared the elderly white-haired and partially bald fellow, I reached out and gently touched his shoulder, speaking only loud enough to gain his attention without frightening him:

"Can I help you with something, sir?" To which, at a distance of about two feet, he turned, looked me right in the eyes, face beaming with the brightest of light and said,

"You must be Daniel."

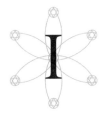

THE GENESIS OF AN ANGEL
The Little Old Man

I t was early morning on July 1, 1989 just after 5a.m. As I leaned against the logs of the cabin, groggily peering into the predawn sky, came a deep sigh of exhaustion. I stared blankly into the heavens, contemplating the day ahead, no doubt in delay to what I knew must come. The dog also resisted the transition from sleep to sober; he too stretched and yawned, then tilted his head, awaiting an explanation for our early rise.

Yet I knew I must awake. Thus with one last rub of the eyes, we began our hike to the far end of the farm. The trek through the darkened woods resembled a horror movie more than a walk to work. Covered from the waist down by the low fog, my legs felt like rubber. I staggered like the undead from tree to tree, the howl of my invisible hound eerily echoing beneath the mystic mist.

Groggy or not, however, I was conscious enough to appreciate the incoming clouds. They rolled in like piles of cotton, still plainly visible against the reveals of intermittent moonlight. *Good!* I thought. They'd make the heat of the coming day a bit more tolerable.

Within the firmament overhead was a dance of celestial timing. The contrast was spectacular: a full moon descending in the west behind the incoming puffs of white strata, while the opposite horizon, still clear, showed hints of sunrise just beneath the morning star. But even in the low light and half-asleep, the scene that mother-nature displayed was beautiful.

The corn was getting taller and this would be our last chance to fertilize the fields: *"knee-high by the fourth of July"* as we used to say. I sighed upon viewing the wagons, their frames sagging from the countless bags of ammonia nitrate. No doubt they were a testament to the lifting I'd endure that day and the next, and I was only too familiar with the back-breaking chore.

Regardless of this, the rural lifestyle was a labor of love. I enjoyed the freedom and solitude of the farm, escaping the noise of humanity and, of course the fresh air. Likewise, the backdrop of the hills and hollows added to the serenity. The view was magnificent and allowed me to collect my thoughts in a way that was otherwise impossible. And though our farm would never make one rich in dollars, the true wealth it brought in heart was immeasurable.

This day, however, the smell was a different matter. The strong scent of ammonia was something to which you never really became accustomed and the air reeked with its vapors. Upon pouring the first bag into the hopper, I bolted from the toxic odor, accomplishing in an instant what a pot of coffee hadn't for an hour before.

But as I turned to catch my breath, the shadow of a large bird flying just overhead caught my eye. It interrupted, even in the low light, the lunar rays that now showed through a hole in the clouds. *An owl perhaps*, but as I peered upward the portal gravitated my attention. It had a grandiose, almost supernatural appearance and I marveled as its bluish-white streaks irradiated the ground below. Like powdered sugar, it softly decorated the landscape with an almost surreal glistening.

I pondered its design as if I'd seen this visage before. It was somewhat familiar, peaceful, but powerful-looking. The audio was perfect as well—the wind mystifying the picture as if the universe was telling its secrets through the word of the whispering pines. I couldn't help but wonder if such things had a deeper meaning and how profound a mere image could be. Oddly I felt a brief kinship to what I saw, as my imagination wandered into some long-forgotten bond.

Within a few moments, however, reality brought me back. The clouds thickened until the visage was gone and so my work began. It was two full days before I finished the task, during which time I thought about everything from hunting deer to paying bills. One loses oneself when riding the endless rows of maize for hours at a time. *Labor?* Yes, but as well a time when every farmer can contemplate his world, his life and his family.

I also pondered the most bizarre dream of the past three nights. It was of a great white serpent, indeed the greatest serpent that has ever been. Before I continue, you must know that I truly hated snakes. We used to kill the poisonous ones regularly on the farm and were all too glad to do so. To me however, *all* snakes were creepy. I didn't like the surprise of finding them in the garden nor their slithery nature, which reminded me a bit too much of a politician.

Yet the serpent of my dreams was, somehow, the most wonderful creature I'd ever seen. It was my friend and I knew it. He was large, as big as a python, and deadly poisonous. Each night in my visions I walked to a distant mountain where I knew this viper awaited. There he would coil and raise. Staring with his golden-yellow eyes, he peered into my soul, mouth open, fangs agape, dripping their deadly elixir.

Surprisingly, however, I was always glad to see him, my soul at ease within his presence. Each time I placed my finger between his fangs, upon them scribed the word; *"vengeance"*. Gently I touched the tongue of the serpent's mouth; it too had a word written across its length, the word; *"truth."* Each time my skin absorbed the fruits of this touch, my finger pricked with the tip of vengeance, then healed with the word of truth that followed; one countered the other.

As this happened, I could read the creature's every thought. I knew his mind and he knew mine. Glowing with a beautiful luminescence, he too was mesmerized in the moment, suspended in marvel with what he saw in my eyes—a reflection, somehow, of himself. Without words he told me that something great was about to happen and that he would soon return to the world. It was then that I would turn and leave.

Even in this dream I was elated with the joy of his promise but also with a sadness that I had to go. Unfazed by the venom, I awoke each time in a restful bliss. Yet between this dream and the image of moonlight that first morning, I was unsure if these somehow had meaning or if they were only the result of having inhaled too much ammonia. Had not the dreams precluded my field work, I would have surely suspected the latter.

Ah but the dreams of a dreamer. One must carry on with the task of making money. A farm the size of ours provided only a supplemental income and required me to work a full-time job as well, as a tire tech at a concrete plant in Louisville. But between that and the farm, I did well enough and wanted for little.

No doubt I was a bit rough around the edges. Blue jeans, boots and a tattered shirt were my daily wardrobe. My hat was my comb. If I forgot my belt, then bailing twine always sufficed. Often, fishing line and a needle were my stitches, and duct tape for the rip in my britches. I was down to earth and truly geared for the life of a farmer, but I was happy and free as a bird.

It was a different day then, a different time. Work rather than relaxation was the norm and I stayed busy. Yet it was still easier to avoid the rat race then than it is today. I loved my life: working the fields, the tobacco, the hay, the hogs, the corn, and the cattle. I even enjoyed changing truck tires. I was in fantastic physical condition, though a bit naïve to the ways of the world. No doubt I was wild as a buck and wired tight—an average, everyday country boy.

I had my tortures, however. Weddings, church, and funerals were always unwelcome endeavors. The real problem was the discomfort of dressing up—the choke of the tie and the itch of a woolen coat. The pretense of show always made me feel out of place, and I could never seem to grasp how others enjoyed such occasions. The whole town knew I was a bit wild; but if so, why then did I have to pretend to be something else as were they?

Yet I'd always attend these gatherings out of respect. With a deep breath, I'd stand up straight and simply play the role. In the end I suppose *respect* is what it's all about and that was good enough for me. That said, I could never reach the farm fast enough and slide back into the comfort of my well-worn duds.

Aside from that, life was my hobby. I enjoyed my diversions: hewing logs, running the woods, hunting—all of which kept me pleasantly occupied. I was honest to a fault, with a genuine love for the truth, whatever it may be, and lived my life accordingly.

I thought about God as well. As with many folks, I contemplated spiritual things: the meaning of life, the origin of the universe, and my place therein. How did it all fit? How did it all happen, and why? I wanted to know. I wanted it to make sense. I wanted real answers.

In context, church I suppose was as much a social-function as anything. Plus, in a small country town it was the only media by which to track your neighbor. There were three churches: the Methodist, the Baptist and the Christian, all within a block. And by no surprise we rotated freely between them. Their doctrinal differences weren't that great (*they all used the same Bible*), so to alternate from Sunday to Sunday was common for all except the most die-hard Baptists. Plus, it kept us close; it preserved the bond of community, as well as the web of support in times of need.

Being from the Bible belt of course we presumed the answers to our spiritual inquiries were hiding somewhere within the pages of that ancient text. It was the umbrella under which we'd been raised, the *rolodex* for our religious questions. Basically, the Bible says *"this,"* therefore it's the *"answer"*—now *"deal with it"*!

Yet there were times it didn't satisfy my craving for truth. Something was missing. Either I didn't like the answers or sometimes my questions were simply too big. I wanted more details than what my preachers could give. The problem was that my ponderings were often socially unacceptable and, according to those who deem themselves devout, *even blasphemous.*

They insisted that the power of the universe has already given us the instructions by which to play the game of life. They condemn with great swelling words of authority too. Yet I couldn't tell if it was heads or tails; was it authority they possessed or *arrogance*? Due to the fact that most folks don't really know the scriptures, we typically have little with which to refute those who are morally confident.

Many *wish* to believe yet have limited options on *what* to believe. Often, free thinking has little place in the world's structured belief systems, thus we only question just so far. We settle back into the status quo of saying, believing, and doing things according to the direction of those in charge of our spiritual beliefs.

It is the short leash of allowed doubting, where questioning is equated to faithlessness, at which point one's salvation is called into question. Next comes the looks of contempt from others, then gossip and even verbal condemnations. Thus for me and for most, the simple solution to prevent eternal damnation was to take the Bible at face value, forget my musings, and move on.

I think a lot of folks fit this mold: We believe in a higher power but still have gaps in our understanding. Subconsciously, however, we fear and are often reminded that to question our religious traditions is, *somehow*, sacrilegious. In my case at least, the years of country living, often wandering the hills and hollows alone, had produced a recklessly independent spirit. At times I was outspoken on the cognitive dissidence I saw in religious doctrine. I was a good kid, but learned early on to think for myself, to assume nothing and to *"take the bull by the horns"* as we used to say.

Though my inclination was always moral, I'd fight at the drop of a hat for what I believed to be the truth. Fear tactics, religious or otherwise, usually didn't work with me. If something was broken, I figured it out and fixed it. If a question remained unanswered, I figured it out and answered it. Likewise my belief in God was no less matter of fact. I wanted to know, and no amount of religious-guilt could stifle my ponderings.

However, aside from an inherent rebellious streak, I was otherwise as normal as the next person. Life was simple then; I had a *family*, I had a *job*, and I had a *god*. At age 24 I worked every day and went to church almost every Sunday. I loved, protected and provided for my family. That of course is what made the next episode of my time on Earth all the more bizarre. Indeed, before the experience of which you are about to learn, I was a typical rural American of the late 1980s; and though my life was seemingly stable in every way, it would all come crashing down in the blink of an eye.

That Wednesday at the concrete plant began like any other. The noise and bustle of trucks, the growl of the huge mixer plant and the smell of cement and diesel all filled the senses. It was a hot day, July fifth as I recall, and we typically left the shop's large overhead doors open on either end. This allowed a cooling breeze to pass through and more light as well.

Around 2:00 p.m. I stepped outside the door on the north end of the building so as to view the lot through which the trucks staged before loading. On the left side of my field of view was the mixer plant itself, an imposing structure, about six stories tall. To the right a bit and in my center-view, was a separate smaller building that contained both the dispatcher's office on the second floor, along with the driver's room directly below. Finally, to the right of that was the parking sheds and gate #3 through which the trucks exited.

The lot was typically muddied from a spray-bar that rinsed the trucks as they departed from under the mixer. This slurry covered the entire drive area, all except one slightly elevated section just in front of the dispatchers' office. As the sun baked this flat, dusty patch, a whirlwind arose that colored itself with sand and powdered cement. It was quite the novelty, harmless of course, but seemingly with a life of its own. I watched as the wind revealed itself through the medium of filth, ascending almost as high as the mixer plant until finally losing momentum.

However, as the swirls dissipated I again lowered my attention to the place where they began, noticing a rather odd sight: an elderly man who I hadn't noticed only moments before. He wore a navy-blue suit and sported an odd-looking red and blue cravat. "*WOW*"; I thought, as he resembled an English gentleman from the late Victorian era. This guy was completely out of place or at least in the wrong century, *I humored*, as was his mustache which, white as snow, also reflected that period.

He was a short fellow, mostly bald, but nifty-looking, well-dressed and equally lost too. What's more, he was standing dangerously close to the lanes through which the trucks entered and exited the factory.

Probably another dreaded salesman, I thought to myself.

Unwanted solicitors were a daily nuisance at the plant. So to see a suit and tie roaming the lot wasn't unusual. We had a standing order though: -no salesmen in the production area-. I'd run off my own share of salesmen over the years, yet this time I was hoping that someone else would beat me to the dirty deed. By the nature of their job, most salespeople can't take no for an answer, and I dreaded the inevitable sales pitch, for which I had neither the time nor humor that day. That said, I had no intention of being disrespectful to someone of his age and frail stature.

I turned to my coworker, Larson, and inquired if he recognized the man, but by the time we looked out again, maybe 10 seconds later, the old fellow was gone.

Huh, perhaps he had walked just out of sight on the other side of the idling trucks, I surmised.

Larson, an older man himself and only two years from retirement, glared at me with disdain as though I'd lied. He was a veteran of World War II and likely due to his combat experience was predictably serious. He cared little for the camaraderie of the younger men with whom he worked. We were always up to something, and, here again, he was distrustful of my claim about the little old man. For once however I wasn't crying wolf, yet I had no illusions as to why Larson didn't believe me.

Whatever, I thought, and went back to work.

Thus we labored for about another hour, processing and stacking a new shipment of tires that had arrived earlier that morning. As a matter of routine, I again walked to the overhead door after completing the task. Much to my surprise, there stood the same little old man in the truck lot, sorely out of place as before.

Was he waiting for someone? I pondered.

Just as before, he was about 50 yards away standing just in front of the dispatchers' building. From what I could tell at that distance, he appeared to have a 10,000-yard stare, randomly scanning some non-existent horizon and completely oblivious to his surroundings. Oddly, he seemed happy enough (*he was smiling from ear-to-ear*), but nonetheless his eyes looked hollowly *through*, instead of *at*, anything. I began to wonder if he was a salesman after all, that perhaps he was senile and had somehow wandered onto the property. I scanned the area for an out-of-place vehicle but saw nothing.

On the second story of the dispatch office was a large window from which Tommy and Eddie could view and coordinate the loading process of the trucks. Likewise they could see me as I stepped outside the garage and waved. They waved back, at which I pointed to the old man and scrunched my shoulders as if to say, *"Who is that?"* At this, they looked at each other and returned the gesture as if they didn't understand what I was trying to say.

Again I called Larson from the back of the shop to see if he could recognize our hapless visitor. Just as before, however, when he walked to the overhead door, the elderly man was gone. By little surprise this merited a brutal but colorful cussing from my fellow worker who was now convinced I was an idiot.

"Let's get to work," he commanded, *"and quit horse'n around."*

(This is a greatly abbreviated and rated-G version of what he actually said.)

Larson was, perhaps, the most fluent curser in the whole world—or at least that I'd ever known. Indeed, Edgar Allen Poe himself would have been hard-pressed to find the words of verbal discontent as well as Larson. And while it would be nice to assume that he meant no-ill by his slurs, my experience told me better. That said, his verbal displays were quite entertaining and made a believer to all those around him. He was feudalistic by nature, born and bred in the Appalachian traditions of eastern Kentucky. Yet it was his crack-whip attitude that forced me to walk the line of proof before comment.

In this case, however, the little old man had put me in bad rapport twice and I was more than a little frustrated. My thought at that point was that perhaps he'd walked inside the drivers' room on the first floor of the dispatch office. It was air-conditioned with a restroom and a Coke machine, so it made sense that he retreated there to escape the blistering heat. Either way, it wasn't my problem now. Surely one of the drivers would either help or evict the elderly gentleman.

At this I walked back inside the garage and took a drink from the water fountain. I suppose however that my curiosity got the better, so I again returned to the doorway to see what I could see. As you likely guessed, there stood the old man once again, this time facing slightly away and toward the north. *"Okay, enough."* I thought, and immediately advanced, determined to prove to Larson that I'd been telling the truth about this illusive individual. *"Great,"* I said under my breath; the factory was loud and would mask my approach until I was upon him.

Now at this point it seemed simple enough to either assist or inquire as to the man's motives for standing in the middle of the truck lot. But had I known what was about to happen or how it was to impact my life, it's quite possible I would have instead run the opposite direction. As I've said before, till that moment I'd lived a mostly normal life: I played ball in school, was married, and worked a normal job. I've never used drugs and, at the time, didn't drink alcohol. From what I can discern, there was nothing that could have induced such an event as that which occurred next.

As the distance closed between us, I further studied his small frame and trembling demeanor. He appeared to have Parkinson's and shook greatly as he stood, seemingly unaware of my advance from his blind-side. At this, I reached out and gently touched his right shoulder, speaking only loud enough to gain his attention without frightening him:

"Can I help you with something, sir", to which, at a distance of about two feet, he turned, looked me right in the eyes, face beaming with the brightest of light and said:

"You must be Daniel…"

Shocked by the fact that he knew my name and having never seen such awesome joy on a human face, I could only stutter,

"Do . . . do I know you?"

"No, but neither do you know yourself. But I know you," he laughed.

At the same moment he reached out and lightly held the end of my still out-stretched hand. As his hand touched mine, I was instantly engulfed with a feeling of bliss and peace beyond anything that I can describe with words. It was an instant state of stupor. I was frozen, completely taken in the moment as if by some magic, amazed, unable to retract my hand and equally unwilling to let go.

And then he began to speak:

"Do you know what your name means? Some people say that it means 'God is my judge,' but they are wrong. It means 'Judge of God' and I can assure you, my son, that there are wonderful things in store. I am here to help you remember."

He continued talking, listing my life occurrences, things that no one, –no one!— knew: things from my childhood, my innermost thoughts, my fears, and even things that I'd never spoken.

"Do you remember when you were in the sixth grade and the bully was beating you up in the bathroom at school? You felt alone and scared, but I was there, then, and have always been with you." (with a bubbling laugh of Joy)

"No matter the circumstances, everything you've suffered was to prepare you for this time. Ah, and what a special time it is. But you sensed it, didn't you? You felt it; you knew it was coming. The truth is so wonderful. You are very lucky, very lucky indeed." (more laughter)

"The day is here; no matter how trivial or how great, it all brought us to right now." (continuing with jubilant laughter) *"Let me share with you …"*

He continued speaking without pause, his trembling not from Parkinson's but from an irresistible joy, the likes of which I'd never witnessed. It exceeded anything

I'd ever seen in a human being. What's more, that same energy was entering through his touch and into me; and as it did, I lost track of his speech, the words becoming an inaudible garble.

Yet a part of me needed to know that someone else was seeing this event. Thus I managed with the greatest difficulty to glance upward toward the dispatchers. My head felt like it was tied to a huge elastic band pulling in the opposite direction, slowing my movement to a snail's pace. I persisted, however, until finally, somehow, Tommy and Eddie were in the periphery of my view. There they stood leaning over their desks, peering downward with puzzled expressions, viewing this interaction between myself and this, (*Okay*), *not-so-lost* little old man.

Immediately below on the first floor were several truck drivers who also peered with equal curiosity from behind the break room's large window. Looking back, I don't know what I expected them or anyone else to do. I obviously didn't need rescue, but then again, my faculties were so overwhelmed I'm not sure that I was thinking at all.

Again with great effort, I turned my head to the right only to see Larson watching me from the entrance of the garage. Obviously I couldn't hear him over the noise of the factory and at that distance, but I could see his puzzled look and the movement of his mouth to the tune of

"What the hell are you doing lil-buddy?"

And while perhaps a part of me was hoping for an intercession from one of these loyal spectators, another part of my soul—*never wanted it to end*. With every second this man, or *"being,"* spoke, I became more and more entranced, frozen and unable to speak or move. Finally it became an overwhelming inward flow of energy and information, a veritable download to which I could only receive and not respond. I was completely catatonic yet I didn't care.

As this occurred, the view between myself and Him faded into a bright, enormously powerful yet soft white light. This was angelic. My senses were completely shutting down, bowing out, to this unfathomable power that had taken hold of my being. My hearing was dampened as if submerged in the boundless depths of the ocean, the surrounding noises of the factory also gone as was my knowledge of who or where I was. The energy of which I speak was like a thousand volts of electricity passing through my body, a force beyond description; but instead of pain and death, it was the most wonderful feeling I had ever felt in my life.

This entire incident lasted for what I perceive to be, *maybe*, two minutes, and then, suddenly, as if violently vacuumed back into reality, my senses abruptly and unwelcomingly returned. I could hear again, only to have him say, and I remember this part clearly,

"Daniel; it is time."

He then paused for a mere second or two, looking me directly in the eyes. His disposition, though still jubilant, was far more serious than before. I noticed in that moment that his glowing persona had ceased, yet his eyes, *those eyes*, now glowing with an overwhelming power and luminescence as they peered into my soul. I knew in that moment that he could see me, that I could not hide my thoughts—that no secret was left within. Yet it was then that he spoke the most simple phrase,

"Okay, good. I'm going now. You'll be fine. Bye now."

And he simply walked away, passing to my left side, me standing there, still somewhat zoned and looking straight ahead, hand and arm still extended from when I first touched him on the shoulder. I'm sure I appeared to be having an epileptic seizure, and admittedly it was quite the shock to awaken alone and in the middle of a truck lot—that and with no fewer than six people staring in wonder.

My faculties returned fairly quickly, however, (or at least I think they did), perhaps within about 5 to 8 seconds. Upon this I turned, expecting to see the elderly man still traversing the large and open area, but he was nowhere in sight. I ran as best I could, legs wobbling as I went, in the direction that he left until reaching the mixer plant. I was sure that I could catch this guy and ask him his name: Who was he? Where did he go? What in the heck did he just do to me?

I wasn't putting two and two together yet; I somehow assumed that since he was old, there was no way he'd had time to reach his car, especially since the parking lot was at the top of the hill and almost a football field away. It wasn't till later that it occurred to me that he most likely didn't need a car. That said, I ran as fast as I could around the main building in an effort to discover, but to no avail. He was simply gone.

Confused by this I dashed to the main entrance of the facility from where I could see all three gates. I knew that, regardless of where he was on the property, enough time hadn't elapsed for him to leave. He had to pass through one of those openings, and when he did, I reasoned, I could stop and question him—but nothing. Not for over five minutes did I see anything resembling a *not-so-lost little old man!*

Again I returned to the scene of the encounter and scanned the area, traversing each and every building, but he had simply vanished. Progressively, as the shock of the experience dissipated, came the growing realization that something amazing had just happened, something that I couldn't rationalize. It occurred to me to question the on lookers in hopes they could identify just who the old man was and perhaps, where he went.

At this I immediately ran back to the shop, went straight up to Larson and, out of breath, asked,

"Who was that guy?"

To which he responded,

"What guy?"

"The little old man I was talking to out there in the lot..."

"What were you doing anyway?" Larson said.

"That's the old man I saw earlier, -did you recognize him? Do you know who he was?"

With a confused look on his face, Larson paused, searching my eyes as if my question made no sense. He responded,

"I didn't see anybody. All I saw was you holding your damn hand out. ...Are you Okay?"

Perplexed by this exchange but realizing further questions would only inflame his predictable temper, I instead opted to question the dispatchers as they both saw and were closer to the incident. I jogged back across the lot to their building and sprinted up the exterior stairway. Though still trembling from the experience, I tried to compose myself as best I could before entering. After a couple of deep breaths I nonchalantly turned the corner through the door and announced,

"Hey guys, how's it going? Having a busy day?"

To which Eddie and Tommy turned in unison and said,

"What were you doing a minute ago?"

"Oh, nothing; just talking to that old man that was walk'n around—which, hey, I never actually got his name. Do you know who he was?"

For a brief moment they glanced at one another after which Tommy said,

"What old man? All we saw was you standing there with your hand held out. What were you doing?"

I stared, dumbfounded, not sure whether to believe them or not. Perhaps today the joke was on me. It crossed my mind that the dispatchers were in *pay-back* mode for the numerous pranks I'd played on them throughout the years as well. Larson at least didn't play games however. That and it was unlikely that an old man whom I'd never met, would stand in the heat that long just to facilitate a hoax.

"No, really," I said. *"Do you know who he was?"*

Again they repeated with a bit of disdain and curiosity. It was now that I felt my first bit of panic. *Oh-no,* I thought. *I'm losing my mind!* Without another word I immediately turned and descended the stairs toward the drivers' room. Again I steadied myself upon entering, trying not to appear as rattled as I truly was. I nonchalantly walked past the drivers as if to buy a soda from the machine.

"What's up, fellas? Boy it's a hot one today, ain't it?"

To which came the immediate response;

"Yeah. Hey, what were you doing outside a minute ago?"

"Oh, I was talking to that old man but never actually got his name. Did you recognize him?"

Three of the four drivers just looked at each other with scrunched-eyes, shaking their heads as to *what* I was talking about. One driver, Victor, said in his typical country slang,

"We didn't see any old man, Dan-el. All we saw was you holdin' your hand out. Are you all right?"

Now I was really getting scared. If there'd been any way to explain the feeling of bliss or perhaps how the little old man knew my entire history, then there was certainly *no way* to deny having seen and touched the fellow. But now it seems no one even saw him besides me! As you might imagine, I was getting nervous.

Ironically, though I recalled facets of the incident, other parts were completely blank, especially when I felt that inflow of information. Some massive amount of energy and knowledge had entered my mind, yet I had no idea what it was—*none whatsoever*. I really didn't know what to think or believe. The illumination I felt when that man touched my hand was unlike anything I had ever experienced and it rocked my world to the core. I don't know how to fully express the magnitude of those moments.

I pondered the incident for the remainder of the workday but mostly avoided interaction with others. My normal self-assuredness was now destroyed; my mind was in a fog, and I questioned how something so awesome could exist without my prior knowledge. For the most part I was a type-A personality, not by nature, but because both the farm and my work conditioned me to be a forward thinker. I always had the answers; I was accustomed to quickly fixing things. But for once I was like a lost child, with nothing to say and without direction.

The religious implications were obvious and I was trying without success to somehow match the event with my own religious beliefs. Till then miracles were restricted to the pages of my Bible as was my faith in God. Admittedly I believed in a higher power, but the majority of my knowledge on spiritual affairs had been taught, not experienced. Now, however, I'd been confronted with something that was forcing me to look beyond boxes in which I'd believed and even far beyond my own rebellious questions.

Like I said before, I wasn't afraid to question my religious beliefs, but not in my wildest imagination did my questions go **this** far. Sure, I had *talked the talk* about God; I prayed before each meal and at church. But obviously didn't really believe that such a phenomenon could exist in this day and age. The grand passage of time between the days in which the Bible was written and my own life had, till now, given me a safety net for my beliefs.

The truth is that the occurrences of which the Bible speaks can either be accepted or *not*. Proving or disproving its authenticity, however, usually leads to a stalemate between believers and disbelievers with no solid conclusion. That actually works in everyone's favor, as neither really needs conclusive proof for what they accept as truth, so long as what they believe is ultimately unprovable.

But now my 1989 had been smacked square in the face with something that would have made Moses himself proud. And while it may not have been the splitting of the Red Sea, it was certainly the splitting of reality in me. It became apparent that my teachings had tailored God to fit into **this** world. My beliefs had molded Him to support **this** life. But now the power I witnessed *did not fit here at all!*

The glory I beheld upon that man's face and felt in his touch was incompatible with the dogma of my tradition. It was *better* in fact, so-much better than what I had thus far believed, and so much more personal than I had ever imagined God could be. It brought an obvious question if I really knew God via my religion, then why was I shocked at the power of that experience? Did this really happen? *Yes*, but it was completely *nuts*…It was *crazy*….and as I'd soon discover, the drama was far from over.

However for the first few months thereafter nothing happened to validate that incident. No doubt I reflected upon it several times each day, trying to make sense of how six people all failed to see what I saw. It consumed my thoughts: at work, during dinner, and while I laid in bed. I had not even a single shred of evidence that the event had occurred—*no* witnesses, *no* proof—yet I knew as sure as the sun that it had.

And then one day while working, just like that, I began to see images—only a few at first, fleeting and flickering across the front of my vision. They were similar to a

14

daydream, only stronger, increasing each hour. They were images that I didn't understand: circles, pictures, drawings and even maps. They were black and white at first, gray scale, but over time, in color. I saw faces too—proud, stern, and with the most powerful visage of strength and wisdom.

Like long-lost memories, they came as a flood; they clouded my view to the extreme. I stumbled frequently simply because my imagination would not let go, nor could I of it. This continued off and on for weeks, months and for many years to come. The images were in my sight and in my dreams. For years thereafter they affected both my work and my sleep and, to a lesser degree, still do after all this time.

It wasn't long however before I began to sketch and file my visions on innumerable note pads. Most of these involved overlapping circles, some detailed, while others not so much. I was never the best artist, but I was now making some truly remarkable pencil drawings late at night and often on the weekends. Likewise, the more still my moments, the more profound the works I produced.

At times though I saw maps within those circles, overlaid or rather meshed together as one. These images drew my curiosity to the maps in the back of my old Scofield Bible. There I began to connect the dots of the towns mentioned in the scriptures as if to reveal patterns upon those pages. I still have that worn copy, its own images now unrecognizable from that which I sketched upon them.

Beyond the images however was an understanding, a genuine comprehension about the past. I'd never read, nor had I been taught what was coming to my mind, to my imagination, but I *knew* it well nonetheless. It was all new and fascinating but maddening at the same time. I had wrestled with that angel, the message from the little old man, with what was happening; yet I instinctively knew that these visions were somehow only the beginning.

I was gaining an unknown yet incomplete wisdom and memory from another time. It filtered into my consciousness like a fog, not all at once, not all at the same time, but in small pieces, *every day* and *every night*. Yet as it came into view, it was nonetheless a new and solid reality, a new world within.

Others, my friends, family and co-workers, noticed my constant distraction. Some commented, some didn't, but I'm sure the changes in my disposition made quite the conversation behind my back. I suppose I couldn't blame them either. I'd wonder too if someone acted the way I was: fine one moment, the next, scribbling circles on a notepad like a madman. My mind was in the clouds, *increasingly* eccentric; odd myself, because now, normality was becoming odd to me.

People are vindictive though. In their ignorance they question and gossip; they doubt and condemn what they don't understand. But they could not see what was squarely in front of my eyes, nor could they feel the elation and joy of that event with the little old man. Some memories brought a tidal wave of emotions from which I could not hide: recollections that couldn't possibly be real, yet were *too real* to be anything less.

Thus the experience was a two-edged sword in that I couldn't share it with those to whom I was closest. I did try on occasion, but mostly my friends and family knew me by the old *Daniel*, the other *Daniel*; and that's who and how they wanted me to stay. More than once I was literally begged to keep quiet, to get my life together and to forget this *nonsense*.

Yet I felt the warnings were more for their own good than mine. It seemed as though the new questions that accompanied my experience made those around me uneasy. These new revelations, however, began to expose certain hypocrisies and vanities within their own social-cliques. And though I meant no ill will toward them, my words were often met with violent rebukes from those who were normally quiet, peaceful country folk. But I gathered their reactions were because I rocked the bed in which they slept more than because I had morally trespassed. No doubt, people wake up grumpy when you shake their bed.

At one point I confided in my minister in hopes of gaining some insight. However, this too ended badly as he was notably uncomfortable with the conversation and subject matter. Instead of engaging in a useful dialog, he too abruptly ended the topic. His plea was the same as others, with a request that I keep the event of the little old man to myself. Honestly, I could understand my relatives fearing the fallout of such an unlikely tale, but the leader of a church who claims to preach miracles, angels, and the supernatural? It struck me as odd that he too would shun the conversation.

It was equally as probable that I couldn't articulate my story. I knew what had happened and that it was real to me, but there were still loose ends. And if I couldn't make total sense of it, how then could I expect others to understand? But the biggest missing piece was the total-meaning of the images themselves, and it was this lack of connection that was most frustrating to me.

Here I was with this larger-than-life experience that in no way empowered practical change. I wanted something great to come of it. I wanted others to be as excited as I was, to know there are things more powerful than *this life* can offer and that real miracles can happen. Instead of helping, however, things were getting worse. People were avoiding me for obvious reasons. I had become the black sheep, the duck-duck-goose, the odd-ball out.

But there was something else I was beginning to see, something that went even further than simple indoctrination and my own stagnant religious tradition. And though I sensed it, I couldn't quite put my finger on it. At times, I swear, it was as if a veil were draped in front of my mind, a curtain through which I could almost see. It was if the movie of my life showed upon this screen every moment of every day, a thin fabric of separation that somehow wasn't real.

Who or what was this dark magician controlling the world in which before I had so blissfully partaken? What possible explanation was there for the contrast between my religious assumptions and what I was beginning to see? The beginning of my world, my life till then, was suddenly having its end, and though I had no idea what lay beyond, I could no longer be the person I once was. As of yet I was beginning to see the depth of a lie, but not its cause or solution.

There were other changes within my personality and the depth of my being. I became much more serious and contemplative. Inventing new and dynamic contraptions became the norm, and though my job required mechanical knowledge, I had never been the creator of new ideas. Now, however, I no longer had the mind of a repairman but was thinking 10 to 20 steps ahead of what I'd ever before considered. Now my creative powers were going full-throttle, *over the top.*

I became quite the polymath, though I was, by no means, before. Over eight new patents and trademarks were filed over the following ten years, not including over two dozen new inventions that I never pursued (I ran out of money): trademarked names, inventions for vehicles, food recipes, disaster-response programs, machinery, product branding, an unbreakable firewall against computer hacking, and even an engine that successfully ran on magnets alone. My mind was taking off like a rocket.

I was understanding things on a deeper level. Every song became a message, a Word from another world, not of which the composer intended, but of the divine message that lay within the lines of its matrix. The numbers and lyrics began to tell a story, the rhythm as a chant, the voice from beyond—a revelation from the blindness of who I thought I was to that which the words now described.

I heard in the music the relationship between the worlds: the cry of desperation from below, the love and hope from above, the countless souls reaching for what was always within. I could track within the choruses a timeline, the development and interaction of the dimensions from beginning to end, the journey that accumulates in this day.

However, the most significant result of these changes was an instinctive understanding of dimensional physics, and with it, the connection between the mental and the physical. It became normal to simply stare at things and understand the most profound lessons about life, deep things, things of which I'd never heard or even considered.

I can remember one example of a beautiful mountain forest: I sat atop Pilots Knob in Red River Gorge, Kentucky, viewing the valley below. There I witnessed the countless trees reaching for the sun in vanity just as humanity does for truth, yet the roots of our earthly existence refuse to let us ascend toward the reality for which we seek.

And with the view of God, I wished to touch them from above, but they could not let go of who they perceived themselves to be. We war within ourselves; we fantasize about extra-worldly things: God, angels, magic, and eternity. We reach within our minds and hope for the heavens but ultimately are stuck to the matrix in which we live. Indeed, we are rooted, no different than those trees, to the ground of our human selves. And such are the woes of a temporal life.

There is a way out: I pondered how fire could change the forest into oneness; how it could make many *one*; how it would free the molecules of the physical into the reality of the air, the spirit of a higher dimension. I realized the advantage of transformation, how the atoms were no longer enslaved to the earth but risen into the liberty of the sky above. It was fascinating to realize that this was the lesson for humanity as well, how an inward burning away of our human self-image would release a far superior creation.

And though one reality would be destroyed, an even better life would be attained.

I fancied the forest, the endless pines and poplars, but also the generations of deadness that accumulate beneath them. Each morning, countless millions of dew drops form upon the limbs, each refracting a bit of sunlight upon the tinder below. For most however, the focus is too far, just beyond the reach of rightness, each drop in itself meaningless. They take no part in the grand scheme of spiritual transformation as neither do we in and of ourselves.

It does, however, take but a single drop in perfection of alignment—in just the right order, at exactly the right distance, and at exactly the right time. It may have been luck, but it happens: On a given day and a given drop, the right distance and refraction, the heat and focus occur to create fire.

It begins with but a slight breeze, the coercion of the invisible, the unseen but undeniable influence of something that is beyond our control and understanding. Indeed the spirit is the key to the consuming fire that approaches. It creates that small, insignificant ember that in turn will destroy everything as we know it. The wind whispers; it summons something that already exists within. It didn't make the fire, yet it pulls from within our hearts that which we know, somehow, is already there. This, I know, is the simile of ourselves upon the coming day.

But the fire of restitution would need to come from within, not without. They must find the Word inside their souls, the change not forced upon them, but that they themselves deemed eternal survival. The fire potential was there, packed away within the fiber of their very being, no different than those trees, within them the light yet unrealized, but by design a new creation.

Throughout the next two decades, I would catalog the images and thoughts of my mind, thousands of them, with countless thousands more yet unrecorded. At first I wasn't sure what they meant, but then, over time, the meaning revealed itself. In dreams and daydreams, small bits at a time, the wisdom would come to dissipate the clouds of confusion. As it did, a crystal-clear understanding emerged of something that was from far beyond this world.

I pondered the pyramids as well; I measured and studied, not to learn, but to confirm. I was possessed to know if others were seeing what I saw. I had to know if this was just me. As I read what others had written, I instead *recollected* what I already knew, an instinct of involvement myself. Somehow *I saw them*, a people; I saw *me* at another time and in another life. The realism was overwhelming; the view from my own eyes, *then*, as I walked, as I traveled, the interactions.

19

I took an interest in my Bible for the first time, not out of religious duty, but because as I read verses I saw so much more than mere history or literalism. I instinctively counted every facet of its content, recognizing patterns and codes of which I'd never heard nor seen. There was beneath its words an obvious and undisclosed study.

Shortly thereafter, I bought practically every religious book I could find: The Jewish Bible, the Koran, many of the ancient Hindu texts, and every single Jewish and Christian non-canonical book that was ever written. I found within these scripts a common thread of exacting information. It was all there: the *same* detailed data. Indeed, they were all telling the *exact same story* beneath their obvious and outer facades.

Over time my insights grew. Yet what I could plainly see only scared or annoyed those around me. This was the paradox, the irony of my event: so much knowledge yet clueless how to use it constructively. It brought me no heaven and, in many ways, only created more hells. Though comforting to contemplate, this new intellect did nothing to change the world in which I lived.

My options limited, I found solace in sleep. Each night I lay in bed, pondering the events and images of my past. Perhaps what I did next was in fact because of my religious upbringing or, perhaps I lacked the skill sets to navigate my predicament with more finesse. No doubt you will think this cliché and simplistic, but I did it nonetheless.

For the first time in my life I *prayed*, not because I was told to, not from religious servitude, but because I finally, *really believed* from my heart that it was the only chance I had at righting a world, *my world*, turned upside down. It was at this point that I made a humble, most genuine request to something I could neither see, touch, nor tell.

As unlikely a solution as prayer may seem, it was the *only* thing left to which I could turn:

> *Thy Kingdom come; above all else, above my life, above my health; above all that I know and love. At the cost of my breath and brethren…Thy Kingdom come. I'm all in. I don't care what you do to me or mine to accomplish, but just do it. Go all the way and don't stop till it's finished. Please bring what you've shown me to the world.*

From then on, for every still moment, day or night, -that was my one and only request of God: *Thy Kingdom come.*

And while I will not argue the practicality of such things, I will assert the end results. Real prayer brought real change, not overnight but over the days, months, and years. Who knows why or how it did, but it *did* nonetheless. At that time of course it seemed miraculous, yet who knows the greater truth. Perhaps if nothing else, prayer created a focal point that I otherwise lacked. Either way, change came.

Hand in hand with my lone requests came the steady erosion of my cares for the things of this world. Reputation, wealth and success increasingly became a mere vapor toward which I no longer reached. Slowly but surely I lost my longing for the whims of the flesh and, in turn, those shackles, those lusts, lost their strength to hold a new thing that welled within my being.

As the old me began to dissipate, I increasingly found comfort with the new me I was beginning to see. A new man was taking over my consciousness, a new mind; and though there will always be remnants of who I was in this world before, memories of my childhood and rearing on the farm, I am largely disconnected from that person now. Of course my interaction with family, my greetings to friends, are familiar. Yet they too sensed the changes that I could no longer hide as my personality flickered between the persona of two ages, *new and old, then and now.*

It was quite the transformation. One minute I was the Daniel everyone knew, the next, an entity that not even I fully recognized. Yet this new man was far more *me* than I had ever been myself. Within him I found comfort; I came to love this new being. He was smarter, wiser, more *still* within. Increasingly I was becoming a new creation; a part of myself with which I had long ago lost touch but was now returning as a dear old friend.

The tides of remembrance came in waves, reckless at first, turbulent and destructive to every relationship I had. But the change itself was relentless, unyielding, and unforgiving. Yet like those trees that I imagined burning, transforming into a new substance, the experience with the little old man was also as a flame within the dry tinder of my life. I wanted the fires of change, and now, *finally*, the fire within had come and had me.

It was the spark of a new imagination. With it came the destruction of the normalcies of the world in which I had thus far lived. Yet the knowledge of which was bestowed upon me was not given but *recollected*, the memories of another time and another life hidden within. But as the fires of change destroyed the old me, the more of who I was *before* would be revealed, the forging of a new reality. And yet the biggest events of all were still yet to happen.

THE SEEDLING

As the days and months continued, my understanding of the images increased. I came to know that the pictorials I saw in my mind were actually describing the verses of the ancient scriptures themselves. In them I began to see a distinct and ever more obvious code. They told the story of a science *visually* and were likewise metaphorically detailed by the verses themselves.

The subject of the science was spiritual, but not at all as literal as the outward stories would suggest. That and the numbers in the Bible and in the images were astronomical in nature. Ultimately they seemed to tell the story of *alignment*, that is, *Earth's alignment*. Exactly *why* of course, at first eluded me, though the answers would come in time.

I found through study that the Earth both spins and wobbles similar to a toy top. While the spin is measured every 24 hours, the wobble takes far longer to complete and is measured every 72 years. At this I found it interesting that there were also 24 books in the Jewish Bible and that Jewish religious lore claims that the Jewish God has a total of *72* names. Add to that the Islamic tradition of *72 "Houris"* or virgins, and the numbers of these ancient religions seem to tell a different story than the literal version would indicate.

Accordingly, the *12 tribes, 12 apostles,* and *12 imams* alluded to the 12 cycles of the moon. The moon's orbit can have either a stabilizing or a destabilizing effect on our planet; its path can literally alter the angle at which the Earth faces the sun. Thus if the moon's orbit is offset as it travels around the Earth, then our alignment with the sun is likewise worsened.

Then there is the mighty serpent, or dragon mentioned in the books of Genesis, Isaiah, Job, Revelation, and elsewhere. This of course is the constellation around which Earth's axis appears to rotate when measuring the 72 year *Precessional* movement. Obviously nothing more than a coincidental clump of stars, this point within the heavens was yet demonized in the lore of every ancient religion; but why?

Next was the number *70*, mentioned repeatedly throughout the Bible, itself an alternate measurement of Earth's wobble. The question I suppose is, why did the authors of those books feel that Earth's tilt and/or wobble was important enough to encode within countless volumes of text? It must have been significant, but again, at first the mystery eluded my grasp.

I found that Earth is indeed tilted almost 24 degrees from being perpendicular to the sun. According to scientists today, this angle alters slightly, perhaps a degree or two, back and forth over a 41,000-year cycle. At the moment, however, it is in fact straightening at an alarmingly fast rate. With this, I couldn't help but ponder if there was a connection to all these numbers in conjunction to Earth's sudden and rapid realignment.

Upon further revelation and research I discovered that there are in fact thousands of verses in the Bible, Koran and Vedas that speak either allegorically or pictorially of what seemed to be an opening in space, i.e., *portal-mechanics*. If so, and if my hunch was correct, then the implications that perhaps the ancients knew of such things thousands of years ago would be shattering to the outer-dogmas of our religious beliefs.

How could this be? I wondered. At that time in 1990, portals were only an underdeveloped theory in Einstein's notebook, where-as the scriptures were literally thousands of years old. No one at the time knew of the data I was finding in the Bible and other ancient texts. How then could the authors of those writs have possibly understood such things?

Likewise I noticed that one of the mind images I drew formed what at first glance appeared to be a geometric flower or lily in its center. The image comprised 12 circles, each with double outer lines and each with 12 pie-shaped divisions. These in turn were surrounded by a crisscross of lines that formed 12 *stars of David*, a symbol that has been identified with Judaism for millennia. I hadn't actually drawn those 12 stars myself; but were the natural result of the lines and circles as they interacted. This in itself was a fascinating incident.

Far more sobering, however, was that within the image's center was the likeness of an *opening*, not unlike the portals we see in movies. In further dreams and visions came the most peculiar image of a man imposed upon it, then *color*, a beautiful luminescent green. The image seemed to relay a powerful message every night as I sleep, but what?

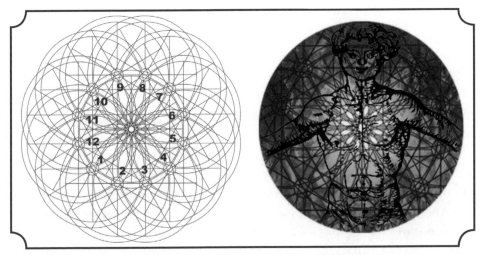

Taken as a whole along with the word-code I was finding, things were getting a bit scary. I pondered, could this have really meant something or was it a mere coincidence? There was a connection here and I knew it, a piece and a part of the solution I sought. I was onto something and it gave me goosebumps to realize what was being uncovered before my eyes. To even entertain that this was *possibly* what the little old man had downloaded that day with only the touch of his hand was surreal.

The problem I was having, and as I would discover over time, was knowing these great mysteries without the wisdom and discernment to articulate and present them to others. Knowledge can bring great power but without clarity, knowledge in itself is vain and destructive. Thus the ancient science that I was discovering would come at a price. More than once I would learn the lessons of God the hard way, not only on how to explain this information to others, but more so, of how to be a worthy recipient of such an unheard-of gift.

But to see these things from the ancient perspective was unique. *How so*, I pondered, could it be possible that a 3,000-year-old text was authored by someone who apparently knew more about the space/time continuum than Einstein? What's more, that identical data was found in not one but multiple religious texts from around the world. Likewise the more I came to understand this science, (I should say, *remembered the science*), the more it also tied into other ancient megaliths, such as the pyramids, Stonehenge and the countless temple ruins across the globe.

No doubt maturity was an issue at the time. When it came to the images, portal science and the scriptures, I was like a kid in a candy shop. I would get so excited, talk so fast, and babel so much, that no one could keep up, much less understand the depth of what I had said. I was untempered, to say the least.

As it were, however, God apparently knew I had more to learn. I was but a humble country boy who had seen little of the world. I had almost zero first-hand knowledge of other cultures, races, or religions, much less the suffering of people beyond the cuts and bruises I incurred on the farm. I worked as hard as or harder than anyone anywhere; I was an animal in that sense. Yet had little appreciation for the plights and views of others around the globe.

I lived in a very small world at the time, not on purpose of course, but because of where I was raised and worked. To be fair, most people around the world are this way. We are naturally wary of others, whether out of ignorance or preconceived ideas. Social and religious stereotypes and propaganda tend to inflame our feelings as well and help ensure that we overlook the viewpoints of those from different backgrounds. Yet again, almost every culture does this to some degree.

I needed life experience and was about to get it right between the eyes. This next event would also happen while at work, and to say that I didn't see it coming would be an understatement. That particular day I was making part runs for the mechanics shop at the concrete plant. The parts truck was a 75 International pickup, a real horse in its day, though by 1990 it had seen more than its fair share of miles, age, and abuse. It did well enough however to drive from Middletown to Louisville and sounded good to boot. The old thrush muffler bellowed the trucks raw power and made quite the show when rolling into a parts house.

This day I was dispatched to a dealership that was in a part of town with which I was unfamiliar. I had little love for the city and even less knowledge of its countless streets and alleys. As you might guess, therefore, I was completely lost in under 30 minutes. Worse yet, we didn't have cell phones back then and it seemed a bit risky to stop and ask directions, considering the area in which I now found myself.

This part of Louisville was comprised of the old row houses that are commonplace in the older ghettos. Their old, worn wood-siding sported ten or more coats of lead paint through the decades, as did many of their sagging roofs with two or more layers of mismanaged shingles. The sidewalks were typically cracked throughout with litter and garbage all around. You get the picture.

The characters in this neck of the woods were a cross section of urban life that usually gets ignored and discarded. Much of their clothing was mismatched, tattered, coarse and varied as were the folks who wore them. The people themselves ranged from tough-eyed and street-wise to the haggardly and homeless. Mostly out of work, poor and with little hope for a life beyond this hellhole, these were the outcasts that almost every city across the world has.

They are tough though, amazingly so, and often possess a wisdom that is easily overlooked by the high and mighty of the uptown social cliques. Growing up without makes one learn to do without, but it can also teach us to find certain bits of joy that the rich and famous will likely never know. There was a depth within the eyes of these folks to which I found myself in odd admiration.

That said, the spirit of darkness also finds itself a place within the streets. There are violent gangs, predators of all sorts, and a lion's share of mental sickness. Theft, murder and crime of every color littered this slum and I took no pleasure in navigating its tangle of treachery.

I pondered what it would be like to lie homeless in an alley here for even a single night. No doubt I could survive the woodlands and mountains as good as any, but this place was a horse of a different color. Here i was a duck out of water and admittedly a bit nervous as almost every street corner had a collection of hoodlums. They were like tigers waiting in ambush for a hapless straggler such as myself.

Any little mistake or mishap could be deadly in a place like that. As bad luck would have it, the truck was down to a quarter tank of gas and running a bit rough that day, putting my nerves even further on edge. The last thing I needed was for it to quit in the middle of a four-way, thus I rolled through as many intersections as I could so as to prevent just such an incident. My only option at the time was to keep driving, taking random turns and traversing the labyrinth of backstreets until hopefully finding the familiar.

However, it was upon this unpleasant detour in which something happened that would change my outlook and life forever. While slowly cruising one of many dark, dank and polluted back-streets that day, I beheld to my right a small girl, perhaps not over five or six years old, sitting on the concrete step just outside the door of an old broken-down row house. She looked to be in a pitiful state. Her face was devoid of the joy and curiosity as any small child should hope to have. Her hair was dirty and tangled. Her face too was darkened with dirt as she stared with empty eyes at the sidewalk beneath her feet, hands trembling from the cold or maybe something worse.

What struck me as hard as anything, however, were the cigarette burns on her face and arms. Standing a couple of feet over and leaning on the house was a haggardly, toothless woman. She was grossly overweight and wearing what looked as much like a sheet as it did a baggy old dress. I could see that the woman was verbally assaulting the child, pointing to her with the smoke she held between her two fingers.

She furiously wagged her arm back and forth in contempt from just behind the child's position on the step. God only knows what she was saying, but by the look of things it was unlikely to be a loving parental scolding or discipline. It was out and out abuse and though I knew it in my heart, I so wanted to make a more pleasant excuse for what I saw.

Next to her, lying on the sidewalk, was a drunken sot of man, equally as haggard as the woman. He propped his head with one arm while grotesquely rubbing the girl's thigh with a sickly sensual persuasion. Within easy reach of his other hand was a half-empty bottle of whiskey. My fatherly instinct wanted to jump out, grab the girl and take her to safety; and I fought every bit of reaction in me to do exactly that. A part of me was wondering if somehow I was really seeing this correctly, that perhaps I misinterpreted the situation, that perhaps there was some logical explanation for what I beheld.

Thus I slowed the truck while passing in front of the child's position so as to hopefully get a better look at her condition. I somehow wanted to see into her eyes, to somehow make contact, to let her know that I saw her and cared. I'm not sure what I expected, but what I saw in her eyes was terrifying and while the glance likely did nothing for her, something within me *snapped*. What I beheld was an emptiness that I'd never seen. It was a hollow and broken soul without love or hope. She was in terrible physical condition, obviously and beyond doubt, a victim of physical abuse and God knows what else…

How could this be? I pondered. *Why would anyone do that to another being? Why would someone burn a little child's face? Why would they treat her this way?* It made no sense. I'd never seen anything like this before and the insanity and cruelty of it simply didn't compute in my brain. My emotions were somewhere between shock and anger. It literally took my breath away, but it infuriated me at the same time.

In the sake of self-preservation, it occurred to me that if I got out and made a scene, perhaps those bums might call the cops. That would have been a good thing however. What else occurred to me, though, is that one of these guttersnipes might also be packing a pistol. The woman was just plain crazy in her eyes and seemed like the type that would be all too glad to end my life on a whim, especially seeing her total lack of empathy for the child. I had a wife and child as well who needed me home that night, and thus I considered my options.

Perhaps if nothing else I could continue to drive around until I found a cop and then return to the scene with the police in control. That seemed like a plan and so I sped up in pursuit of the same. However, after another 15 minutes of becoming even more lost and with no police in sight, I was feeling ever more hopeless about the situation.

Ironically it was then, by complete accident that I actually happened upon the parts house that was the original goal of this trip to begin with. It was an odd stroke of luck as not only could I now get the parts I needed, but also I could call the police while I was there. I did call too, but was heartbroken by their response. In my shock of the moment I had failed to get the street name. I offered to try to find it of course, with the help of the police, but they'd have none of it.

To be fair, the police don't typically dispatch a patrol car to follow someone who themselves is lost and on a wild goose chase. Then came the questions:

"Were they hitting her?"

"No."

"Was she trying to get away?"

"No."

"Was she injured?"

"Yes, she had at least a dozen cigarette burns"

"How do you know they were cigarette burns?"

"Because they were!"

"Are you sure it wasn't chicken pox or something else?"

"Yes"

"How do you know?"...

By no means am I throwing the police under the bus. Their questions were simply the nature of police protocol and entirely legitimate at that. I get it. Police can't make determinations based upon what you *feel*, but upon the *facts*. That said, I know what I saw and the defiled nature of that situation. If every other part of the girl's condition could somehow be explained as innocent, the spirit of abuse and neglect was still guilty as charged.

Defeated, I got the parts for which I came and left. The drive back to the concrete plant was surreal; a snapshot of the girls face and eyes permanently etched in my mind. I had already challenged my religious beliefs, but I was now questioning my belief in the justice and love of an almighty god. *How could he allow such a thing?*

I found a cognitive disconnect in my beliefs: that a loving God was watching over us all the time, that He was always making the world right even when it was wrong, that God created us and even showed me the mysteries of the universe, only to thereafter allow such doom upon the innocent. Worse yet, I realized in that moment that the child I had seen was in all probability only one of millions in similar or worse conditions around the world.

I made it through the work day but was only too glad to get home that afternoon. Instead of going straight to the cabin as usual, however, I instead drove to a remote dirt road at the back of the farm and parked. I needed to be by myself for a bit and sort this out in my mind. There I sat for at least 20 minutes, fidgeting and nervous, desperately trying to make sense of this in context to my beliefs and what I had thus far learned from the little old man.

A storm was brewing in the clouds overhead as a front moved across the farm and quickly darkened the skies above. Within it were the powerful rumble of thunder and lightning; the wind also swaying the trees seemingly to the point of breaking. It was to be indicative however of the real storm that was building in me.

Something was happening; something was churning within me—a love for that little girl, a love so strong that I could not let go, a love I had never felt before in my life. It was a love more powerful than anything I'd ever known, but with it, within me, was *a rage*. I felt betrayed by God and I wasn't humble about it in the least. In fact, I was mad as hell.

Where was His great concern? Where was His compassion, I marveled? He created us. He created *her*, but for what? For her to be a dog at the feet of the devil; a drunken molester and despicable wench? I spoke aloud:

> *(Trembling and vindictive in tone): How wonderful my own blessings; thank you, dear God for all the wonderful mysteries you've revealed to me. Weren't you so thoughtful... You've given me everything; a wife, a child, a house, a home... I've got money... I've got a job, food, and, never mind the people in my life who love me... That's great, just special. Lucky me, right?*

> *(A brief pause, then screaming at the top of my lungs):* **How dare you! How dare you** *give to me without cease yet take from her, the helpless.*

> *(I burst forth from the truck, now yelling at the sky):* **How dare you**

bring a soul into this world and allow it to be treated this way! **Nice of you**, dear Lord. Thank you for my salvation that you promised, and the curse you've laid upon one more worthy of blessing than myself!

(Picking up rocks now and throwing them at the sky): **She's done nothing to deserve this**, and you've done absolutely nothing—nothing to fix it!

The more I spoke, the madder I got, tears of indignation dripping from my eyes:

Oh, "Show respect" I hear. **No, -you show respect.** (Another rock at the sky) An all-powerful creator who showed himself once 2,000 years ago, supposedly, and then went AWOL. **You think I'm afraid of you because of a threat of hell-fire and brimstone? You can't intimidate me—not now, not after what I saw today. You want somebody to pick on, somebody to curse?** (Poking myself in the chest as if to dare God) You want to burn me in hell for speaking what I know to be the truth?! **Then do it!** You do what you think you have to do, and I will do the same *** **** thing! But I will not believe in a god that does this. **Because if she can't have you, then I don't want you!**

And I meant what I said too…

And wouldn't ya know it, my friend, but at that exact moment, in that same instant in which those words left my mouth, something really did, for real, leave me. *Hope left me.* All hope, beyond all doubt, vacated my very being. All I could see in that moment was darkness, not outside, but inside myself. My whole outlook on life changed in that moment: all of my aspirations, all the good feelings and vision for tomorrow—these were gone but in a blink. The significance of my past and future, meaningless. Every bit of everything in me was over, done, *finished*. I had nothing. I was empty; my body was alive, but my soul, dead.

I fell to the ground, limp with desperation, every ounce of energy and self-preservation abandoned. There I lay in the mud, in the rain and lightning, groaning the genuine call of one who lie in hell. It was the groaning of the my spirit, the sorrow I felt, the pity. I felt the *horror*; I felt *her* horror. I lost cognizance of where I was or what I was

31

doing. All I saw was her face and now my own nothing. I felt no responsibility to family or friends. I saw no need to move from where I was; the instinct for survival, gone.

I was wet and cold and didn't care. Something in me had snapped. I passed out, even in the cold. I'm not sure how much time transpired, maybe an hour or two perhaps. I finally awoke still hopeless but bored, unsure what to do. I was unsettled where I was, as where I would be; this emptiness, a seemingly perpetual condition that I knew would follow me.

As much out of habit as to duty, however, I returned to the cabin soaked to the bone. I was home yet feeling so far away from everything. My wife also was home, fixing dinner—the routine. She was accustomed to me working in the rain, yet somehow noticed the glazed look in my eyes as I passed.

It was the 10,000-yard stare and straight to the fake-rain of my shower. My mind was demented now and disconnected. I felt nothing as I sat on the shower floor staring upward at the scalding spray that thawed by body but could not thaw my soul. I had ignored my daughter on my way in and now she too knocked on the shower door. *Daddy, Daddy, Daddy, daddy.* I never responded, nor could I. I was somewhere else, lost in a hellish mindset that words can never truly describe…

Later that night, I explained to my wife what had happened. She of course heard but didn't listen, which only served to deepen my depression. Later I arose from bed, still tormented by the image of injustice. I made it about as far as the family room before lying in the middle of its hardwood floor. Oblivious to its discomfort, my mind still spinning as in a never-ending fall, I again passed out in the groaning of one so lost.

My spirit was crossing the great nothing, its own dark night of the soul. Regardless of what you may imagine that place is like, until you've actually been there, you can never truly know how empty it really is. Many people have been there since the beginning, but not all. Once there, very few ever make it out. It was forever in every direction and now I was smack-dab in the middle of it.

There was no horizon there, but only dark gray, with no earth beneath me and no sky above. In that place there was no right side up or upside down. It was endless and without the possibility of hope. I no longer cared if, or what, the Almighty took from me nor that He apparently did take something, *my hope*, the very thing that we so often take for granted on a daily basis.

There, the *game* of life is over; in that place there is no rescue. My salvation too was gone and I knew it, yet in the very middle of that great abyss was still me, lost, and the image of that little girl. No matter how I got there in that awful, awful place, no matter the power that put me there, there was *no* power powerful enough to take her from me. Somehow, I found myself caring more for her than I did for escape from the hell in which I now lived.

I fell asleep on that floor. I remember nothing of that night till the next morning. I didn't dream or toss or turn, but was just completely out. I awoke to the call of my name, my wife looking down in bewilderment as she tried to wake the dead; *Daniel*, **Daniel**, **Daniel**! As I arose and wiped the drool from my mouth, the first image I saw in my mind was that same girl.

And so that day was the same as the last. That night, however, I called and spoke with a relative about the incident. It was difficult in my zombie-like state of mind, but I managed as best I could. After talking for a bit, I seemed to recall a verse in which the apostle Paul spoke of sacrifice. She remembered it off the top of her head: Romans 9:3, in which Paul stated that he wished himself *accursed* from Christ (i.e.,-*salvation*), for the sake of his kinsmen.

It is a bold statement to wish for such things, but oddly was exactly what I found myself doing only the day before.

"Paul actually said that?" I asked.

I suppose in all my years of indoctrination, I had come to believe that only one person, two thousand years ago, could do such a thing as that. That was Jesus' job, *wasn't it?* Beyond that and then, it was unthinkable that anyone else was in need of such a gesture as forfeiting a prize such as salvation.

Yet in all my learnings and revelations, it was the one thing I missed about the true nature of God, in fact, the biggest thing of all about God: that it's not about what you have, a hope and salvation, but about whether or not the love in your heart is powerful enough to lay it all down for the ones you love; in this case, the person God put in front of me to love, that little girl.

Yet with nothing more than that realization, my sanity began to return. I just kind of snapped out of it. Still dazed a bit, I pondered for the next few hours and, honestly, till the dawning of the next day, but I awoke the following morning feeling somewhat better, though still deeply concerned for the child's welfare. I so wanted to believe that maybe, just maybe, there was something more to God than mere vain blessings of health, wealth and wisdom; that maybe the lesson of the cross wasn't just a one-off deal; that maybe something unlikely and good did happen to that child as a result of the very real, though short-lived, hell I suffered.

I would never again have validation though. What became of the child or whether or not she was still in that horrible situation was as much your guess as it was mine.

I did drive back to that area of the city again that Saturday, but once again became lost without ever finding that same street and house.

Weeks went by, and so life goes on. Most of what my job entailed at the concrete plant was changing truck tires, yet the day would come, almost a year to the day later, when I would again find myself making a parts run to the same place I had the year before.

I suppose because I hadn't found the parts-house correctly the last time, I had programmed nothing to memory about how to get there correctly this time either. I really hated driving in the city and by no large stretch of the imagination was once again lost. Here I was again in the same slums as last time and with no idea how to navigate the labyrinth of roads.

You can only imagine what I was thinking, however: *Not again*. My hands began to sweat, and I was itching from head to toe. I was nervous but was beginning to realize that God doesn't do accidents and coincidences. I was nowhere near the mark of perfection in this respect, but was learning to go with the flow of what life/God put in front of me instead of fighting such circumstances.

I knew in that moment that I was going to somehow wind up in front of that same broken-down house that I'd seen a year before, and the next two turns produced exactly that. My heart sank as I recognized the street and, at a distance, the same house. Unlike the last time, however, the sidewalk was now devoid of people, nor were there any cars along the curb.

As I slowly rolled down the street, I noticed that several of the homes were now boarded and vacant. It appeared as though they'd been condemned or perhaps were slotted to be removed for new construction. Seeing no signs of occupancy, I at first chose to keep driving, still slowly idling past the rows of empty and dilapidated houses.

After passing the old house, however, I simply stopped in the middle of the road. With no traffic, and no one behind me, I ground that same old clunker of a truck in reverse and backed up till I was squarely in front of the step upon which that little girl sat only one year before. There I paused and starred for a moment before finally shutting off the engine…now reliving that horrid moment in full reflection. Oh how my imagination wandered in wonder of what had happened, where she had gone or her fate…

Now, I can't exactly explain what happened next, yet I know full well what I saw. After a few minutes of pondering and perhaps even an unspoken prayer, I continued on my way. After making another couple of right-hand turns, I emerged onto a larger and somewhat nicer street. It was lined with small businesses of all different sorts. After driving only a block or so on that street, I found myself passing what appeared to be a children's home. I didn't actually see the name of the place, however simply because something greater caught my eye.

Just to my right, walking down the sidewalk in the same direction as I was driving, was a woman. She looked to be perhaps in her late 30s or early 40s. She was well dressed and not bad looking, smiling as she trucked along. In her left hand she held something as she walked, something that I thought perhaps I recognized.

What she held was the hand of a little girl, perhaps about six years old now, happily skipping alongside the woman as they went. The child was also well dressed, a stranger I suppose, yet somehow familiar. Surely this wasn't the same tattered being that I saw the year before. Her hair was combed and she was clean. She had energy and life. She had a caretaker who was happy with her as well.

Surely I had it all wrong. Surely this was someone else and I had again misjudged the situation. But then, just as they were about to enter the front door of that building, I stopped again, smack dab in the middle of the road and looked to see what I could see. I couldn't help myself; I had to know if this was a mirage or maybe something else.

The little girl also stopped in that moment as well, ironically, instinctively, resisting only slightly upon the tug of the woman with whom she walked. She then paused for a short moment as if to follow an internal ticking of the brain, a feeling of something within; she looked at the sidewalk under her feet. Then, as if by some supernatural instinct, a bond that we now both felt, the little girl turned and looked up and looked me directly in the eyes and smiled…

It was *her*. I couldn't believe it but it was *her*. I froze in shock as my eyes looked and locked onto hers, my daughter, not by birth or genetics, but by the spirit of God within us, a kinship forged in the fires of God's kiln. The miracle of this was overwhelming and my eyes immediately welled at the fantastic sight I was seeing. Then, playfully, she tilted her head oh so slightly in curiosity of the same. It was then that she raised her free hand and squeezed a few clasping waves as only a child can do. She too knew; I don't know how, but somehow she knew.

And just like that, she was gone into the building and out of sight. But I had seen all that I needed to see and all that I would ever need to see to believe in the power and love of God. This was the lesson that I needed to learn: that all the greatest revelations in the world are for naught, without knowing first the heart of the God who gives them.

Unfortunately I feel that our modern world has made us complacent in this respect. In this day, men have become lovers of pleasure more than lovers of the truth that leads to the highest reward of all. We shun the greater work before us just to feel good for the moment. We desire a god that brings comfort. Yet in this we forfeit real salvation with much less ado than I did that day during the storm.

I think in that moment a year before, while on that road at the back of the farm, unbeknownst to me at the time, I made God blush. I had no idea that my rebellious response was exactly the reaction He'd desired all along. The storm that day was not the wrath of God but rather the calling of the spirit of the storm that was in me. It wasn't God that was the problem after all but instead my perception of God that let me down. In the end, I didn't curse God that day, but the false image of God that I so wrongly had built in my mind.

God is the master of getting what He wants. No doubt He is also the master of knowing how to get blood from a turnip too, and he did exactly that in me. He pulled from within exactly what He needed me to see: the next step of operating the real power of the cross. It was not a lack of faith as some would say, but the very manifestation of God's love that had emerged: the laying down of your life for another. In the end, God didn't take my hope, but rather allowed me to forfeit it in trade for her hopelessness. This is how it works.

Before this, God's power and love were separate from my understanding; I was, till then, on the *outside* looking in on the subject. But now this deity was on the *inside* *as* me; God in *my* form working a very real and personal power; looking inside that little girls, little life; and more important than healing her body, was the healing of her soul and *her hope*. Now God had birthed the real miracle of His love in my person, and I did the exact same thing to her. I had rebelled, not out of ignorance or disrespect, but against the false god that society and religion had given me.

In the end I did exactly as a child of God, my own *little person*, was supposed to do: I lived my own Romans 9:3, becoming accursed from all that I had in this world that another might live. Yet the hope I lost was in fact the burden of that young child, the burden that she had carried for God only knows, how long. Gladly I took that burden that she might live in hope, and now, -she did. From the very moment I looked into her sweet, sweet, beautiful eyes only a year before, the power of this world lost its grip on her, a transfer of energy, an exchange of situation and circumstance.

We see this in the story of Christ: that one lay down his life and salvation for the lowly and the meek. That is the job of every angel, every drop of God within us. As a result, the great nothing could not hold her, and it could not hold me. In the end, what God really took from me was my illusion of who and what He is.

Only one choice, however, and only one of the gods I have mentioned can actually give you salvation, the passcode to heaven that we all seek. It is not about the longevity or condition of the body, but the eternity of the spirit within. Thus as that spirit becomes us, we trade it to those we find while here; we give the Element of God that lives within to that which needs it.

The problem of bitterness toward God that many people today have is in fact our own misunderstanding of the divine nature. Educated societies have a grand misconception of the divine, much of which is the result of millennia-old religious imagery. These base perceptions were of course necessary at the time in that early cultures needed something on their level of comprehension as a moral guide and focal point. Simplistic religious beliefs allowed people then and now to cope and to hope in an otherwise brutal world.

Unfortunately, however, while our education standards typically increase over time, our spiritual knowledge is often still stagnant. God does sit on a majestic throne, within your hearts and minds. Thus it is we who can articulate the power of the God-Element. We must let go of our dogmas and instead let the power of God do its work through our experience. So ultimately I wish to tell you the story of transformation: that the miracle of something greater does exist within our own inner being.

It is not a fluke or a fantasy that I bring you, but the fact of a long-lost element of which the ancients knew and of which we are about to rediscover in full. It is real; it works perfectly; it can and does bring visible change. It is the tool by which we ourselves repair and are repaired in God in this world.

Are there still people fighting a dog over a rotten carcass just to get their next meal somewhere in the world? Is there suffering, horrible abuses and handicaps around the world, every moment of every day? Of course, and there always will be in the dimension in which we now find ourselves. But *that* isn't, rather, the *body* isn't and never was the real issue, was it? The point is that the person of God be awakened to function as it was always intended within this fallen world.

Feed not the body of the flesh and consider yourself an angel, but *give of yourself*, of your *spirit*, as food for those who are starving spiritually. This is where love surpasses even faith. This is where the saying comes true:

"When that which is perfect is come, then that which is in part shall be done away".

Thus Love is the connective tissue between ourselves and the world around us. But there is no love like God's love. Nothing else is so profound and so powerful and so deep.

The logical mind desperately tries to stifle this process of understanding. I had underestimated the divine plan. Once again I failed to see that God was preparing and purifying me for my job. Yes; my job is the same as yours; to function within the love of God and to renew the conveyor belt of salvation.

I use the name of Christ to identify the spirit that I know to be true and real. What is important, however, is not a specific name, but rather to correctly identify the spirit of which I speak. God forbid we get hung up on the specifics of religious names and terminologies, but instead to identify the person of God and His workings within us. If one could neither see, hear, read nor be taught, they could still identify a given spirit within, _without name_. Thus I don't care what name you use to identify the love of God, so long as you understand the nature of that spirit correctly.

That person gives of itself instead of taking. It loves instead of hating. It forgives instead of crucifying. It does so in an understanding of its purpose in the grand scheme of the dimensions. It is not needy but full of the knowledge of God and works the power of God in everything it does.

Yet there was another purpose for me: to bring you the mysteries of the universe and God—but not only to bring them, but to remove the veil which had in fact made them a mystery. It was this episode with the frail, abused little girl that finally brought me closer to my own personal graduation on this journey. This is when I finally began to grasp that my life here on Earth was as it must be. It was through this event and others that I was allowed to carry this message to you and the ancient mystery that will be revealed by the end of this book.

It is knowing when to fight and when to concede that wins a deeper relationship with God. God will always win, yet knowing when to stand for the truth at all costs, even at the expense of salvation, _will_ win you His respect as a father to a trusted son. In the end, He wants you to know the depths of His love; in the end this is what must birth forth from your inner being.

The wisdom of the ancient science cost me much; it cost me who I was before. Not all at once, but in steady and deliberate steps I lost who I had once been. That small, frail child in that Louisville ghetto was only one of many such strides in my life by which I came to wisdom and understanding. Her contribution in the revelations that you will see is, in fact, immeasurable. Everything costs something. God bless her soul, for she paid dearly for the things you are about to discover.

The hell that she suffered and that I suffered with her was, _I say_, worth it. The statement is true that death is only the beginning. In fact, death and taxes are not the only sure things, but *life from death, that is what you can count on*. I brought life to that little girl and, thankfully, through the power of the real God within, she brought life to me as well. What unfathomable energy is it through which a tortured and innocent child could unknowingly save the soul of a man such as myself? But she did…

III

Ascending the Portal

I am without variation and form.
I am present everywhere as the underlying of everything,
and behind all senses.
I attach to nothing, neither am I freed from anything.
I am the pure bliss of consciousness; I am.
Make no mistake...I am.

Over the course of the next two years, the visions would continue, always new, always intriguing, every night, and often during the day. It became a routine of sorts that I grew to love. Often I pondered what lay in store for the morrow, what new image would appear and perhaps some new understanding. Yet in that, things began to settle and the profound in itself became routine. Things calmed somewhat, perhaps a bit too calm for the almighty.

I went to bed on that night just like any other, lying on my back, staring at the ceiling, reviewing the events of the day and contemplating those of the next. After a few minutes I began to doze. As I did, I felt my body lighten and my mind begin to loosen. I'm sure you know the feeling—those moments between wake and sleep. It was a feeling of freedom, and as I faded into the world of dreams, I pleasantly began to float just above the bed.

Wow, I can remember thinking. *This is nice; this is gonna be a good one!*

My spirit lifted through the ceiling and roof of the house, ever increasing in speed as it went. Seldom, if ever were my dreams so vivid, so detailed and so meticulous. I

41

could plainly see the lake and dam, the trees from above and increasingly the entire farm. It was surreal yet so real that I couldn't deny the experience. In a mere wisp, however, I was sped away to a place high within the clouds. I gasped at the feeling of speed, even in my slumber, the miracle of flight—*amazing*. Once there far above the earth, I looked downward through a hole, many thousands of feet below. Even at that range, however, I could still see my log home, now but as a tiny speck.

Stillness ensued for the next several moments as I hung suspended amongst the heavens. What a wonderful vision. I thought, as even within the dream I pondered the realness of what was happening. Though I could not feel the touch of the wind, I could hear its rushing and even see the clouds as they passed through and around my position. I felt secure in flight, oddly now disconnected from the cabin, as though I lapsed in memory. I had forgotten who I was in that moment and was amazed how comfortable and normal this experience felt.

Suddenly, however, a beautiful light radiated from behind and above my field of view. Its rays shined past me, a soothing energy wave, mostly white in color yet mixed with faint hues of emerald and sardine stone. The light was familiar, yet I knew-not how, yet so unlike the light of the sun or moon. As my being slowly turned to see the source of these rays, I noticed that within them were sparkles that gently floated outward from a source.

The flickers were quiet in presence yet somehow *alive*, as if containing a mind. I saw in them a design, a structure, that was completely unaffected by the wind. The sparkles were within the same space as was I, within the clouds, yet completely untouched by the physics and weather through which it dwelt.

I marveled at this visage to which I was drawn. I could literally feel the light pulling me toward it, my focus still slowly rotating to see what was sure to be special. It's hard to describe, but I felt so at ease, as though I was somehow going home, not back to the cabin, but to some long-forgotten place that I could not consciously recall. My turning continued however, until at the very moment the light came into view, *just as I was being pulled through*, a brief, fleeting glimpse of an unbelievably overpowering brightness and then—all was still and total blackness.

In the next fraction of a second, I was violently vacuumed back inside my body. There I lay in bed within the cabin, now wide awake, my eyes opened in amazement of what had just occurred. Within my mind, I couldn't help but wonder if I was dead or dying. But as I lay there now petrified, I heard a voice, an undeniable voice, and a powerful echo within: I literally heard the words

"You will not be allowed to remember what you have seen".

Shock ensued as I stared at the ceiling, unsure whether or not to move. *Holy s...!* I thought. *That was by far the most real dream I've ever had. What was that light? What just happened?* I lay there and pondered for at least ten minutes, not quite sure what to think about the realism of the experience.

Finally however, I got out of bed, went to the kitchen and made a pot of coffee. As I drank, sitting upon the counter top, I tried to convince myself that this was just a dream, a night vision of my mind and nothing more. Doubt however, was winning against my better reasoning and logic. I mean, the *light*—it was so-real, and the *voice*—I really heard that ...*didn't I?*

Why of all things would I see something really great and then not be allowed to remember it? That makes no sense. And who in their wildest imagination sees the layers of the ceiling and roof as they pass through them in a dream? That's not normal dream-material, or at least it wasn't for me.

I rationalized that dreams are sometimes just that way, that maybe it was the result of events that my mind had somehow contorted and arranged. I suppose that's very possible; our mind can manipulate things, right? Our worries, fears or thoughts can be twisted into an illogical combination of results. I humored that at least it was a fun dream instead of a nightmare, though the voice at the end still seemed a little too real to be a mere illusion of my sleep.

That said, I had the strongest of suspicion that this was, somehow, more than just a dream. It felt *real* and even more than just a *really good dream*. It actually felt, well, kind of, -supernatural. All my thoughts gravitated towards the light which drew me in. What was it? I wanted to know and so that event played on a continual loop within my mind.

Great, I thought, *so now I'm batting-zero for sanity.* Let's face it, two years prior I was made a complete fool in front of multiple witnesses while babbling about some nebulous little old man, after which I began to draw a bunch of circles, maps and grids, and now, a magic-carpet ride to nowhere and of which I had no recollection. That's just great, by all means, sign me up for the nut house... *Thanks, Universe!* So this is what it feels like to lose your mind! *Why me, and why are these things never clear?*

The next morning I told my wife about the dream and she, *by no surprise,* down-played the event. Resentful of her condescending tone, I thus became all the more steadfast in trying for her approval and/or, at least, a two-way conversation. As it became obvious that I wouldn't quit talking about it however, she too, like so many others in my life, shied away from the subject altogether.

Wonderful. How is it that they can talk about God at church on Sunday, but somehow my spiritual experiences are taboo? Besides, even if it was just a dumb dream, why can't we at least talk and have some fun with the subject? Oh, I get it; that would be outside of our religious programming. God forbid we do anything outside those chains. That makes sense to me. In the end, the dogmatism was enough to make me pull my hair out.

Ironically, the realism of the occurrence had only strengthened my belief that there was something real, something more tangible beyond what I would see in this world and beyond the status quo of God and church as I'd been raised. I was already in rebellion against my social and religious programming and this only made things worse. Indeed it only reinforced and somehow connected the lessons of the little old man.

However, the more that I latched on to the possibility that a *real world* existed beyond the routines of this life, that perhaps heaven wasn't just something to talk about on Sunday, the more I also became alienated in this world. Indeed it became increasingly difficult to cope with the normalities in which everyone else seemed satisfied.

I recalled a verse in 2 Timothy that rang true to the pretense I saw within the social cliques of society, to those who spoke of God, those who went to church, and those who considered themselves righteous, yet ultimately showed enmity toward the subject and reality of heaven when it became uncomfortable:

"Having a form of godliness, but denying the power thereof."

The more I embraced the miracle of the little old man and the vision of the portal, likewise the less I doubted my own insanity and instead suspected the sleep of those around me. At one point I evaluated my increasing self-confidence as either a form of narcissism, self-delusion or, perhaps—*spot on.* Between all that, life, God, and whatever, had simply thrown too many things my way to be mere coincidence. Either way, it was quite the predicament to realize that either I was crazy or perhaps the rest of the world was, but at least my search was narrowed to one of those two. No doubt this brought a certain amount of comfort.

Little did I know however, that life would take another bizarre and unexpected turn, one that would dwarf the occurrence with the little old man, the endless images, and even my dream of the portal. Three years had transpired since that dream and, like all things, we move on to what is in front of us. I had to work, I had to eat, and I had to make money to pay the bills. Yet I was still stuck with the nightly visions of circles, grids and faces from another time.

As usual I awoke around 2:30 to 3:00 a.m., unable to sleep. It was then that I arose to either draw, design, invent or just listen to my favorite music. It was peaceful at that time of morning, and I loved the quiet. I found solace in song; I had immersed myself in music since my collision with the little old man, saturating the mind with the meaning of the lyrics, the count, and the beat of its rhythm. The wave-patterns intertwined with the matrix of who I was and myself into them. I melded into the music almost as though we were one.

On one such unsuspecting Friday night, I sat upon the food bar and mended my favorite hunting shirt. I had taken the liberty to prep my clothes for the upcoming deer season, checking tabs, sewing the numerous rips and tears that inevitably occur while romping through the woods. My garment was old and tattered; it had seen years of service and certainly was in need of retirement.

Familiarity however, is always the issue. It is hard to part ways with that which we are accustomed, but ultimately the time comes for all things *of* this earth to pass. Letting go is always easier said than done; but in this case, I was stubborn and made the maintenance, determined to get just one more season out of those skins.

I was wide awake, listening to my favorite CDs while I worked. The kitchen island was located just in front of the sink and stove area. This was the counter upon which I sat while I sewed; the radio to my right, my bedroom to my left at the far end of the house. I had closed the door to the bedrooms so as not to wake my wife and daughter and lowered the volume as well.

At the moment I was listening to a song by Enya, the words:

Close to home feeling so far away...

As I walk the room...

There before me a shadow...

I adored that song as much now as ever, but now the beat began to change. It suddenly slowed without explanation. The radio itself was plugged into the wall-socket, thus dead batteries were not an explanation. Rather however, something was slowing down in me; yes, *time changed.* Within my mind, time itself was coming to a crawl. Did it speed up, or did it slow down? Honestly, it's hard to say and I know not which...

From another world

Where no other can follow...

Carry me to my own

To whe r e I can c r o s s o v e r...

I failed to catch the irony then between those words and what happened next, though I would certainly make the connection later. Suddenly, I was jolted from the daydream of those tunes by a sharp pain deep within my chest. The severity of it shocked me as it was quite unlike anything I'd ever experienced before.

I immediately straightened from my semi-slouched position, quickly pressing my forearms to my chest, thus dropping the shirt, needle and thread with which I was sewing. Much to my horror the pain did not subside, but in only mere seconds had completely sapped my strength. My breath became short and laborious; my arms frogged as well—all the iconic symptoms of a heart attack.

...It hurt and it hurt quickly. I knew in that moment what it was, as do all who have felt its pain. I didn't need to be told what was happening, yet in an instant I was powerless to do anything to change the outcome. I tried in desperation to turn toward the bedroom where my wife lay sleeping. I tried to yell for help but the pain was simply too stunning. Somehow I hoped for help in those fleeting moments, but I was overcome with the spasm of this attack on my heart.

I knew this was it—*that fast*, I could not breathe and I could not speak. I could not move further. I knew this was my end, and I must say that it was surreal beyond words. I knew even then however, that no one would hear me fall and that there would be no rescue: that they would find me dead in the morning. Ironically it was hopeless, yet somehow, hopeful beyond what you might imagine; the feeling I was feeling was somehow—*amazing*.

Within only a moment however, I was falling uncontrollably, forward off the counter toward the floor. I was blacking out, yet there remained one last bit of information that I would recall before my consciousness ceased. My eyes made contact with the rotary clock on the old stove. It showed ***3:27a.m.*** and was changing at that exact moment to ***3:28***.

Each new minute on the clock took about 3 seconds to rotate into place, but I only managed to see it half way between the 7 and 8. It was the last thing I remembered of this world, the last image I saw: a flicker of something, a swift gasp, blackness and . . . *out*, through the top of the house and into space, far, far above the Earth, traveling as speed I never knew was possible and with a freedom I never knew existed.

Yet in that same moment as the body and being I had known till then collapsed and surely died, within the same instant, someone else came to life. Indeed as one part of my being fell from the counter, shed with no more value than a single leaf that falls from a tree, another somehow awakened anew. It was not me who ascended, yet somehow a new part of the same person. I remembered something pleasant and something present—a new man who was free of an old garment, an old body.

With great speed and no will of my own, I now ascended to the heights above the Earth, far beyond the atmosphere. As this occurred, a menagerie of colors illuminated my path: *blues, purples, greens, yellows and reds* came and went. My vision was at first focused upward towards the stars beyond and so this continued until well within the blackness of space.

But then, after only a few brief moments, sudden stillness; my spirit stopped. I was in complete awe of this new state of existence yet somehow still at home within this unbelievable feeling. It was then that my view began to rotate from the heavens and back toward Earth.

There my new being hung suspended, viewing this third rock from the sun, a planet that had till then been my home of 27 years. It was as if this new man was bidding a final farewell. From there though, I remembered nothing of what was. Silent, still within, I stared at a place that I barely even recognized.

I could recall nothing, neither my family nor friends nor self as I had once known them. I knew not my name as Daniel, nor any of his life and times. As a butterfly that emerges from its drab cocoon only to show its beautiful colors, I too shed the cares and worries of life that was before. I was disconnected from that world now, as I too saw colors, now a deep luminescent red around me.

After only several seconds of this peaceful viewing, this new bodiless self, turned again to the great abyss of space. It was then that came an explosion of speed, *unparalleled speed, -beyond anything that one can possibly imagine,* as I rocketed into the boundless expanse, beyond this solar system, ever faster until even the speed of light was dwarfed. It was as the tachyonic particle, only far faster.

It was traveling as the speed of memory, the velocity of an imagination come to life. I had instantly gone from being the atom to the Adam, the micro to the macro, the mere mind of a man, to the mind of this entire universe. It was the speed of becoming everything within these boundaries of the physical.

In this I began to see, to become, *lives, countless lives* from the past. Like billions of streaming videos at the same time, they all came into the vision as memories. And though disconnected from them physically, I yet became their consciousness. It is inexplicable to my mind now to explain how to feel and to understand all those beings, all those moments through which I passed, all at the same time. There were so many humans, so many countless creatures of all shapes and sizes and from around the universe—not only humans, but everything from every planet that ever was.

As this occurred my being ballooned in every direction and with ever-increasing speed. I no longer traveled in a single direction, but increasingly in all directions at the same time. I was becoming one with everything I saw and through which I passed. In this I remember the deaths of every conscious creature. *Why* I cannot say, but the *deaths*, their moment of passing, are what I recall the most. There is no way to list the countless trillions of these beings coming and going from all directions as was I.

A French soldier: The cold shown my breath. To my left and right, long ranks, a long bowed line of men that disappeared into the fog that rose from the field. We advanced up the incline of that open plain. Nearing its crest we could hear the muffled tromp of our enemy as well; our forces hidden from one another but by the morning haze and crest of the hill.

Bayonets fixed, we readied for the onslaught, ours and theirs that approached, separated now, surely by mere yards. The suspense, the helpless terror of the imminent destruction that was about to happen. It was bizarre as I could feel through the ground the massed footsteps of both parties, us and them. Yet it was nonetheless sudden and surprising. There, for a fleeting moment, a micro-second, everyone paused; time stood still. I remember the length of their coats, better for the cold than ours.

By command and instinct we *all* lunged, our lines and theirs, crashing into a desperate struggle for survival—this a tragedy of the human condition. The fight, the training: *parry, thrust*. The panic, the madness. I can remember my own final moments: I fired from the hip into a soldier only five feet away and then plunged my bayonet into the man to his right only to immediately feel the bayonet of a Russian deeply within my own ribcage. I can remember the shock of being all three men at the same time. I could feel their fear, but not their pain. I knew and lived those moments, that event on the battlefield, *mentally*, not physically. I was there . . . *I was there. . .*

I slowly fell to my knees and then to the ground as the fighting continued around me. He gasp for air, holding both hands on the hole in the side of my chest. I laid there, a dying stare, face to face, only inches from the dead man who killed me. Both our eyes, wide open in death, white, foamy blood still running from his mouth and nose. The shock of knowing that I was dead in both their forms—then—*nothing*.

The boy lying in the fence row: I played within the edge of the woods next to the field. I could see the farm house a hundred yards away. I saw my father approaching. He was hunting, his shotgun at the low ready, barrel pointed downward and to his left. I hid within the grasses of the row just beside a post.

The mind of a child: I giggled in anticipation of surprising by beloved father. Now only feet away I sprang from my concealment mimicking the roar a lion. He didn't mean to; it was an accident. I startled him. The gun fired, and that's all I remember; and now I remember being the *father*.

The *father*: the utter horror of realizing I just killed my son. In that moment my universe stopped; my existence plunged into the hell of blackness, my whole life and sanity ruined within but a moment...*All I was trying to do was bring home food for my family...wha, what have I done?* The extreme guilt, the madness, the horror were beyond words. Glimpses of the screaming mother, the other children staring in shock and disbelief of what had happened. Then -nothing.

The little girl who watched as her family was murdered with spear and jagged-daggers: It was a village, somewhere: I could hear yelling and screaming all around. Suddenly I was jerked by the arm and flung through the air, thrown into the fire of my home as it burned. I remember spinning into the flames, the shearing pain of burning alive. I tried to stand, then—*nothing*. Yet only in my mind did I feel this.

A man, *drowning*, trapped under the log: under the ledge; tangled and running out of air. Panic and the feeling of cold water as it flooded my lungs—then, *nothing*

Falling from the tree, the shock of having lost my grip....the crunch of my neck as it broke—then *nothing*.

The lion came from nowhere. A fleeting *"wha..."* before its teeth plunged—then nothing.

The lion too as it heard loud pops and felt the hot stab of bullets passing through my body . . . it was always my body, no matter the creature.

The whimpering torture of the dog being beaten...

the wreck
the miserable disease
the murder
the plane in its uncontrolled descent before crashing
freezing
scared
alone

footsteps
-fear
-fear
-fear

Countless tortures and abuses of both adults and children. I will not mention them. The worst part was the hatred I felt from within mankind, -the evil that lurks within this species above all others, an evil that before I did not know existed.

Do you know how many people I have been? How many times I broke the rules of this world's nature? How many times I rebelled against its restrictions? How many times I have been poor and destitute, a prostitute, a beggar, a thief? I was them all: one who had nothing, one who had everything... And what of the down trodden and handicapped, all in all, the lost in who we are, never knowing something greater, handicapped in our minds. I was rich, I was broken, I was black, and white, eastern and Indian; every mix and every creature from everywhere.

I did everything in all those peoples: the do-s and the don'ts, the rights and the wrongs, the faithful and taboo. Who was I but all? I was drum and did drugs, the good and the bad, the loved and the hated, accepted or not.

Not all of the visions were devoid of pleasure, fun and good, yet the positive was so outweighed by the ultimate horror of death that all things suffer in this dimension. What struck me most about this collective mind was its never-ending search for permanence, eternity and glory without success.

Yet through the experience of suffering and death in and as these innumerable creatures throughout this universe, I never once felt the physical pain of anything but always the *inner* suffering: the realization of mortality, the termination of this life, and that it was about to end in those moments. It was the collective mind of this world, God in His first form. I was connected to them all emotionally (at least to a degree yet disconnected physically as though watching through a movie.

Then, oddly, out of the madness of dying in these countless forms came a moment of complete stillness—an *early-man*, covered about the midsection in a rough cut fur. I stood upon the edge of a cliff overlooking a beautiful valley. It was springtime and there was a slight breeze that I saw within the movement of the grass and leaves. I scanned to see what I could see. This man, in him, *my* spirit, was *unusually* still. It was a special moment among so many that I saw and became.

I'm not sure what it was, but perhaps the grandiose view. It was as if suddenly, I, as that person, briefly entered into a higher state of mind. In it I knew something greater, something bigger than just myself. I entered into peace. I became assured, beyond words, that there was something beyond this daily life-and-death struggle, something beyond the survival-mode in which I lived. *I loved that moment.* I loved it and somehow knew who I was. It was a wonderful feeling that had a special significance.

At this point even the galaxies sped by as mere flickers of light. The velocity was such that my mind began to expand, not in one direction, but *all* directions. My consciousness was becoming one with the whole of this physical universe; and in the same capacity that it takes no time for a thought to travel from one side of our brain to another, so was my new brain becoming *all* within this dimension. I was seeing *all* things, I was becoming *all* things, here—the past and the present of every occurrence within our dark universe.

This can be understood by realizing that the light we are seeing from the stars at night is literally millions and even billions of years old. Like an old recording, we are not seeing the stars as they now appear, but as they once did in the remote and distant past. At that distance and even at the speed of light it takes their visage countless years to reach your eyes.

Likewise every occurrence that has ever happened within this physical universe is recorded in an ever-expanding visual journey as it travels across that grandiose distance of space. It's like a history of our universe past, yet it arrives as a live-streaming video feed to the collective consciousness of this world. Likewise, if we see someone running at a distance of only 100 feet away, the speed of light brings us that image almost instantaneously.

But what if that same occurrence could be seen at a distance as far away as the sun? How long would it take for the images to appear? The answer: about 8 minutes and 20 seconds. Now, just because there isn't a human eye to see it doesn't mean that the visual occurrence isn't still traveling across space. Indeed it is still traveling much like a streaming video.

Every moment of everything that has ever happened is still traveling across this universe in which we live. From the time we are born to the time we die, a never-ending broadcast of our life is given to the empty space in which we travel. Spreading outward from its center and still-going, visually, across space, is every single moment that has ever happened. *This* is how the universe expands.

There are only so many things that I can tell you as even in today's sky-is-the-limit age, there's only so much the human mind can hear and receive. What I will say is that the mind of the collective saw all things from one end of *this* universe to the other, past and present, _all at the exact same moment_. There is no way to list them all; there is no way to imagine them all. There are no numbers that will count how many moments of how many lives I witnessed. _So many odd creatures…_

They were all the same too, in that they were all creatures of the same form-ing-physics of this universe. Whether from Earth or a life-form from other planets, all the beings I saw were formed from the **mental matrix** of this dimension. The physics that forms one, forms the rest. I hesitate to tell you simply because it's so beyond the accepted norms of our beliefs and knowledge, but I swear I saw them all and _became_ them all.

In the mind and state of existence in which I found myself, I could view and comprehend all of these images simultaneously. The wild thing is that I viewed those videos from two perspectives: from an outsider's viewpoint, as well as from the mind of the creature itself. The view from the creature's perspective was unique in that I ex-perienced their lives first person. Not just creatures however, but everything, even star explosions or other events. I was absorbing it all.

Just like the light that is arriving from those stars from millions of light years in the past, they are still arriving to our eyes as brand-new and omnipresent images. Likewise, just because we ran across a field as a child 40 years ago, doesn't mean that the image isn't brand-new as it arrives at ever-farther locations throughout space. The recording of our entire life is the same way: traveling _forever_. This of course is only a metaphoric attempt at explaining the experience of which I speak.

And yet I would find that even the scope and scale of all this experience was still only the collective mind of _this_ universe. There was so much more to come though the scope and scale of the experience that thus far was astounding. The enormity of this universe and the countless experiences within it are unbelievable beyond words!

The boundary of the physical universe is not so difficult to describe. It's like the edge of our thoughts perhaps, much as the limits of our learning—a bit fuzzy and gray to the imagination as our minds expand. We push to perceive, but beyond the limit of our comprehension it begins to get cloudy… Behind it however is that which we _do_ know and articulate, the solid matter and reality that follows everything we learn.

The edge of the universe and the mind of the collective within it are this way as well. It is far from being well-defined yet still expands into nothingness, from nothing into something. There, some of the dust and stars follow it as it goes, though most is empty space. I saw the edge as dust, smoky and gray, yet ever-pushing and expanding. Beyond this I can't say…but beyond this was the _ungrund_.

But then it all stopped; all my seeing, all my being, all the grandiose size ceased.

My mind was gone again, narrowed instantly. I found myself, an individual soul again hanging in space and peering across the great emptiness. It was like looking in one direction as far as you can see on a clear night across the stars.

Then behind me, that light. Behind my mind's eye, a glorious and overwhelming white brilliance. It resonated in power as it shined beyond and past my being. This was just as it had been from three years before in my dream of the portal. The sparkles, they were… *atomic*; each one glistening, descending as the waves of a gentle sea. Like the serpent of my dream years before, the light emanated truth and wisdom; its waves slithering into space and time. They were—*alive*, within them a mind, that mind. . .

Once again my view turned to see the source of the light and what it would be. Like the replay of a movie, every part of this was the same as before. Here I was, in the unfathomable expanse, presented before the great attractor, an irresistible presence and the doorway to another dimension. Just like before, I felt its pull upon my being, my soul reconfiguring as I hovered ever closer.

This time was different however, for now I felt its rays piercing the very depth of my soul. I not only saw the light but was becoming it as I neared the *portal* to which I turned. This time I knew full well even before I beheld its visage: a pleasant comfort and the secure embrace of its power. This was my own event horizon, the threshold of another reality that I was about to cross and into.

Finally in full view: an overwhelming sight of beauty and power. There it was, a rip in the very fabric of space, seemingly no bigger in circumference than a simple door is tall. It seemed that size, but round, beaming with a silent magnificence and an energy beyond description. My speed now increased toward it. I felt my being absorbed ever more as I went through—a quick vacuum as an irresistible power took me across and through to the other side; a mere blink, and I was gone forever. . .

As this occurred my consciousness instantly changed. There, in this new dimension, there is only so much I can tell you. It was a different knowing, a much higher understanding, a wisdom and love above all things in this universe. Yet it was the same familiar burst of energy that I'd felt many years before when a little old man touched my outstretched hand while standing in that dusty, dirty truck lot. This time it was even more powerful; and this time I was *one* with that power, *one* with that wisdom and *one* with that unfathomable love.

This new dimension was unlike anything that can be uttered with human words or expression. Words like *"beautiful"*, *"boundless"*, *"eternal"*, *"without end"*, *"love"* and *"God"*, are all pitiful attempts from a pitiful creature to explain something that flat-out is not of this world. In that dimension there is no such thing as time or space; there are no separate beings; there is only light unlike the light of this world. It lasts forever inside of a glory and power infinitely beyond human understanding. It is both perfect and powerful yet entirely peaceful beyond imagination.

The world in which we live *spins*: everything *spins*: the Earth, the sun, the planets, the galaxies, a black hole, and even the universe itself. Here, we spin as well; our minds twist and turn in struggle every day: *"What should I do?"* and *"What should I say?"*—manipulation, control, dominance, strife, advantage. But there, in that place, there was no more spin, but only peace and power beyond all words or understanding.

It emitted yet without space or time—endless, priceless, beyond quantification, beyond description. It was—*forever*, without words or language, without race, creed or gender. There are simply no words, *no words* to describe that—thing, that place, that being, that mind, that light.

It is eternal, without time, outside of time, beyond it. It goes on forever and without end. It is the power of eternity and safe beyond all corruption. How can pure, undefined light be so fulfilling? Because therein is the transformed essence of every thought and every experience that the universe has ever had. Whether grand or small, every imagination in this universe, every being that ever lived and died, is changed and absorbed within that light. It is a *purified Element*: un-dark. There all the negative explodes into an infinite multiplication of glorious power.

Whether that world is large or small is impossible to say simply because it doesn't exist in space and time. I suppose therefore, it is neither. In it however, I heard a pulse somehow, a rhythmic pulse of reverberation, the constant deep voice of a choir in unison: *rumm, rumm, rumm, rumm, rumm, rumm, rumm*—like a heartbeat. It expanded and contracted with infinite power. I could feel it without ceasing, *the breathing of God.*

There was no me there. *There*, I was *that* mind and I was *that* dimension forever, without end. The experience lasted forever—more than many millions of years, but all in a moment, the measurement of time, inapplicable. It was not a consciousness as we know it, but rather a *super*-consciousness—so far beyond thought or deed, yet quiet as even the most still waters, serene beyond imagination.

The word *"love"* cannot communicate the depth of the person we call *God*. Love is not something He *has*, but rather who He *is*. It is—*He* is, the end-all, be-all entity; it exceeds anything else and everything else; it is so much more than I had ever believed in or hoped for, far deeper and more profound in every capacity than I know how to tell. In that love, everything before it, everything of all space and time has its perfect purpose: the past the present and the future all as one. There everything made sense in perfect rhyme, reason and sequence, even the horrible suffering of this world. To know what God knows; to see what God sees; to have the God-consciousness of all things.

But for all of its grandeur, for all its impeccable perfection, its indescribable peace, love and joy, that glorious dimension still sees this world and stands in awe and admiration of its sacrifice, an irresistible beauty in its weakness as even the Almighty knows it will bring Him an heir of life. This is not a mythical history story, but the spirit of sacrifice that all our lives have been. It knows that the pain and sufferings of this world are, in fact, the bloodline that feeds that higher dimension; that our sufferings here, though unintended, keep Him alive *there*.

It is this great conveyor belt of life that also ensures our eternity as well, for in Him we find ourselves or nothing at all. Indeed, in the same way that our food dies to bring us life, so does our suffering and death become the lifeline of God in Heaven. There, we become Him.

Some will say; *"What if the sun dies? What then? As such there can be no portal and thus no food for Heaven."* This universe has many such restaurants from which God can eat, many planetary arrangements and creatures from which to pull the suffering of this dark dimension. Likewise, the Earth upon which you find yourself, is only one of many. Yet even when this universe eventually dies, as it eventually will, there are countless other universes all of which supply the one and only dimension of Heaven.

So while the divine has quite the harem of physical universes from which to choose, all of which bring life, by the very matrix of its makeup there can be only one Heaven. This is the nature of the divine, for in that transformed dimension He is a giving God, a loving God, a God of all and the same God in which we will all one day partake. The Father, the Mother, the child, are all only pictorial of the dimensions themselves, each of which are ultimately only different facets of the same person of God.

God is all-powerful too. Yet in the anatomy of God, things work a specific way simply because it is the only way that things can work. Upon the sharp tip of a needle is the whole of Heaven, for therein is the way and the life and, for what you will come to learn, the resurrection. Surely I lived this, I was this, and I remember this *forever*.

...Suddenly however, as I lived within that wonderful bliss, in a moment, all things stopped; the peace, the power, the glory, all ceased. Now was a new stillness. I found myself, the mind of God, again suspended within the abyss of space. I entered if but only for a moment, this universe. There I hung quietly upon the edge of some invisible force that surrounds this planet. I rested upon the cusp of a magnetic-energy, God, upon it, a part of that mind beginning to tangle within it.

I beheld this planet with a focus that before didn't exist within the light. What I saw was a dying people to whom, somehow, I was pulled toward. They were lost, *so lost*. Within me was a sudden pity for this place, now the essence of a tear within me. It was very powerful and very precious; the awareness in that moment. I knew that they had all forgotten, each one oblivious to those around them. They did not know me; how could they not know me? I felt a sudden weakness in the question.

I began to feel myself drained of energy, a separation of my being into two equal parts, a split in my mind and of who I was. I saw souls, many small flickers of light being sapped from the Source. Like so many bits of energy floating from behind me and downward toward the Earth, and with them I too was being drawn ever farther from the light. I was entering space and time.

With this discomfort a realization, myself now in two, a conversation between them. Now a giver of will and an obedient-receiver of that directive, the exchange between a father and a son. It came as a simple yet solemn command:

"I send you: -I go"…

Upon this the light of the portal behind me extinguished. With it now the God-consciousness instantly ended. I fell now at great speed upon a seemingly predetermined arch of descent. The fall was terrible, violent, screaming in fear, a shriek of uncontrolled terror and confusion as I was hurled toward this hapless mass of rock.

It happened quickly; that energy that had me, propelled me at an unbelievable speed, -the speed of the magnetism that had somehow captured my mind. Yet I remember, vaguely, colors of light in a blur followed by a slight slowing as I fell through the clouds, then the shock of a horrible crash.

With great violence I was slammed inside some vessel or container, -a lump of flesh and blood: *and then*, for a brief flickering moment, I sat there suspended, no longer in the body of God, but in the body of one who I knew not—*still* falling off the counter, the clock *still* changing from 3:27 to 3:28. No time had transpired since the beginning of this miraculous journey, not even a moment.

…Yet oddly, somehow, I remembered falling like this before. I remember this horror as if a rerun from a long-lost time. It was long, long ago—a *déjà vu* from another chapter in some distant past. I recalled in that moment not only the horror but also the recollection of a parched desert just before a great mountain. The images were vague but real.

I awoke, then, I remembered, -in the body of one. Who he was, at first, I could not say—a strange being like so many others in this universe. I awoke in him, naked, yet aglow with the power of God. There I stood upon the edge of that place, barren and desolate. To the horizon, its appearance, purplish-blue, a distant range. *Where was I? Who was this person?* Yet somehow I knew this was where I was supposed to be.

He began to walk, with no food or water, fed by the fusion within, irradiating the creature in which I walked. I took that body, not by choice, but by proximity. In that body, I assumed control, the choosing not of my own and even less of his: no thoughts on how to sustain the life of this creature in which I now dwelt.

I was driven by a knowledge, the power of who I was. *Who am I?* I am; *I am.* With no shame or tepidness, only great strides of confidence, I walked as one possessed; I focused upon those hills nonstop for three days.

I weakened over time, a cooling of my being—and then—*SMACK!* I hit the floor like a bag of bricks, eyes wide open, my being stuck in some foreign mass. I lay staring at the base-board of the cabinets, in shock, but somehow still radiating with the *love* of the creature I was before—not a possession mind you, but the *Element* that I was in the light of Heaven. There I lay; I did not and could not move.

This is where the real problems began, because as I lay there, I didn't know *who* I was or *what* I was. I didn't know my name or even what a name was. I didn't know where I was or why I was there. I began to hear a loud groaning. What was this noise? It was me, this entity, this being, from the body I now inhabited. *Oh my God, the pain.* Weakly I called: *Help, help!*

Over the course of the next hour my consciousness returned, slowly of course, yet I could not recover from the shock. I still reached within for the light. I lay upon the kitchen floor, motionless. I awoke to the realization that the overwhelming pain I felt was normal. Pain is part of this life, yet because we have nothing with which to remember or compare, we instead accept the agony as *"feeling good"*.

Remember, I had just left perfection, the highest of all dimensions in which there was no pain or suffering. Now I found myself in wretchedness, a trap, a nightmare, a torture, this humiliation, this *hell*. I understand now: this is what the angels did before me. They too fell through that same doorway, those same flickers of light from the portal. Yet where did they go? What was their fate?

Over the next three days I said nothing. My wife, understandably worried, asked her mother for help, to visit and to talk. They were concerned and completely clueless as to what happened. Yet what could I say to explain? Speech was meaningless and pitiful. What was there that I could say or do compared to that experience and that place?

"Daniel; are you okay?" The question was pointless and not worth answering.

"Please tell us what is wrong!" How could I even begin to answer?

Finally I remember my mother-in-law asking me,

"Did you see something or what? What happened?"

This at least got me to look up and into her eyes. I struggled again to respond, but there simply wasn't anything I could say.

I wanted to communicate, to say something, *I suppose*; that I had *seen…*, that I *was…*Wait, what's happening? It was all so confusing. I couldn't say *"Heaven"* or the *"Glory of God"* for even the word *"God"* was a pitiful lack of respect for the light of which I had been. Everything was beyond words. Finally I shook my head as if to acknowledge that I didn't want to talk.

By the end of the third day however, and seeing the torment that my silence inflicted upon others, I managed with great effort to communicate *what had happened*. It was strange to relearn who and what I was in this world, a complete reconfiguration of mental matter into this lowly state.

The gibberish coming from my mouth and the mouths of others; what was this brutally low form of communication that I heard? In this case I would find it was called *English*. The whole thing was bizarre as I couldn't even recognize the language of my thoughts much less the words of my wife. It's hard to believe this babel was once my native tongue.

Some part of the brain however, must have had memory recall. Otherwise how was I breathing? *Aha! "Breathing"*, which would imply some form of life. Yet if this was really life then let's eat and drink, for tomorrow we die, but now, I was already dead in this separation from the light. I was now a prisoner to this body, a *bad dream*, spoken in English. *Yes*, I remember the meaning now; that must be what this is: *a bad dream*.

Finally when I could speak, it was brutally forward so as to bring immediate ridicule. As I explained what had happened, their response was typical for those who have forgotten, again protecting the boxes in which they slept:

"Oh, I wouldn't tell anyone; just keep it to yourself! It's not worth it. Please, please just keep this to yourself. You'll be alright."

God forbid, of course, that we talk about God from self-experience. *What will people think? What will they say?* Oh the scandal of not being a sheep led to slaughter. Oh the chains of this world and the fears under which we live, our cares for others' perceptions. *Damn* our lack of insight. I was frustrated yet exhausted from this whole ordeal and slept better than I had in years. Within the shut of my eyes I found solace, a respite from conscious thought and the horrible fact that I was lost. For a while at least my dreams and visions of the grids had stopped. Sleep became my friend, a welcome reprieve from the hell in which I found myself.

There was however, a residual effect that lingered from the other side. I knew their minds now, *their minds*. I could see their thoughts, *everyone's* thoughts. I knew their pains. If their knee hurt, I sensed it. If their hearts ached, I could feel it. I was not so much an empath now, but rather extra-sensory. I could see their posturing usually before they were aware of it themselves.

Humans do that, you know; they calculate one against the other. Seldom is the mind within man straight forward or genuine, nor can it be. They maneuver for advantage on an almost non-stop basis and, for those who can see it, it is the very hallmark of evil. They do it through the manipulation of words and questions, through politics, through religions, through money, through family structure, through everything.

I could see these evils that accompany a world of separate souls. We call this *"normal"* of course, but it is not. We call it reality, but it is wrong. While here on Earth however, this is the nature of a mind divided. There is no real oneness, but only division, and with division comes contention and warfare. We search for oneness no doubt, but it is an unlikely thing, a desert walk with no water.

A madness ensued from my predicament. I became quite the thrill-seeker, doing almost anything for the sake of adrenaline; anything for the sake of energy. I starved for the energy that I'd lost since my fall. My risks, though calculated, showed a blatant disregard for the body that my mind now recklessly used. To be free of gravity, to jump from an airplane, to climb a cliff with no rope, to run, to dive and to drive like a maniac. Anything for adrenaline and endorphins.

My mind bullied my body into doing whatever it so-chose, no longer in consideration of its pains. Cynical of the body's weakness, I pushed it to the point of collapse. I taunted it from within my thoughts, somehow hoping for release. Suicide was an option and duly considered, but between the *promise*, the *portal*, and the *face of my children*, I could not justify such action. There had to be a reason I was here. *Oh,* but the insanity of this existence.

I was not out of body, per se, but at odds the flesh and blood chains that had me. There was *"Me"* and then there was the body to which I was unfortunately stuck. I was *just crazy*, crazy to the point that I once jumped off a 55 foot high wall at a sand-pit into a pile of sand no bigger than a car. It was a shortcut at the time to where I was going, and I did it with no more thought than walking down a sidewalk.

I was *crazy* to the point of jumping from a cliff onto a nearby tree or treetop only to shimmy down without rope or harness; *crazy* enough, now, to jump from that tree into the top of a sapling to only ride its bow to the ground; *crazy* to the point of, having forgotten my tools by which to disassemble a barn one day, I instead used my feet and fist and easily finished the job by myself and by that afternoon.

Too hot or *too* cold was the body's problem, *not mine*. Its woes, its weaknesses meant little to me and only revealed the frailty of the physical creature I inhabited. I did not hate my body yet resented its limitations and rightly so. It could not compare to who and how I was before and within the dimension from which I came.

On a pleasant note, my interaction with the natural world was taken to a whole new level. An energized feeling would occur, similar to the one I'd felt when that little old man touched my hand. When it did, I could approach any animal, whether it be a wild deer, bird etc., and instantly touch or hold that creature. In those moments they trusted me; they knew me and I knew them as well.

There were often witnesses to these events too, and while I could never make it happen at will, when it did occur, it was as real as the sun in the sky. One Saturday morning I, my wife and children were eating breakfast at the kitchen table. My daughter, having spotted a blue jay at the window, tugged on my shirt-sleeve to show me. It was looking not at us through the glass but at me. Thus I *knew*, I felt in that instant, as it did me—*our souls*. It wanted nothing special from me, but the inward food of union that I also sought.

There we both sat, frozen in stare, speaking more through the eyes than any volume of words could ever explain. I arose and walked to the door, went outside and around to the corner. The jay, typically a mean-spirited and territorial bird, met me half way, perched upon the limb of the Bradford pear. Oddly as it twitched this way and that as birds do, I knew his mind, as he also knew mine. I was inside his mind already: not his mind, not my mind, but a connection, a mixture of the two, not separate, but one.

Without pause I extended my arm to which he simply hopped from the limb and onto my thumb. And so I stood and stared as did he, content with this connection as was I. My wife and children, seeing this, were only steps behind, gathered around to witness the spectacle. At the time it was as natural as *falling off a log*, as we used to say.

I gently cupped the jay with both hands and let everyone take turns touching him in awe of what was happening. After less than a minute I reached him back up to the limb to which he disembarked without fear or flight. The ensuing conversation brought a multitude of questions and speculation: Was the bird sick? How did I know he'd let me hold him? Could I do it again?

So again I reached, to which the jay ascended, a foot or so beyond my reach. I spoke to him in his native tongue and walked closer: *Come here; it's okay*; to which he again lit on my wrist. Again for another 30 seconds or so we all marveled at how wonderful a thing this was. And then the feeling, the bond, quickly began to fade, a connection that I could not fake in a thousand years. As it did and the energy of the moment left, so did the bird; flying away to another tree far out in the field, probably himself wondering what in the world he was doing in a human's hand.

I too was wondering what had happened, how I knew and how the bird knew. But the fact was, deep down inside, I *did* know what had happened, that it was an after-effect of the portal experience. It was a power beyond thinking, beyond *thought*. It was not *doing*, but *knowing*; it was not *thinking*, but *being*. However, it was far more than just being in harmony with nature. Indeed it was *supernatural*.

A month later was an incident with a deer. It was a doe who loitered in the field behind the yard. It too felt the attraction, that overwhelming energy. Again I have no clue what activated this event within that particular animal and at that particular moment, in myself as well, but it happened. The energy projected itself in great power within and when it did, the rules of nature changed in an instant.

I walked to the deer as though to a sister, a familiar old friend. As I did it grazed and then raised and met me half-way. There I rubbed her back and scratched her shoulder as she continued to graze. It was wonderful to see and I can remember as my mother marveled at the sight.

Again however, the energy began to fade after about two minutes. When it did, I could progressively feel the nervousness of the deer within my own being. This too was a shared energy and natural for the deer. So as goes the way of nature, so did the deer. Shortly thereafter she bounded away for the safety of the woods as I too returned to my house.

My genius was followed by complexity. I was as simple as a child, yet no longer simple to the ways of this world. I saw everything in great detail. Who was this man I'd become, this memory that had invaded my human life? The depth of it, profound; the love, beyond description. This mind and its understanding. I had become *touched* as now I also touched the world with the dimension from which I came.

The God-Element continued to fade over the next three months. When it shined, it shined oh so slightly. At times they could see the glow, barely discernible, *but there*, a layer of luminescence that they could not deny. It infuriated many and astounded a few more. Most seemed to hate it because they could not explain or control it.

But the changes within were also at odds with this world. The new me made it difficult to maintain relationships. Almost every conversation was awkward as I had little or no subject matter in common. I was an eccentric now to whom almost no one could relate. As a man blinded, I saw only the desire of my mind, the need to connect with that energy from Heaven. Thus the races and games, the parties and politics, the family and finances, all became the mundane.

I was a bit odd and I knew it. Often even I wondered if I'd lost my mind, and why not? Everything from my understanding of life to my understanding of the scriptures was changing. Not only had my focus changed, but the drive that we have for the things of this world was gone as well. I was miserable yet could not take my eye away from the experiences I'd had. Though seemingly powerless now to make them return, they were yet too real to deny.

By little surprise, as the glory within me faded, came the return of those confounded circles and grids. All I wanted to do was return to that higher dimension; but if I couldn't be there, then I at least wanted to learn more about it via the means before me. Thus I took a new look at the grids and now dissected them mentally. I sensed now more than ever that they held the key by which to return home.

Yes; I still wanted love and closeness while here on Earth, but even that eluded my grasp as did every other endeavor of human life. I had no one to talk to; no friends to whom I could confide. The fact was, that my hunger for life was no longer filled with the health, wealth, and wisdom of this world. As a result of my changed-focus, I lost my money—*all of it*. I lost relationships too—*almost all of them*. I got divorced, and with it my reputation was destroyed through a series of bad choices, bad luck, and an outlook to another world that simply didn't fit. So was it my fault or Heaven's?

But even in depression and financial ruin, the hells of this world were unable to snuff that one tiny moment in eternity; an event that I could not touch or smell or see nor even prove had happened. Yet those experiences were infinitely more real than my everyday life. With this more than 27 years of vibrant youth, physical wellbeing and social and financial good standing as well as a stable marriage were instantly exchanged for this new mantle.

Then came the deception. Now having been touched by another world, I too wanted to touch and to express my inner being. I had a message that I wanted to be heard and so I turned toward any inward-leaning ear. In this there were those who told me what I wanted to hear to get what they wanted for themselves. Yet I too was lured by opportunity.

Unable to find that energy from beyond the portal, I became deceived by my feelings. I fell for the allures of natural attraction, the *female physique*, for those who promised a similar love and interest for the divine. In turn it was an opportunity to connect, to find some sort of bond beyond what I could find alone.

These actions were in contradiction to my own beliefs. I had come to hate this world, yet found myself with no better option for oneness than sex—not just sex for the sake of sex, mind you, but a desperate search for energy through some type of union with another. I indulged in sex and gravitated towards every beautiful woman I could find.

The Element, though faded in all but my eyes, emitted just enough emerald to entrance their minds. With a mere look I seduced them, *not I however*, but the remnant power of Heaven they beheld. It was the visage of my eyes, what had become *steely* eyes, a telltale sign of what lay within. Thus the truth was confused by the flesh, not only them, but myself as well. I became quite the cad, that era of my life a story in itself.

It was this that began my downward spiral even further from the reality of Heaven, for in it would come a series of affairs that destroyed everything. In this process I made a lot of mistakes and did a lot of very stupid things that I regret. Ultimately however, experience was my best teacher for what would come.

In the end I would find that while in this world, I truly was not of it, that no matter who I am here in the flesh, it in no way defines who I am in my ultimate form. But I had to, -*had to*- lose everything first to see it. And not only loose it, but actually have a changed hope—*so changed*—that the loss of this life no longer mattered, that the loss of reputation, love, relationship and money meant nothing. He had to be able to trust me first. He had to make me unshakable. So now, a delusion and a dream became more powerful than my despair. It's all quite amazing really, for in time, even despair would turn to faith.

Now I knew what the little old man had told me. Aside from the visions, he was preparing me; he was training me. It's why I had a dream of the portal that I couldn't, at first, remember. Before, I simply wasn't ready to know the deep things of God though they were still registering within my subconscious all along. Until I was broken of myself however, I could not be entrusted with what I saw or experienced. That said, even more correction would be on its way.

THE SACRIFICE

Every second and a half to two seconds, for an hour at a time:

chop . . . chop . . . chop . . . chop . . . chop . . . chop . . . chop

Hand hewing logs with an axe and broad-axe was hard labor, *-brutally tough*, but, at the time, so was I. However it was equally rewarding as well. Not only had I built the log-house in which I lived, but made some of the most beautiful hand-hewn mantels around.

And while it had begun as a hobby, it had grown into a means by which to rid myself of excess energy. My run-in with that seemingly hapless old man brought more than one side-effect as did the event of the portal. Not only did I live in a constant state of increased brain activity, but now my physical energy had spiked as well.

My thoughts raced, not in confusion, but in clarity. I became an empath of sorts and a mere look into someone's eyes gave me volumes. I could feel their hurt, their hate, their lies and fears. My mind expanded in creativity as well, far beyond what I ever imagined possible. So regardless of those happenstance, whether real or imagined, they had certainly caused some very real changes in me.

As you might guess, I was becoming a bit maddened with these turn of events. It got to the point where I could hew logs for 10 hours a day then still run 3 or 4 miles in the same boots and blue jeans in which I'd worked; soaked in sweat but still beaming with a power that simply didn't make sense. There were times, even after all that, I would lie in bed unable to sleep, literally trembling with energy.

My mind darted through the thousands of grids and the constant movies of my memories. Frequently I would get up in the middle of the night and write a thought or sketch an image, only to finally doze off in the wee hours of the morning. Even with this I could often jump out of bed the next morning like a springboard, straight to the coffee maker, throw on some duds, slop the hogs, pour the coffee, and out the door. It was a fact that I simply couldn't slow down.

So while I loved the boundless energy, the downside was that it became increasing difficult to function within a normal social setting. Not only was it difficult to sit still for very long, but I became increasingly intolerant of normal human interactions. *Keeping up with the Jones* simply became *plastic*; small-talk felt *fake,* and the norms of life, unbearable and vain. My mind was elsewhere now, the images being far more entertaining than a sparkling clean car and having my grass mown exactly 3.4 inches tall. I became quite the slob, unorganized, hap-hazard and increasingly eccentric.

I came to resent not only the shallowness of others but even my own physical needs. I was part animal, at least I should say, *locked* in an animal's body, always forced to yield to its needs and lusts. I was nowhere near the portal now, still certainly in *this* world, but just as sure *that I was not of it.* Yet I could not escape.

As a result, my daily walk in life became an endless series of distractions. I ate, but despised that I had to. I worked and even enjoyed the feeling of accomplishment, but resented through my teeth the need to work for money. I hated money, yet with a modern family in a modern world, I obviously had to have it. I would often begin a hobby only to quickly begrudge the vanity in which I partook. This world was cruel and boring by comparison and I constantly sought things, *anything,* to distract me from this harsh reality.

There was only so much that I could accomplish with the mind-images I saw, and thus with the good came the bad. Increasingly I felt trapped with the memories of a life that I could neither prove nor pursue. Thus, work became my friend in that it brought the diversions and exhaustion I desperately needed to escape conscious thought.

Increasingly nothing seemed to satisfy. My soul was in full rebellion against the limitations of this world and at times I became a bit unthankful for the things that I did have. Yet while in this body I fully realized there were bottom-lines—money, food, water and breathing; all things that simply could not be circumvented. At times I pondered the madness of my transition: the birthing process, a life moving from the familiar into the unknown. I was in the birth canal of consciousness, literally somewhere between two worlds—unwilling to stay within the norm, yet unable to ascend into something better.

I pushed forward, however, sensing that somehow there was so much more to be had—and thus my reckless abandonment of life as I'd known it till then. I still hunted, even though it too was losing its appeal. I had always hunted for substance; *nothing went to waste*. We ate what we harvested; deer, rabbit, turkey etc. So while I fully accepted the dynamics of the circle of life, that something must die in order for something else to live, whether a carrot or a quail, a beet or a buck, I began to see the vanity in all things. Few things, besides an angel, choose to die—*food for thought*.

I obviously couldn't stop eating but found myself questioning why I had too. I was never a bleeding heart, but now pondered the madness of even life out of death. The religious folk in my life confidently asserted God's intentions that the plants and animals were made for our consumption. They pointed to Genesis 9:2 and other verses as proof to their point.

Yet I couldn't help but wonder that if the process was so great, why didn't they join the food chain? It seemed hypocritical to think it a *"blessing"* to kill and eat yet a horror to be killed and eaten. In other words, if being *killed, gutted, skinned, and eaten* was so great, then why were there no volunteers?

Ignorance is bliss I suppose. Cognitive dissonance is the coping mechanism of all creation. What's more, humans even have scriptures to reinforce such beliefs. How else would we manage in our own little worlds, small as they are, to know the truth? What would happen if we awoke to realize the horrors of our doing, the state of separation and ignorance: that, in fact, every living thing feels; that all things desire life; that the food we eat also felt and feared, and that many mourn the loss of their own just as we do?

On the other end of the spectrum came the argument that we should all be vegetarians and thus stop the inhumane killing of animals for food. But these folks too seemed cowards in my eyes, for at least the deer had a chance to run away, while the plants in their garden had no chance at all. Just because you can't hear a plant's plead doesn't mean it wanted to die for you.

Besides, if being a vegetarian was so pure and moral, why pray tell do so-many plants grow thorns in defense? Why, if devoid of consciousness, would they concoct their own poisons to prevent consumption? Ironically even the plants and animals often have more faith than do we, instinctively believing in what lies before them instead of the accepted norm of political, religious and social programming. *Oh to be back to that light again.*

Indeed, while the sheep may be for slaughter, we in fact often lead ourselves to slaughter. Our minds are separate, each bit of God asleep in billions of bodies, each going their own direction. Instead of harmony however, come the wars of race, religion and regions. We wage the battle of the sexes and the daily grind all due to our separation from the realm I witnessed.

Make no mistake, almost all life in nature chooses to live just as you do. Yet they too partake of this world's madness and the brutality as well; they too battle for space as does humanity. In our fallen and blinded state we perceive nature as *beauty*, but why? Show me the mythical *"ecosystem"* in which we fantasize about trees and animals living in harmony. No less than the barbarous human, the trees also choke and crowd to gain advantage. As a war is slow motion, each seeks to rise above the rest, each to own the sunlight, as does man's religion to own the light of God. This is in fact the fight of this world in which we are all blindly joined.

I had come to terms with the fact that real death is not of the body; that real death is in fact the dimension in which we live. *Death* is *a state of mind*, a mind separate from the knowledge of God. Had this not been so, then nothing would ever die. Yet it all does die, not just at the end of life, but every moment of every day we fight the struggles of the un-illumined.

Our soul struggle from the moment it is born; it cries out from the moment of its conception. From the bed upon which it enters this world, to the bed upon which it dies, it mourns. Indeed, our deaths begin at the very beginning of this flesh and blood life. Are there moments of happiness? Of course; but temporary they are, as all things in this physical world.

Strangely, however, something else was now controlling my destiny. I was changing. Increasingly I found myself being fed inwardly from another source, *fulfilled*, not with that which I put in my stomach, but by that which emitted from my heart. It was a heart within my heart, not flesh and blood, but a very real spirit-Element. And the more I remembered Heaven, the less I felt obligated to partake in this world's affairs.

There was a great shift in my consciousness. I was consumed by that event, *the portal*. Like our food, my thoughts now digested into a new mind; my very being absorbed into another, increasingly in union with *its* mind, *His mind*, my life in this world now laid upon the alter of transformation. Progressively I was no longer my own, a man of this world, but a man who remembered something beyond as well as a long forgotten past here on Earth.

I saw a reflection from a former life; I beheld an ancient face, in my imagination, the image of a *Wiseman*. The one I recalled was stunning, his eyes aglow with the light from another world. The intensity of his stare, the power of his persona—*supernatural*. He was just barely contained in his body; translucent, transcendent, nearly able to sail the skies but by the will of his mind.

Who was this person and what did it mean? Yet somehow he seemed oddly familiar: *Is this the creature that I had forgotten? Is this who I really once was, perhaps who I had once been?* In the mirror of my mind we came face to face. There he stared directly into my eyes as if awaiting a response; alive and looking at me.

More and more the memories returned, not just from the beginning, but to the very beginning. From far before the fall, and into the *ungrund* I could see—I envisioned eternity and now, evermore clearly, what the little old man told me. I could see in my mind his face that day when he said he was here to help me remember. And now I *could* remember. My Lord, my God, *I remember . . .*

With this came the realization that the countless images I'd seen were not created by another but were indeed of *my own making*, by *this same ancient man that I now beheld*. Now also I knew why I had made them and exactly how profound they truly were. Most bizarre of all, however, was that my fall from Heaven was not in this *life*, in 1991, tumbling from that counter in the kitchen as I had supposed, but instead many eons ago. I was ancient indeed, but only recollected my prehistoric fall that night. Indeed 1991 was but a flashback from a long lost time, a post-traumatic incident in which the past came back to haunt me once again.

The more I remembered about that life and time, the faster its memory returned. I saw others as well, a small group of beings. I recalled their faces and pondered their names. They were, *we* were, the ancient magicians, *the real magi of old*. As crazy as it sounds, I recalled the grand undertaking with which we were charged. Their stares beckoned me to action, to wake and to work. With only their thoughts they commanded, *Open the seals; tell them the truth; tell them the science; tell them everything. Daniel—it is time.*

I came to realize the great wealth of knowledge and wisdom embedded within those sacred images. I knew now that I hadn't dreamed about the portal, but that it was real, that it had closed immediately after the ancient fall, but also now how to open it again. Now I understood my attraction to the ancient scriptures and that indeed the formula on how to open the portal was hidden within them.

There was a connection, a sacred thread that the magi themselves had penned all those centuries before. How precious those works, those words that were written, a gift for your cultures to read, a perfect spell that would realign your Earth to open the gateway to a place you call, Heaven. They are not what you think they are. Those words are not what you were led to believe. Now the revelation of the ancient mysteries was complete in me. Now I saw as they saw, and I knew what they knew.

Yet the *fall* haunted me ever more. Indeed I beheld its horror nightly as the pictures played across my imagination, mixed with a childhood dream. They all started the same: each time I walked toward the bluff that overlooked the valley of the old farm. I had come there to fly, and as I approached the edge of the cliff came the feeling of separation, my mind from my body. The rush was fantastic and enveloped my being—the chill-bumps of ascension through the air and true freedom.

But then, just as my spirit soared, flying high above the clouds nearing the precipice of escape, came the predictable jolt—falling again through space identically as I had that night, screaming uncontrollably. The outcome was always the same: I awoke in bed with a shock, sweating, pondering that I was still here, still a prisoner to this world of insanity. Each time I was left with the same thoughts, wondering why God had led me to this end. *Why* was I given a knowledge so grand but that yet led to nowhere?

Either way it matters not, as I see now how the scriptures were designed to manage our barbarism for a time. The goal was not to teach the human animal truth, but for a far greater cause than even the life of the human itself. You see, dear friend, it is *God* who hunts the suffering of all things in this world. We indeed are the garden of his choosing, the sacrificial animal that brings life to Him. *Humans* do not own the food chain as we supposed but are at the bottom of God's own need of life. Yet in Him, we are all truly one…

Now I will tell you: I never saw the little old man again, *never*; but I did however feel his presence, inwardly, more than once. I heard his voice within, and I still hear him today, in my mind and as my own imagination. He scolded me once, very rightfully so; a story of which I'd like to share:

Many of my relationships had faltered; some, the cause of which others had contributed, but much of which I could blame on no one besides myself. In hindsight, this one was on me . . .I had not spoken to my father in over a year, and harbored a bit of resentment for some *seemingly* poor choices he'd made in recent years. It had accumulated into a lot of unnecessary drama that complicated the lives of everyone else in the family. He was quite the enigma however, the best of times and the worst of times.

Dad was certainly old school in his outlook and would have easily matched the Hatfield's and McCoy's for toughness. He'd grown up through the Great Depression and learned how to survive in a way that many folks today simply can't understand or relate. He demanded respect yet seldom yielded it in return. No doubt he had his demons; he could be harsh and unforgiving, but underneath the veneer he had a heart of gold—*usually, but certainly not always.*

He was old and frail now, hunched-backed at 75 years; his eyesight was failing and was quite the pitiful sight. That said, he was still quick to anger when provoked and was a fearful entity even as an elderly man. In his youth he was known for his fists and now, even now, for his skill with a pistol. So, naturally I respected him as both a father should be respected but also at the cost of strong retribution had I forgotten my place.

What he had accomplished however, is what a father is *supposed* to do: he worked, put food on the table, and protected me from harm until I was a man and out on my own. He spared not the rod of correction and, I think at least, did not spoil the child. Beyond that he was there for me even when I stumbled as an adult and on more than one occasion.

He had raised me to be fearless as well, though I probably will never be as naturally bold as him. He taught me things about people, life, honesty, dishonesty, farming, fighting, shooting, hunting, equipment, trucks, logging, and love, you name it—a luxury of practical learning that many never have. I was lucky that way, yet his occasional mean streaks were often excessive and downright ornery.

What's more he was probably the most unapologetic individual I'd ever met, sometimes to the point of narcissism. I will admit that he was a product of his environment, the end result of a life full of hardships. The man had suffered more than most ever knew, much of which wouldn't come to light until many years after he passed. To discover the depth of abuse in his childhood and what he'd kept to himself all those years would one day change the way I looked at much of what he'd done.

We had always been close, but I had finally had it with his stubborn belligerence. His insensitivity in matters of relationship had in fact terminated most of his friendships. I wanted him to hurt, as he had hurt the rest of us, and I knew that my avoidance cut deep. This evasion was fine to a degree, but I'd admittedly become a bit self-righteous in this game. Indeed I had broken my own rule of simply spitting out what I thought. I was playing the cat-game instead of confronting and telling the truth about how I felt. What's more, I felt superior in my decision to act this way as, at the time, everyone else in the family was also disgusted, thus justifying my own feelings—or so I thought.

He knew, too, that the family was unhappy with the path he'd taken. I myself had purposely avoided him in the last year, hoping it would force him to look at things through a new lens. Avoidance was easy too, especially considering that he was basically blind in one eye and couldn't see out of the other (A country slang for generally poor vision). That and the color of his truck was like a beacon and could easily be spotted at a distance. It was a bright *raspberry-red*, of all colors—derived upon from his favorite drink: a *Big Red*: This was a concoction of his own invention, consisting of Bourbon over ice, red grenadine and topped with of all things, his favorite fruit: *a raspberry*.

Now, I need to switch directions for a moment so that you can understand where this story is headed. Let's go back about two weeks before. It was mid-November and I was deer hunting as I had every year since I could remember. One day while in the woods, I heard a gunshot on the property next to ours, not over a couple of hundred yards to my right. The shot made a shrill, shrieking noise as it crossed the open field, ending with a dull *thud*, the familiar sound of a good hit, presumably a deer. As it were, within only a moment or two a buck jumped the fence, wounded and badly limping. There it stopped and stood within 30 yards or so of my position, breathing heavily and bleeding profusely from its rib-cage.

He had an uneven rack, his right antler being normal, bowed well outside his ear and was very stately, while his other was deformed and bent straight down in front of his face. I'd heard of this deformity before, typically the result of a prior injury, but it was quite the sight to see. Not wanting the animal to suffer further, I too shot, hitting the deer squarely in the boiler room and knocking him flat. But for some reason, instead of staying down, he quickly recovered and ran off as though uninjured. Baffled by this, but convinced that he couldn't possibly run the length of another football field, I began to track what was sure to be my dinner. As tracking goes, this one was easy; his blood left a distinct trail and I was confident I'd be filling the freezer with meat by the end of the day.

However, after tracking the buck for over a half mile, *blood everywhere*, I decided to stop and let him lie down, and die (*which they typically will if not pursued*). After a couple of hours I continued and, sure enough found where he had bedded down, bled a lot more and then continued on his way. Again I tracked him for another half-mile or more, still to no avail. The sun was waning and it would be less than an hour before dark. Seeing as the blood trail had stopped, and not wanting to lose the harvest or protract the animal's suffering, I called a couple of friends to help me track.

Thereafter the three of us looked for the buck well into the night but with zero luck, searching over 100 acres and with two dogs, both of which were good trackers. Needless to say, I was frustrated for the failed hunt, and more-so for the deer's suffering. I wasn't opposed to the harvest yet felt an overwhelming pity for the pain and fear of a creature that simply wanted to graze the fields and woodlands yet was now doomed to a slow and agonizing death.

Now, what happened next is where the science of the ancients parts with the dogma of modern thought and reasoning. I understand and agree that the outer mythologies of our religions were often childishly simplistic. I also comprehend that much or even most of these myths can be neither validated nor confirmed in a historical context. What's more, it makes sense that people want proof of what is real and what is not. I get that.

As you are going to see, however, those mythologies were only a *cloak* for the real knowledge that lies beneath their surface. So I have promised to show you the ancient study in detail and I will. Before I do that, however, I would first like to share the power of the Element into which the ancient science tapped. What happened next with that deer is indeed exemplary of this greatly misunderstood substance, but only a mild example of its potential.

The substance or, *Element* of which I speak and of which the magi knew, was more than the raw results of input and output, numbers, formulas, and the like. Indeed, the science of the ancients delved into and quantified the very matrix of the subconscious soul. Here we are immeasurable, countless, and without limits. In this science, things go beyond the boundaries of periodic tables and atomic structure. Here we plunge into the *infinite*.

You see, while I walked the woods that night, searching for the predictable and likely outcome of physics—two bullets, both squarely placed within the heart/lung area of that deer, shredding him terribly, bleeding profusely, having lost more than enough blood to already be dead—something equally unlikely and unpredictable occurred. It went beyond the science of *one-plus-one-equals-two*, yet nonetheless added perfectly in me: *I heard Him*; deep within the recesses of my mind, a small still voice that said,

"This is the way;"

—*clearly*, but as a solemn command and with the most serious tone, the voice of the little old man. *Aha*, I heard him in my mind.

"Insanity," says you.

"Perhaps," says I.

. . . But the mind; the boiler room of all i-*magi*-nation; the forge of all reality; and in it, if you choose to listen, the most important things of all. It is the most unprovable place, yet the very thing that we use *all*-day, *every*-day. *Yes, inside my mind I heard Him*:

"Go to the hillside and find the sacrifice that I made for you since before the foundations of the world"

Hmmm, I thought. *What hillside?* I mean, *really*, all we have here is hillsides. But I went anyway, obediently, to where my instinct led.

Once there I actually found a blood trail that I had tracked earlier in the day but opted not to track again as I already knew its outcome. Not knowing what to do next, I simply sat down and became still, listening for something else, *another* clue, *another* voice in my increasingly ruined sanity, *anything* would have been nice—but instead, *nothing*.

There I stayed for over an hour until convinced of my own madness, I gave up and went home, chalking up the experience to bad luck and the seemingly imperfect and random dimension in which we live. I think what bothered me most however, is that a wounded animal was suffering. I hated that feeling.

The next morning was Sunday and I awoke with a feeling of guilt. I considered that maybe life wasn't all about the food; that maybe the animals that I ate had a mind and soul as well, that maybe the proverbial *"sacrifice"* also felt and feared. Thus I arose and searched the same area as before, desperately seeking to conclude something that once seemed so natural but now condemned the very depth of my soul. I walked for miles, scanning every patch of brush and retracing the original trails until finally accepting the futility of my actions. Like it or not, I had failed, but hunts are sometimes that way.

So, that was then, but now over two weeks had transpired and sooner or later you let go and move on. Farm work typically slowed during the winter, so I resorted to hauling dirt and rock on the weekends to help pay the bills. One such job found me at a new home literally on the other side of the county and in an area I'd never been.

It was beautiful country with steep winding roads and a grandiose bluff that overlooked a river. The owner needed a pile of dirt moved to another location, but he was late so I parked in his driveway at the top of the hill. There I shut off the engine of the truck and waited, enjoying the scenery and peace.

After about 20 minutes however, I began to wonder how much slower one could be, that and now my contact wasn't answering his phone. Here I was on my own clock and trying to pay my bills but thanks to him, was accomplishing nothing. I pondered the rudeness of making one wait. But suddenly my thoughts shifted from a mild frustration to the realization that something wasn't quite right; *something suddenly felt wrong.* For lack of a better description I will simply say that the moment became still, -eerily still. The wind quit blowing and the birds stopped chirping. There was nothing but pure silence. You could have heard a pin drop from a mile away. It was ominously quiet both outside and, somehow, *inside* my mind.

Then it happened: I could literally begin to hear, *no*—not hear—but _feel_ the words rise within my being. That same familiar voice:

> *So you still think you've got it all figured out, huh? That somehow this has all been an accident—the lost deer, the sacrifice I intended for you? You say you believe, yet doubt what I have accomplished. You desire respect, yet are unwilling to give respect to what I have given you. You see the high and mighty; you detest the blindness in others but yourself fail to see what I have set in motion even in this life.*

> *Somehow you still think, in your arrogance, that you know what is best, and after everything I've shown you? You flaunt the story of a little old man, and I know you desire to see me again, yet are oblivious to the work I have done in front of you every day. You wish for others to reach beyond this world yet yourself seem unable to see or hear beyond your own physical senses . . . and by doing-so, you trivialize My power and ability. You fail to appreciate the true gifts I have given. You fail to see the very thing that you insist of others—**to see Me**. Yet you, in your own vanity, wish not to be questioned? Who are you?*

75

So strong, so undeniable was the voice, *the conviction*, that I hung my head in shame during almost this whole time; but the realization continued:

> *It is the gospel of "you" that leads to destruction. You know it is evil [and in that moment I did realize it], as though somehow there was ever a separate "you" with which to contend—or maybe you want the gospel of "Me" and "you," That way you can take the blame for what seems to go wrong, while giving me the credit for the good,...but therein is still the evil **you**, unwilling to cede total control of where you find yourself. Seldom though have I heard you say; <u>just God</u>, regardless of the outer circumstance. You either trust that **<u>I am</u>** the path set before you or you don't. You don't know as much as you think or pretend.*

> *Did I not tell you before, that everything in your life has happened for a reason, <u>everything</u>, and that I was there all along, forming you to My reason, and My good will? So what will it take to get you to believe the real depths of what I do and have done? I will tell you that you are not here to haul dirt, but that perhaps the dirt exists in your own unbelief. Raise your head—now, and see the sacrifice that I have prepared for you since the beginning, the life I have <u>ruined</u> for you, that you might understand. For if he had not been exactly who he <u>was</u>, you could not be exactly who you <u>are</u>: the man I need you to be in this day. Receive the one whose blessing I took, that you could become what you must be for <u>Me</u>. He is **<u>My sacrifice</u>...for you**...Be **not** unthankful, for the work that I have done.*

And at that very moment I raised my head to see something that should not have been where it was, this far from home and on a Saturday. The sight was beyond what should have been or could have been. *My God!* It was not only unlikely, but *impossible*. A little truck headed up the road in my direction—not just any truck mind you, but a raspberry Blazer, slowly made its way, turned, and pulled straight up to where I was sitting.

I was choking up as this went way beyond a coincidence or mere *voices in my head*. There he sat, I could see even through the glare on the windshield, my dear old dad, himself, eyes welled with tears, hoping against hope that I would come and speak to him. Trembling now from this undeniable miracle, this unfathomable occurrence, I ran and opened his door. I could not reach him fast enough.

Having not been spared the rod of correction from my heavenly father, I humbly embraced my earthly father in appreciation for the sacrifice he'd been, myself seeing things through a different lens: the optics of faith and understanding, certainly, in this capacity, for the very first time. Never in my life was I so glad to see him as we both stood there unashamed to share the sniffles of Joy.

However, the change in that moment was not within him so much as it was within myself, in my understanding of what I had missed about the facts. It was not what my father had been doing wrong but rather what God had been doing right all along. And to think that I had completely mistaken the point.

The little old man had set me straight and I loved it. It was a voice from beyond the portal that had somehow reached across to teach me this unfinished lesson. A voice had led my father as well that day to the most unlikely place: a remote road in the remote countryside where neither of us was likely to be and had never been before or since.

But you never know about Faith, who will hear its calling and who will not. That day at least, one of us, *my dad*, had listened a little closer than had I. He was never the religious type, but had learned to listen to a deeper instinct within. It is a small thing, a small still wind that whispers, "*This is the way, walk ye in it.*"

Yet it taught me to listen a little closer too, to believe in where I was and what, perhaps, God was doing in my life. That no matter how "*good*" or "*bad*", happy or sad; to not call it vanity or madness, but instead the reasoning of God which far exceeds all expectations of man. It is not the hill where we would go in life, but rather the *hill* where the spirit leads us that matters.

It is not as we would have it be, roaming high above the clouds in a dream, the ideal life, but as He wills in every moment of every day. Therein is where the Joy and, for now, the *Glory* is to be found. And if we could only see that servitude to Faith is indeed the beginning of freedom and the perfect life that we all ultimately seek. In the end, to see as God sees will bring the real miracle of flight of which we dream.

Like the gold that is tried in fire, I too was being purified for what would shortly occur in my own life. God's refiner, *His Word*, was destroying all that could be destroyed in me so that only that which could not be destroyed would remain . . . Listen well my friends, to that small still voice of love, peace and the direction of God . . .

Through this experience I learned many things. I felt the profound depth of God's love, His unfathomable power even on this side of the portal, the stillness of His voice and His desire that we put aside the negativity that this world brings. It is here that I see the fallacy of becoming entangled in the darkness of the physical. I speak of the human life; its never-ending drama, constant problems, fighting, arguing, and discontent.

Indeed we are in this world but not of it. The spirit of God is in you, in your imagination and this is who you truly are. And though the Element of Faith can reach beyond our physical-senses, it also brings rhyme and reason while here. In turn, realizing this truth is the very tool we need to survive in the *now*. That there is more to come is indisputable, yet for now *believe* that we are already 100 percent <u>exactly</u> where we are supposed to be in Faith, in Him. This is God's perspective.

Yet even after all I've seen in Heaven and Earth, *here* and *there*, I still can't say which is more beautiful: the glory of the eternal or the precious sacrifice that we are in this world for one another. One is forever, the other temporal, yet one is nothing without the other; something must die in order for something else to live, thus both realities have their place, the lesser bringing life as food for the greater.

It disappoints me, I suppose, considering our time here is *so* short and *so* precious, to yet see so many people who waste each day in the doom of unbelief, always forfeiting the riches of love in the moment for dreams of another day. Why is it we holdout for the Cinderella dream instead of seeing that the perfect mate is God in the moment?

The next moment in our lives here is never guaranteed; thus do you really want to waste the ones you do have? The magic is always in the moments, and in them we shall all be changed (see 1Corinthians 15:52). Though foolishness to this world, <u>*believing*</u> in the moment that God sets before us is in fact the beginning of wisdom and the road that leads to the portal.

To see this requires a change of perspective. *Repentance,* it is said, is a mere changing of one's mind, a choice to turn our back on the old way and come face to face with the new. It means deciding on what we are going to believe and call reality. In this we stretch beyond the brutality of this physical world, standing before the threshold of Heaven, the breeze of liberty upon our face. Yet it is a conscious choice that begins the process of transformation.

Many times each day that choice must be made inside your heart and mind, to see what God sees, to choose what God chooses, and to allow His mind and will to become one and the same as yours. And that, my friend, is the science of defeating death: by ignoring the outward circumstances, no matter how obvious or treacherous they may be. One must look *through* the physical, *past* the veil, and *into* the divine reasoning. As crazy as it may sound, turning your back on the seemingly obvious and accepting this deeper reasoning is the <u>*only way*</u> to eternal life.

The day will come however, I promise, that the struggle of seeing beyond will end. The time will arrive when those who believe, that is, the *inner-man*, will simply walk out, rather, ascend-out of the dimension in which we find ourselves—a *New Earth* at first, but then through the portal and into our Heaven. Yet even the portal is opened by the magic of believing and this was the key all along: *believing itself, is* the key to the power of God.

And while the magi built Faith into the Word, God built it into you. There is nothing, *no circumstance* that believing upon the Faith-Element can't overcome. In the *now*, no mountain is too tall, no problem insurmountable. It heals all things, transcending the *past*, the *present*, and the *future*, and with it, a peace that goes beyond all understanding.

It really is a sacrifice—the forfeiture of one life and one reality. Everything that you know and believe and see and feel in this world—you have to let it go, all of it. It *seems* impossible, but it isn't, and as the divine-source trusts our intentions and works, things will accelerate in these end times. The rate at which Faith changes things will increase and the results will quicken. It will get easier though, I promise.

Faith is *not* an abstract concept, yet neither is it an attribute of the human. Faith is not a possession of self-will and determination. Faith is not natural; it is *super*-natural. It is the person of God incarnate, the very real Element that lives within us; the remnant-source that melded into the world all those eons ago just after the portal closed.

In this world, for now, there is just a tiny bit of that light in each and everyone and everything, but it is the same light that I remember from the other side. It only exists in small doses but is still, *by far*, the most powerful substance in existence. Thus it only takes a little to do the job, just a drop, but we are all in fact drops of God in one another's life just as my father was in mine.

Indeed Faith is the <u>new</u> tangible; the <u>substance</u> of things hoped for, the <u>evidence</u> of things not seen: It chooses for us the path we take at every cross-roads; it separates what appears to be real from that which *God says is real*. It is a match-maker of the *impossible*. It can bring a raspberry truck to the most unlikely place, a little old man to the mind of a reckless youth, and even open the portal that will save the world.

For what it's worth, I saw the <u>exact</u> same deer the next year, ironically not limping, but running across the field by my house. My father passed away the very next day . . .

*Faith heals **all** things. It is the <u>infallible Element and Substance</u> of God.*

FLASH BACKS
My Transition to the Past
The Destruction of the Temple

"I have remembered the days of old, the years of ancient times." —Psalms 77:5

Many decades have passed since then. Now I sit alone with naught but silver hair and memories that span the ages. No doubt I am a man fallen from the graces of the world. The cabin is as old and run-down as myself, seemingly as broken and sad, a gray relic of a more carefree time. Eventually I lost it all: *money*, gone; divorced of wife and largely shunned of family. Now I sit as an eccentric: *"The strange old man who lives back on the hill"* is how they know me.

Everything was so simple before I met the little old man. I remember the farm and the years of my youth. I reflect upon those days with pleasant imagination yet know full well why they departed. Life is funny that way, here one day with joy and newness; the next, health and happiness a thing of the past. He took what I had from me, the status quos of this world: normal views, normal desires, and normal goals.

The best laid plans, of course, but my former aspirations were fleeting; my love for land, wealth, and good fortune are gone. Yet these were all replaced with things far better than that which the eye can see. My daughter envisioned it many years before. From the mouth of babes: at only 12 years old, she awoke one morning, sobbing from the memory of a sad dream. She walked at a ridged pace straight to the kitchen where I readied breakfast.

As she neared I could tell she was crying. She hugged me tight and told of her terrible visions. In them many years had passed. It was a dreary scene, cloudy and cold, the leaves gone amidst the dead of winter. The farm lie in tatters and now myself at the bottom of the hill as I labor to cross the drive and dam of the lake. Where I was going, she could not tell...

She noted as I recall, near silence in her dream, all except the stark sound of a *tap* . . .*tap* . . .*tap*—my cane as I walked upon the gravel, each step the struggle of a worn and elderly man. I lived in solitude. Disregarded; my value to friend, family, and the world long gone.

"You were all alone except our shepherd," she sobbed.

The scene of her dream now switched to the cabin, itself devoid of all furniture but a single lowly bed, the haunting echoes of emptiness adding to this dreary stage. I know full well the creaks of the floor and the music of the whistling wind between the logs. There she recalled, I lay in that bed, held by a monster who desperately tried to kill me. It was an evil, dark being, and very powerful. Each night it screamed a most fearful bellow in an attempt to extinguish my life.

She said I was subjected to this demonic barrage for years. Sobbing in great heaves, she said, *"No one would help."* Little did she know, that no one *could* help. True to form, for decades, night after night its weighty burden was laid upon my mind. Though its power can no longer hold me, I recall many restless hours; often I tossed and screamed as one who burns in a fire, my regrets, paying dearly for my lack of insight and a wrongly directed belief in this world, every ounce of human self-esteem and identity stripped away.

The demon was the voice of guilt, from mothers and fathers, family and friends, the do-gooders of God who so ridiculed in the name of the very devil they worshiped each Sunday. Always denigrating in tone, always condescending, they merely spoke what the master of their minds commanded: *"Do this." "Don't do that." "Work more." "Get your life straight." "Get your head out of the clouds." "What is your problem?".* Though I had surely tried, in the end nothing I could do was enough to keep up with these Joneses.

Other, far crueler things made their way back to my ears as well, their opinion often gnashing at the core of my soul. This was the source of darkness that held me down each night as I lay terrified of my failures in this life. It haunted me with the reminders of their words, the fault and the blame. Not till well into my 50s would the monster of condemnation lose its grip. It was then that *guilt*, the fuel that fired this burning of my mind, finally ran out.

But this is the whip of God, the very tool that has readied me for the work that God Himself had devised. Thus it is only right that such things should come to destruction. Yet ironically within that darkness is also a treasure that is little understood, a true paradox of hardship and glory. In it I have learned so much, never turning my back on the lessons that lead to the Wisdom of God.

The dream continued, however; she noted that early each morning, the demon would stand-to, powerless to proceed. Thereafter she would see me again, each time crossing the same dam, somehow revived with an inexplicable smile of joy. In that smile was a victory that made no sense. How could something so powerful fail to kill such a frail and seemingly helpless old man? What was the resilience that she saw within the emerald sparkle of my eyes? It gave her a sense of hope in an otherwise hopeless nightmare.

Still pouring her tears, she said that I finally died alone. I was rather, *"just gone,"* she said. Accordingly *"they"* found, as it were, only one remnant of my life, one unsuspecting reminder: my <u>cane</u>, wrapped in countless coils of thin paper-like bark. *"People came from somewhere, the government and scientists I think, they took it away to study it."*

They unwrapped its bindings to find that it told a story beyond what they could understand. They struggled to find out how I knew of that which was written upon its rough script, how I came to this knowing, but they could not. Upon those sheets was the story of what I saw and knew. She recalled that they took the cane and its wrappings to a museum. There people came from all around the world just to see it—upon it things that were never before heard nor seen.

Ah, but it was all just a dream. I realize of course that in today's world, few believe in God, devils, demons, and angels. Religion is fading as perhaps it should be; the desire for dogma, the belief in unbelievable tales, often traded for seeming rational pursuits. We point to our education that we feel brings awareness. Such high understanding thus negates the need for ancient belief and superstition.

Don't misunderstand my intentions; in the end, *believing* is what it is all about, yet it is the conflict of our beliefs that cause so many of the world's woes. The root of course is the religious playbooks we were handed from the past. These are the scriptures of elusive interpretation, the boxes that our cultures shook in an effort to guess their content. Though billions herald these texts as truth, hardly any two people agree on the totality of what that truth really is.

The Bible itself makes a wonderful example: For over 2,000 years, *all* have speculated as to its one true interpretation—over _30,000 denominations_, that is, _30,000 guesses_ of the same book revered as truth by believers, yet so often the core of their bitter and even deadly religious rivalries. How could that be? And how embarrassing would it be to find that they were _all_ wrong?

The truth is a sharp sword: the Catholics and the Protestants, the Sunni and the Shiites and so on. They all shook the box; they all picked their poison, the book and interpretation of their choice, the Hindu and the Jews as well; the countless doctrinal bickering of the Bible, the Koran, the Vedas and more. Some were our own guesses; others those that tradition gave.

We aligned ourselves with those guesses as well. We found within them a sense of righteousness, rhyme, and reason. How ironic that our search for truth would bring such ruin: the archetypes of bigotry, bias, and hatred. Was not our differences in belief and doctrine the prelude for every religious war that has ever occurred? As history has shown, we fight to the death for our _"truths"_ that we believed, wrongly-so. To find in the end that _the real myth_ was our misunderstanding of those same scripts and scrolls.

All things evil must one day perish, and so with the deception that hides the truth. Wouldn't we all love to know, _once and for all_, exactly what lies hidden within those ancient boxes from the past? To open, _finally_, and see, without guessing, _the whole truth, the real truth_? And in this, to find our real place within the world, to finally realize, on a grand level, why we are here? To know that we are more than just our senses, more than just a temporary creature in this archaic universe? In the end, to realize that we were never intended to _"fit-in"_?

There is only one interpretation that puts _every_ verse of _every_ holy book of the world in-sync. The primer is deceptive in that it is, _in no way, shape or form_, literal or historical in nature. Once you see it, there will be no more questions; there will be no more denominations; there will be no more strife of religious doctrine and dogma, one against the other. Indeed, once we find that primer, _that code of truth_, it reveals a science far greater than our minds till now could comprehend but also puts to an end every _guess_ that came before it.

Let's face it, you seek evidence; you need evidence. You already know that something big is about to happen. We feel it subconsciously in the very depth of our being. The scientists have already discovered the God particle; we are close to this thing, this discovery of which we all await. Somehow we sensed it; we knew it was near.

Thus what I offer is validation, not by a new or futuristic discovery, but from the ancient past; that indeed there is something more, something bigger than the status quos of this life. Here something greater emerges about who we are and where we are from. Here, now, the unlikely becomes the probable, the visible, and the miraculous. Now there will be no more guesses but only the truth that lay before us all along.

That is what I offer you, the seals of the ancient texts removed: *Your* Bible, *your* Koran, *your* Vedas, the pyramids, the megaliths, the ancient past, will be opened and understood as they were meant to, in this day and at this time; to show you the mysteries that <u>someone</u> from long ago left for us today.

True to my daughter's dream, true to her prophecy, I am alone yet with an indomitable joy within. I learned of course to keep it to myself, *my cane*, the *images* and *truths* that sustained me since the days of the little old man. What I knew all along I kept till the end. I wrote it for you that in the end and after I was gone, you would have this, that all of humanity would partake in the fruits of my estate.

It is my gift to you, the sheets of information that you are about to read. Herein the rough outer bark of scripture is removed to reveal a scientific treasure that defies imagination. This is the wealth I leave to you. Indeed it will change you forever, whoever you may be. In it is the one and only way out of death and, beyond your greatest hopes, the path to *immortality*.

Some of you will understand it, some of you will not; but it is the truth, and no one will <u>ever</u> prove it wrong. It is the grand finale of those who once roamed your planet. It is <u>what</u> they knew, an intellect they hid within the sacred books that we all shook as mere children in a child's game of guessing about God.

To them however, it was not a guess but an exacting science. They gave it to us in code, encrypted within the wrapping of literalism that we believed. Therein was the greatest performance and the greatest drama of all time. What they did was incredible; what they knew was incomprehensible to the primitive human mind. Yet it is a screenplay of which we are all still partakers.

We are at the climax of the single greatest engineering feat ever accomplished, and the fruits of their work are about to be reaped. The miracle, I suppose, is that you will find in the end that the supernatural is not a myth but instead a super-science. So while the outer stories we absorbed were but a mere distraction for children, an even greater truth is about to be revealed.

People like to say, *"Abortion is a sin and the Bible says so. Adultery is a sin and the Bible says so. And so on . . ."* We throw our stones no doubt, based upon our perceptions of the ancient books, behind each cast the might of popular religious opinion and interpretation. But if only you knew what was really meant by those *verses*, those *stones* by which people so-arrogantly condemned one another for millennia—to find that the authors of those texts were themselves *cruel* by the standards of men; to find that they cared less about our humanity, *that is*, who died, who lived, and the moral purity of the world.

What they did, they did for one reason and one reason alone: They were sent for salvation, yet not of the human or human kind. To them there was only one creature here worth saving, one you've never seen nor met. It is the greatest creature to ever inhabit this earth and, haughty as we've become in our perceptions of truth, it is the real truth that will condemn our own religious judgment and condemnations . . .

My memory is keen for a soul of such age, the images still crisp after all this time. Some say I am delusional, that I see nothing; I suffer, they contend, from old age and hardship, the imagination of a madman. I suppose by the appearance of things I am inclined to agree. My eyes aged and failing, my mind somewhere between this world and the next—what possibly could I know? Admittedly the line for me is a fine one, a razor's edge, the boundary between genius and insanity, what is real and what is not.

In my defense, consider the seclusion to which I was subjected. For too long I was a captive in the most brutal of hells: my past—a very long road of tortured memories. Now I live as a hermit, half-crazed and alone with what I see in my mind. Like a movie, my tour in time replays over and over again, a journey of the eons.

Madness then, I suppose, is the prerequisite for what I am about to tell you, the only greater lunacy of which would be to say nothing at all. But perhaps I should let you be the judge, whether outstanding or outlandish, real or imagined. Hear, then, my story, from beginning to end.

It is my contention that I remember these things for a reason, that regardless of how bizarre or unlikely my tale, I was touched, not by the peculiar, but by my own past. Indeed my recollections are the only record in existence of a people and information that has all but been erased. And while I am not the last of my kind, unto me it was entrusted to reveal the secret, the code, the *magic*.

Yet no matter how far removed from time and ages gone by, the images I see are not thousands of years old but of yesterday. Indeed, fresh are the pictures: the Temple Mount, now only ruins of pillars and stones that were once so grand, so domineering. I was there from the beginning and at the end; I sat upon the remnant of my world, all that I knew and lived and loved—now only ashes. How could a place, I ponder, a spectacle of such reverence, come to such treachery? I try to remember it as it *was*, before the Roman hordes plundered our creation.

Humans—I had traveled again to Jerusalem as chief of the magicians, that is, the *magi*, to oversee a city gone mad. Rampant chaos in the streets, corruption in the priesthood, zealots who, in full rebellion, have drawn the ire of the legions and now almost a million bloated corpses rotting in the sun. Almost every Jew in the city was slaughtered. To no avail, those who did survive were taken to the far corners of the empire as either slaves or entertainment for the games.

And while I loved the Israelites, like all humans, they were prisoners to their own lies. They could not see beyond their physical selves, a fact reflected in their fight to preserve a physical holy land. They perceived the scriptures and Israel by the *flesh*; that the Messiah would be an outer being, -*physical* as were they, and that somehow the temple of God was of *this* world.

But the message was far deeper and far more profound than that. I put the patterns before them, not only them, not only in Israel, but everywhere I wandered throughout the world and throughout the years. I showed them the symbolic sacrifices of the calf, the lamb and the two fishes—these the ages of Taurus, Aries and Pisces. It was in these epics that the truth was slaughtered via the ignorance of man, dead within *all* of humanity, their own blood the cost of drunken sleep.

It was in these ages that the glow of the heavens finally receded. The light had existed for millennia, but by the beginning of the age of Pisces was gone except within the skies above the Earth's poles. And with the end of this illumination, also came the suppression of their inner eye. Now they, the human creature, saw only with its *physical*-eyes, now a lust for the things of the *physical* world. They had forgotten the ancient wisdom, the real wife of their youth, and thus their memory of the world from which they came.

But only the Jews of all people valued money enough to eat it. They filled their guts with gold and silver coin in an effort to hide it from the invading Romans, oblivious that the real treasure already lay hidden within them. Yet with this absurdity they lost both their money and their lives. The Romans disemboweled them by the thousands, crucifixions lining the hills and roads around Jerusalem.

I pondered the blindness of the world in which I lived, how only a hardened generation would trade the inner love of God for a lust of outer *things*, forfeiting the eternal for the temporal. But they simply could not see. They defended their perceptions to the last, crowding within the halls of the treasury in a last-ditch effort to prevent its theft by the legions. And now myself beneath the city of tunnels, trapped as were they. I could hear their screams above me as they burned alive.

Gone with them are the stockpiles of the treasury, the tithes of their temple. Like every lust of the eyes, the riches they harbored were fleeting, taken to Italy as plunder in a caravan that stretched beyond the horizon. And though the outer Temple is destroyed, it survived long enough. It served its true purpose and, as you will see, offered a peculiar treasure for us all.

All was not lost; I saved many of the *Sacred Maps*, the magic sheets of the heavens. This was the greatest treasure and the real secret of the Temple. The last of my couriers made their escape as the Romans encircled Jerusalem. They fled for the Judean desert, to the caves of Qumran; and though they buried my mystery within those sands, they could not save themselves. They too were eventually surrounded and slain.

I myself survived by a fluke of faith, for as the Temple collapsed it trapped me within the storage cellars below, safe from the warfare that raged *outside*. I remember sitting in the blackness of those secret tunnels, a willing *prisoner* once again, my body silently and safely tucked away within the sanctuary of God. Yet as I stumbled in the gloom of those caverns, I found more sheets, more scrolls that hadn't escaped.

They were rolled in parchment, the *skins of beasts,* and sealed with the mystery of God, *encoded* with *the <u>real</u> truth* that was forbidden until the time of the resurrection. It was I who scribed their lines, who measured each word, every letter counted, added to perfection. Each was placed in its own rounded case and though my refuge was darkness, the light of these passages was still visible in my mind.

Sadly, while I could not save those sacred writs, I did at least save myself. After three days I escaped from beneath the Temple Mount, crawling from the collection pool that drained the blood of the altar. There I emerged from above the Brook of Kedron and ascended to the stench and destruction of the Temple ruins.

My cloak covered in the blood of animals, the Roman soldiers stare in contempt, themselves unsure of my pale complexion and unusual eyes. They could see that I was no Jew, which, some would say, saved me from the fate of my comrades. Yet the barbarity of the Romans was no match for the visage before them. My glare *chilled them to the* bones as they walked wide circles, their arms full of stolen loot.

But whatever the excuse for my survival then, it was faith itself that ensured my memory through the ages and, now over 2,000 years later, would preserve the truth for you today. It was meant to be, written long ago that the words *are* sealed until the end. And here I stand, in proper order, to tell you my keeping of the ages.

And what of my involvement as a magistrate within the great cabal? How shall I begin? Time fails me to tell you everything: how we traveled the ancient world, to *Greece, Babylonia, Egypt* and of course, *Israel* too. Contrary to what the historians say, we crossed the mighty oceans millennia ago; we established the traditions of the *Incan, Mayan, Aztec,* and even the *Chinese* cultures. We went southward and northward to the frozen poles as well; *you will see...*

That we traveled the globe is evident by our calling card; the iconic *"dragon"* or serpent who was part of *every* ancient-lore. In prehistory this flying monster terrified the primates as it circled in the skies above. Its fear forever etched within their instinct, we used its legend to portray a far greater and real monster who has you.

Yet even today the serpent survives in your myths and modern festivals. You will find him in your scriptures. Indeed his likeness still haunts the Aztec and Mayan pyramids, still painted upon the cliffs of the Mississippi, and molded into the dirt of the serpent mound in Ohio. I will show you who and what the dragon, the fallen serpent, truly is.

Draco the Ancient Dragon*: Known as both a serpent and/or a dragon, this ghastly-beast was the chosen hallmark of the Magi. Its imagery is found in every ancient religion from around the globe. We used man's instinctive fear of this mythological creature to instill obedience upon the cultures we formed and controlled.*

There is more evidence than mere dragons however. We did things, seemingly impossible feats, and yet the arrogance of modern man still refuses to believe. Guess, if you will, how our Sumerian text was found on ancient clay bowls high within the mountains of Bolivia, an unlikely place, don't you think, for those who were unable to cross the oceans? Ponder, if you will, the perfect symmetry and alignments of the pyramids. Consider our scriptures, thousands of years old, which your cultures still use today. More so, not only these physical creations, but the secrets encoded within them.

Indeed the Magi were the masters of early civilization; and though warrior-kings ruled the armies of the world, it was our cunning that controlled the minds of the masses and even the kings themselves. We were not only the creators of these civilizations, but the unseen authority of *every* nation that hailed from ancient times.

THE ORIGINAL MAGI:
THE BEINGS FROM NOWHERE

"And the Sons of God saw the daughters of men that they were fair; and they took them wives of all whom they chose" (Genesis 6: 1-5)

Though our memory of the original luminaries was erased long ago, early humans drew, as best they could, the illuminated beings with whom they once existed. These were the original magicians.

They came as it were, in the days old before there were any nations, and *from nowhere known to man*, I assure you, -a people. These *"people"* took the outward form of humans but were, in no-respect, the beastly savages that before hence roamed the planet. Their brilliance was beyond that of the human, as if a light burned from within their very being.

They seldom spoke and with a most ominous glare: *those eyes*, those *steely* eyes, and within them the glint of eternity. They seemed to know things—*everything*, possessing a wisdom beyond comprehension. To see one face to face was both intimidating and yet the most powerful, most beautiful visage that can be imagined. Yet beneath this stunning presence was somehow, always a quiet smile. Barely perceptible, it emanated the confidence and might of a creature that <u>***was not* from this world**</u>.

Their power lay in both thought and Word; for what *they imagined* was in itself a spell, and what they *spoke* literally made the earth tremble. Indeed they were masters of the mind, the unseen, the invisible things of creation, and it was this ability that enabled them to survive in this physical realm. They were not extraterrestrial but *interdimensional* beings, a string from the higher worlds—*angels* per se to the quaint and primitive. For millennia now they've been trapped in your world, this foreign land, to them a prison.

Thus as usual the concept of angels has been woefully misconstrued throughout the ages. It is here then, that perhaps I should clarify exactly who and what they are. Try if you will to imagine a greatly elevated consciousness, a type of genius that has no physical embodiment nor relies upon anything of the physical world. In its purest form it is a *mind* that exists outside of space, time, and matter.

Within its dimension of origin, it is not a separate being but rather a singular spirit of illumination, a part of the whole of God, a mere drop of water in the endless sea of the Almighty. They are to humans as the fifth dimension would be to the first. Yet the mind of which I speak is beyond the gauging of physics, an invisible and completely incompatible matrix with this world. It is able to view and see us, able to penetrate our every thought, yet itself only discernable within the lights of the super-aurora that once existed on Earth. Here they angelic-energy shown as beautiful beams of pure energy, a ghost of flickering hues and color that astounded the imagination.

But also envision what would happen if a part of that mind, *just a tiny bit*, became separate from its source and was forced to exist within the physics of this world. Like air bubbles that get trapped in wet cement, it eventually hardens into the medium of its imprisonment, taking the form of its captor, embedded within the weight of this earthly domain. Likewise the angelic remnant would also dilute, weaken, and solidify into the physical realm. It would separate into individual entities and over time, into evermore visible/physical forms.

That, however, was a very remote past. Sadly these luminaries were long ago forgotten by history and are remembered today only through the fog of ancient lore and misinterpreted archaeology. They were the *angels*, or, as some called them, the *Sons of God*, and though they were here for eons before recorded history, their most recent imprint began a mere 18,000 years ago. It was at this key stage in human-infancy that the most miraculous mutation since the beginning of life on Earth occurred.

THE DIVINE PURPOSE

Before that time, the Element brought improvement to every species on Earth, its logos sifting through the fibers of creation, much as you might imagine a breeze blowing through the forest. This interaction brought rejuvenation. In small steps it altered the DNA of all living things. Through an intense level of imagination, it stimulated the addition of neurons and even the improvement of genetic structure over time.

The end results were modifications of existing DNA, *point mutations* that were almost imperceptible. It initially happened over millions of years, slowly, gradually, in almost indiscernible increments. Fossils don't lie, however; the changes are plainly seen. Preserved within the endless layers of rock are an observable evolution, an undeniable record of transition for all to behold.

The day came however, in which the physics that guided this ancient interaction were compromised. There was a portal, a very *real* portal, of which you will learn, but this bridge between the worlds was broken or, destroyed I should say, thus entrapping some of the Element within the physical world. Its options thus limited, and with a desire to return home, this interdimensional life form did what it had to do.

It was then that it greatly accelerated the process of melding. It was a quickening of the modifications in which *evolution* became far more akin to *creation*. The Element did so, *not for the sake of your species*, but out of desperation for its own ends. It needed, for its own purpose, to quickly create the beast that today is known as *man*. This undertaking involved two distinct efforts, both of which were founded upon *genetic layering*: The Element could not mate with a physical creature, but could however, impress its brilliance upon them.

This was similar to being exposed to radiation, only in a good way, which altered those animals into a higher state of consciousness and stature. This first melding was a hastened upgrade in geological terms, a rather compressed timeline of the last 45,000 years. And while early humans were the end result of this metamorphosis, there would yet be an even greater transition just before the end of the last ice age.

Ironically the Element was fully aware that it would suffer death if it joined with flesh and blood. And though these early human hybrids retained some of their luminance, the melding with physical beings was also a genetic cancer for the energy that once illuminated the heavens. Thus with each generation of human offspring, the Element was further divided and diluted, even the lifespan of the creature progressively shortened.

It seemed to be the end of this energy from another world—*or so it appeared.* As a result, the light and mind of a once infallible being faded into the human race; its glory was no longer visible and the memory of its existence finally erased.

Yet the story of life out of death exists not only within the primitive ecosystems of Earth, but also as a tool for this stranded life form. Indeed there was a method to the madness of the melding; a plan of escape from the physical world. In order to repair the way home, to reopen that portal, it would require a power greater than that which the Element now possessed.

As you will see, the one and only answer for salvation from this prison away from home—the key of escape itself, was none other than *death* itself. As a seed that falls to the ground and dies, this energy from another world was also forced to self-sacrifice, to become a temporal creature with the hope and plan of a future resurrection.

In this, the Element literally bred itself out of existence, its DNA now lying dormant within the human creature. And like a tree that absorbs waves of light from the sun and hence now contains its energy within its very fibers, humanity likewise contains the hidden dimensional light of the God Aurora. The implication of course is that mankind became nothing more than a slave, a cocoon that, ugly as it was, would someday, hopefully, give birth to something far superior and far more beautiful than itself.

PERFECT WORDS: THE INVOCATION OF THE MAGI

Not all of the Element bonded in the melding that made man. Some was purposely and consciously held in reserve for the second phase of the most ingenious plan ever devised. Indeed the first melding gave us the volume we needed: the mouths and improved speech by which to affect our solution. We had, for reasons you will come to understand, only a finite amount of our self, of our *Element,* with which to work. Thus, humans are far from being overly intelligent or articulate. They were by no means genius, nor was genius required, but only the ability to express and verbalize complex sentence structure.

That said, we knew full well that the construct of this world would eventually force our remaining consciousness to solidify into physical beings; but how to do so intelligently? It is said that walking is nothing more than a controlled fall, and we likewise fell into your world, *not by choice*, but now in measured steps that we used to our advantage. To our own benefit we melded along a logical path or else suffer the eternal results of failure. You see, the garden of humanity in which our DNA was planted now needed a keeper to till it.

Thus the remainder of our Element again bonded. This time however, it was concentrated within a few select beings, offering us the best chance by which to articulate our genius. This second event produced some spectacular individuals who in pre-civilization were of great renown. These half-breeds, the children of two dimensions, were called the *magi*, and would later develop and control *every* religious circle of the ancient world.

This of course began the next phase of our two-part plan that involved the grouping and teaching of humanity. Like a moth attracted to light, early humans were mesmerized by the glow and wisdom of the magi, who possessed an overpowering presence. Thus we used this power to obtain people's subservience and to organize them into arranged civil societies.

And this is how such great intelligence suddenly emerged from otherwise primitive cultures to form the great civilizations of old. Egypt, Babylonia, Israel, Greece, China, and even the Aztec, Mayan and Incan cultures were all the end result of the great magi. Again, we didn't do this for the benefit of humanity itself, but as a means to an end for the Element within them.

We needed, for reasons you will come to understand, humans to speak; to emanate the power of Word; to vocalize a *séance*, if you will, *of perfect words*. Magic spells are real, that is, at least ours were. Thus we wrote the *God-Spell*; the real *gos-pel* of the ancients that would be our ticket home. Yet in order to accomplish this, the magi first created a format through which humans were compelled to repeat the magic we created.

The remnants of these systems are still visible today in the religious megaliths from around the world. But even more important is the survival of our scriptures within the Christian, Jewish, Hindu and Muslim faiths. This was the advent of organized religion, a simplistic but effective tool by which the magistrates controlled people's actions, thoughts, and words. Through these orders we accomplished not only moral compliance of the cultures we controlled but also ultimately the powerful voice of millions of followers who heard and repeated our magic as directed.

Humans: *The direct result of the first angelic melding. Not all Element diluted this far however; some remained luminescent for centuries. These few, the cabal of the magi, once led these human tribes.*

So as a guide is to the blind, we led a creature who walked in darkness. We didn't give them the whole truth, but merely what they needed, and thus gained what we needed from them. They knew not which way we took them but trusted us with fanaticism. And though each religion polarized into sometimes dangerous and even deadly opposing traditions, the end goal of enabling their voices for us was the same throughout.

Truly the outward stories of each religion were designed for the simple-minded folks of that day. Early cultures were barbaric at best. On a good day they consisted of hunters and gatherers, foragers who scraped out an existence from among the jungles, deserts, and woodlands; but on an average day, they were nothing more than savage brutes with cannibalistic tendencies.

They were loosely configured nomadic groups with no formal education. They were violent, thick in their minds, and could not grasp the profound wisdom of the magistrates. Early man needed something on their level of comprehension, and the mythologies—the superficial stories we created, filled this need.

However, underneath the words of the outer myths was a far more serious plot. Indeed, every religious script and scroll from ancient times was encrypted with a numerically precise magic spell. This includes **the Christian Bible, the Hebrew Bible, the Vedas, the 12 Epics of Gilgamesh, the Odyssey and Iliad, and, to some degree, the Koran**; were all designed from the sacred geometry of the heavens.

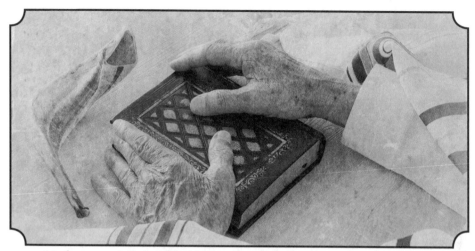

Math, you say? *Codes? Magic?* Yes, of course, the magi, in their genius, integrated within these stories a numerical catalog of divine information. We knew that nothing is truly separate from the dimension from which we came, that the invisible things of God are clearly understood by that which is seen, *math* being the most precise novel of all. Thus, if the math was perfect, once converted into Word, it would provide our way home. This celestial math, once vocalized, *is* the <u>Word of God</u>—aka *the true God-Spell.*

Not all magic spells are instantaneous; some take literally thousands of years before they come to fruition. Similar to a radio wave, the Word of the Book carries both energy and information. More importantly, once spoken by mere mortals, these magic spells would someday, over time, summon, better yet, *awaken,* the *"Sons of God"* whose life was now imprisoned within the human DNA.

And just as their genetics are now intertwined, so too are the magic and power of the Word. Like the sunlight that summons a seed from the dark earth in which it is buried, so would the perfect wave pattern of God, when spoken through man, resurrect the light of God from the creatures in which it is entombed. Likewise, the more these scriptures were read or repeated, the greater the effect.

Unbeknownst to humanity, the words were a <u>*resurrection machine*</u> through which the light ensured its own survival. How ironic that it would happen through the mouth of babes; the unknowing, hapless rabble of humanity that would repeat the magi's verses and make this machine function. For thousands of years humanity would be a blissful host, not only to the holy remnant, but also as the rescuers of our collective soul.

As impressive as the magi were, however, the backbone of our efforts were simple: the quest for resurrection into the dimension from which we came . . . Indeed, we viewed the physical world as a mere picture, a *map*, if you will, of the mind of God. At night when we watched the stars, it was as if God had printed a huge story, written in the sky, waiting to be read by those who could discern its hidden language.

Truly our mythologies camouflaged a far more profound and secret wisdom of which only we knew. Beyond the outward fables was a story that humans simply could not and would not perceive, something so-powerful that it was necessary to hide it until the end. Unto the Magi it was given to know these mysteries, but unto humanity, in parables—that in reading the Books, they might not see, and in hearing the scriptures, should not understand. But with this, the magi would defeat death itself, the last enemy of this dimension, and in return, through their rebirth, the super-aurora would return and the dimension of God would become alive here on Earth—*all in all.*

The first Luminaries from the higher dimension as drawn by early humans.

VI

THE GREAT WHEEL OF GOD
The Hidden Gospel and the Secrets of Symbolism

How we opened the portal to Heaven

"*U*nto you is given to know the mysteries of the kingdom of God; but to others in <u>*parables*</u> (*or symbolic code*), *that* <u>*seeing*</u> (*the literal translation*) <u>*they might not see*</u> (*the code*) *and* <u>*hearing*</u> (*the literal translation*) <u>*they might not understand*</u> (*the symbolic code*)" Luke 8:10

Peeling away the layers: *Beneath the unassuming stories of the Bible is a fully developed science of which only the magi knew. In the end, you will find that the literal stories of*

the scriptures never actually happened, but were a cloak for something far greater and far more personal than we could have ever believed. We did this for a reason; let me show you why, for now is the day of understanding.

Within this chapter and the rest, are the actual images I saw beginning in 1989 as a result of the touch of that little old man. Along with those images are the explanation for what they mean. Therein are the mysteries of the magi, the magic of old and the code of the ancient scriptures.

This is not just any code, mind you, but in fact, *the* code, as in, *definitive*. As a result this chapter is a bit technical yet reveals the secrets that were destined for this day. Herein I will explain the details that are necessary to understand the ancient science, how we designed the holy books, and the truth of their origin. It will be worth it, I promise.

I have so much I wish to share with you: that nothing within the ancient texts is what it seems; that beneath the surface of their unassuming stories is something infinitely more profound than mere history or moral directives; a *hidden-mystery* that will be revealed by the end of this book. This is the time in which everything will come together, the revelation of the ages, *right here, right now*.

This information was lost to time: what the ancients knew, what man forgot, and what you are about to relearn. Much of what you need about the science of opening a portal is included, thus preparing you for your future. I realize there is more science here than some prefer, but there will be many questions, all of which will be answered in this book and the next. Thus for those who desire proof, the proof is included.

Again, some of you will understand it and some of you will not. Increasingly though as something divine awakens within us, comprehension will come. The data herein will eventually be accepted as the real end goal of those who wrote the scriptures. Take your time; read it slowly; digest and dissect this information to your satisfaction. It's a lot and perhaps a bit redundant, but once you realize its significance, it will change the world forever.

But what possibly could a magician tell us that we don't already know? Perhaps then, that it doesn't require a college degree to realize that the Bible contains a cryptic layer of information. The most obvious indicators of course, are the redundant numbers integrated throughout the body of each and every story. Therein is an unbroken chain of astronomical digits such as 12, 24, 70, 72, 144, etc. Likewise, these patterns exist within every ancient scripture and tale from around the world and are a bit too coincidental for mere chance.

Everything from the chosen 144,000 in the book of Revelation to the Mayen baktun stela of 144,000 days; from the 12 labors of Hercules to the 12 apostles of Jesus—these parallels are always the same regardless of the continent or ancient culture of origin. While some call this a coincidence, others call it suspicious. In the end however, we will find these patterns are not an accident but the flawless design of an otherworldly intellect.

Though these digits should help us to dissect and discover the secret itself, the primer has thus far remained elusive. Over the last two millennia literally thousands of scholars have attempted to decode the Bible's passages as well as the mysteries of the pyramids with only limited success at best. In the end, all have fallen short of the -*who, how, why and where* of the ancient code. No doubt bits and pieces were revealed along the way yet typically without true perspective and full revelation.

The truth is, we purposely designed these things to remain secret until now. The magi were co-dimensional beings, flesh and blood, but with the mind of what you would call *God*. Thus we used our genius to mask the scriptures from even the sharpest minds throughout the centuries. That same genius lies within you however, and is just beginning to awaken in this day. Therefore in order to understand our code, you must learn to think as we did and to access your creative capacities in greater depth. I need you to see beyond the face value of the Bible and other ancient texts, that you may understand their true, intended purpose.

As Luke 8:10 plainly states, there is an underlying mystery to the scriptures as well as an outer symbolism that conceals its secret. Thus there are two opposing gospels, a lesser story that camouflages the greater story, or perhaps the mythological that hides the technological. In this age, we are privy to the revelation of the mystery itself, a message that will mark the awakening of a real, but long-forgotten Element that lies dormant within our human vessels.

However, before you can wrap your mind around this secret code, you must first comprehend the science that it hides. It is actually quite simple: There was once an opening in the fabric of space that existed just beyond the outer edge of the Earth's magnetic field. *Portals* are not just the stuff from which movies are made; they exist, they are real, and it was through this celestial gateway that we came to your Earth. On the other side of the portal is an entirely different dimension, a reality in itself, yet with a unique and far superior matrix than what we experience in this world.

The realm of which I speak doesn't exist in another place, but rather in the space between space. It is amongst us, in our very midst, connected yet separated from the physical universe but by a thin membrane of consciousness. Similar to vinegar and water, it exists within the same enclosure as you, together in the same glass as ourselves, *touching* yet without mixing. It is a different state of matter and energy that is inside, outside, through and all around, within everything and everywhere.

It is possible however, for the two worlds to interact via the one thing they have in common: *gravity*. Indeed gravity on a planetary-scale is the only thing powerful enough to alter or tear the invisible boundary between the two worlds. It does require certain conditions in order to create these gateways; a near-perfect combination of magnetics between a planet and its host star, in this case the earth and sun.

But something happened: Earth no longer faces the sun to the degree in which it once did. Its axis has developed an eccentric *wobble* and *tilt* that today are about 24° (degrees) off-center. Earth's wobble motion, similar to a spinning top, has always existed, yet had now exceeded the required alignment by which to produce an open portal. As a result, the focused energy of the huge magnetic fields were disrupted to the point of failure, thus closing the bridge between the dimensions:

OUR PROBLEM

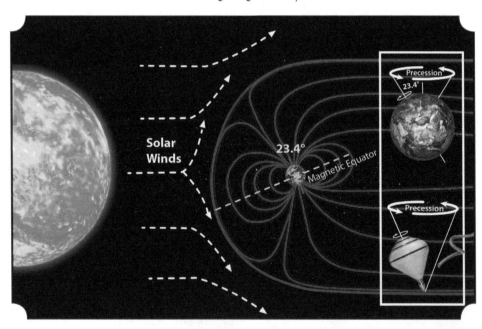

The same computer-models that say the Earth has never tilted less than 22.1° (degrees) also failed to decode the Bible. They are wrong, as the Earth once tilted only 15° and will again eventually decrease to only 12° tilt. Everything we worked to accomplish revolved around this issue.

OUR WAY BACK HOME

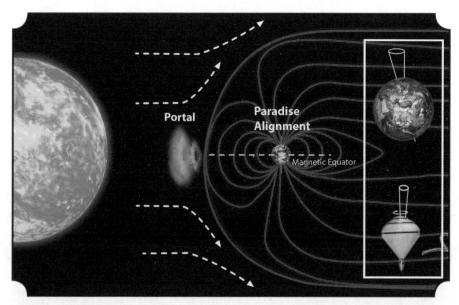

This is the Paradise Alignment, a more-perfect interaction between the sun, Earth and moon that will reopen the portal to Heaven. This re-alignment is achieved via the frequencies we created and their impact upon Earth's magnetic-field. Likewise we hid those frequencies within the words of the Bible and other ancient texts that the world still uses today. Our motives were singular; to return to the dimension from which we came and we did whatever we could to make this happen.

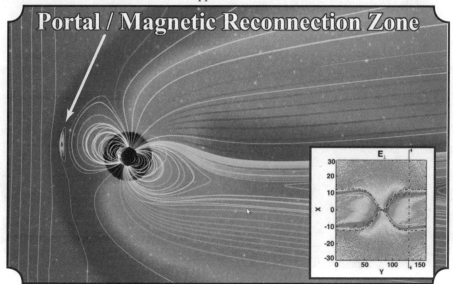

Even NASA is learning that portals exist: In this visualization from NASA Heliophysics, the resulting glow of magnetic reconnection is plainly visible. The portal is not open in this image, yet the mechanics by which it occurs reveal themselves. The Paradise Alignment will start the engine of this huge resurrection machine. The literal tearing of the fabric of space is exemplified in the Bible with the story of the torn veil of the Temple. (Image: Goddard Space Flight Center and from NASA's Polar spacecraft, circa 1998, which provided crucial clues to finding magnetic X-points. Credits: NASA)

The planetary forces of gravity are immensely powerful. Likewise, though gravity and magnetism are not the same thing, they both affect the fabric of space and time. Not only can they warp the space/time continuum, but under the right conditions they can literally tear the *"curtain"* (Matthew 27:51) or fabric that otherwise separates the realms. These openings generally occur on the day-side edge of Earth's magnetic field where the combined forces of the sun, Earth and a full-moon create the greatest, single, stress-point.

There are other forces that affect a portal as well, including Earth's orbital-speed and the resulting *Lagrange points*, as your scientists now call them, specifically the location of *L1*. Add to that the angle at which the Sun's magnetism impacts the Earth and the complexity of the portal-equation is quickly realized. More importantly you will see that the magi understood and manipulated these studies thousands of years ago and with means that were truly ingenious.

Before the portal's closure however, and even for a long time after it closed, the Element energized the gas layers of the upper atmosphere and thus revealed itself in a *global display of aurora*. Indeed much as a prism divides white light into the colors of the rainbow, so did the Element refract into a beautiful color-show within the heavens. As a result we later named this impacting quantum, the *"Glory of the Lord"*. This is in fact the origin of that long misunderstood term.

*The **Super-Aurora** was the result of an open portal in which the gas layers high above the Earth were bombarded by positive energy structure from the higher dimension. It once existed around the globe and was visible 24 hours a day. This color-show was labeled within the scriptures as "**The glory of the Lord**" and/or as the "**angels**", the later term in English derived upon from the fractal "**angles**" of light that were emitted.*

But as a result of the portal's closure, a small amount of Element from the other side became marooned here on Earth. Now separated from its source and unable to cycle back through the portal, it tended to dilute within the Earth's magnetic field until finally no longer visible. In essence it had become dormant and subconscious within the ionic-structure.

Thus the goal of the *"angel's"* physical-descendants, -the *magi*, was to reopen the portal by correcting the Earth's wobble and tilt back to a necessary-minimum. This in turn would realign the magnetic-fields, awaken the trapped Element and open the way home. Not until that time however can the angelic-Element escape its earthly prison; not until that *day* can it coalesce into its original, singular, state and back across the dimensional-bridge.

The key by which to accomplish this exodus, bizarre as it may seem, connected both the magnetics of your Earth, the spoken Word, as well as the matrix of your mind. The question is how to use those three things to realign the planet. What possible interaction could they have to fix such a grandiose problem? The short answer is that the scriptures of your religion contain a specific mass and gravitational field that, when spoken, affect Earth's own magnetic field and thus pushes its axis back into a perpendicular alignment with the sun.

The long answer is that connection begins with math; not math as you know it today mind you, but a dimension to mathematical-science that was long ago forgotten. Numbers don't lie, thus we found the power of how to realign the Earth within the *dialect* of its own cycles and seasons. We knew that therein was the hidden blueprint that could return us to our home; a place that as of now you call *Heaven*.

This was another level of math, a *metaphysical paradigm* by which we discerned numbers on a mental plane. Rather than *forming* a solution however, we instead, extracted it from that which nature had already provided. Essentially we made math talk. With it we formed a solution that could then be *spoken by you* in order to fix the problem.

This was the true *art of arithmetic*, a revolutionary dissection of math that acted as a fractal or prism of the divine consciousness. As well it was a medium through which a physical science could now be manipulated via *your* thoughts and words. With this form of calculous, we literally *changed the alignments of the solar-system into words*. Now math was not only a universal language, but an *interdimensional*-language as well.

Where it becomes interesting is how that math is camouflaged, rather, encrypted within each and every word of the Bible, Koran, Vedas, etc. Thus each of these documents act as resurrection-machines. With the Word of these scriptures, we were able to direct the verbal energy of millions of people around the globe by which to literally push Earth's magnetic-lines back into alignment so as to open the portal and the path to immortality. Those scriptures also tell us on another layer, the information of *when* the portal closed, *why* it closed, *when* it will reopen, and, many details about those who designed this ancient science.

Understanding this information takes us from our uneducated pondering of the super natural and brings it into the light of a comprehensive super-science. This of course required a genius beyond that which modern science can accommodate. Indeed, the science of the magi produced something truly *magical*, something *so-powerful* that it is defies human-logic. Not only can it rip the space/time continuum, but the mental continuum as well.

However the scriptures were only one method by which we applied portal technology. There were actually three types of resurrection-machines, all of which manipulated either sound waves, magnetics, and/or mental structure.

1. Our first attempt was the **Pyramid-Method** which basically functioned from mass, shape, alignment, and proximity. Though somewhat effective, pyramids functioned <u>without </u>the Earth's realignment and were limited to only a brief period of function each year during and near the equinoxes. Indeed they can and did open smaller, temporary portals that would "bleed off" a small amount of dimensional DNA but could never really capacitate the total quantity of Element that was trapped.

    Something of interest is that a pyramid-portal is symbolized on the back of the American dollar bill. The *"all-seeing eye"* represents the angelic wisdom and is positioned at the tip of the pyramid which is also accurate. More later on the details of pyramid design and function.

Up and Out: The huge mass of the pyramids once formed mini-portals by focusing the geo-magnetic-energy of the sun and Earth. Via this method of resurrection machine, the angelic-genius could cycle between the dimensions in small quantities and only at specific times each year.

2. Second was the **Sound-box Method**: A hypogeum functioned from certain baseline reverberations and frequencies. Once again this is the manipulation of wave-patterns. When isolated, these harmonics loosened the angelic consciousness from the human mind. These enclosed rooms were **_unable_** to open a portal, but did allow us to temporarily shed the burden of thought so as to access information that would otherwise be mentally inaccessible.

   Likewise similar harmonics were built into the acoustics of most ancient temples and helped promote spiritual association for the masses as they worshiped. It brought a feeling similar to the lyrics of a touching song, only better. We also toyed with chants and *ohms* which tickled the fabric between the strings of the universe. They worked, somewhat, bringing illumination and peace, but never gave the ultimate solution we sought.

The hypogeum in Malta. This and others were designed to loosen the God Element from the restrictions of our own physical-being via harmonic vibration. This in turn allowed us to meditate far beyond what is otherwise possible.

3. This of course leads us to the ***Scriptural or "Word" Method***, which was our final and, *by far*, most effective solution by which to reopen the portal. Though more complex than our prior attempts, it offered a real, long-term fix to the Earth's tilt and wobble predicament.

   Unlike the physical-mass that was required with a pyramid, the scriptural method used *people*, lots of them, to achieve a *mental mass*. Thus the Word was especially effective when spoken in large gatherings and congregations but was also affected by the time of day in which specific verses were employed. Unbeknownst to those who spoke or read the scriptures, these verbal signals functioned as an invasive, wave-pattern technology that in turn impacted and altered the Earth's magnetic-field.

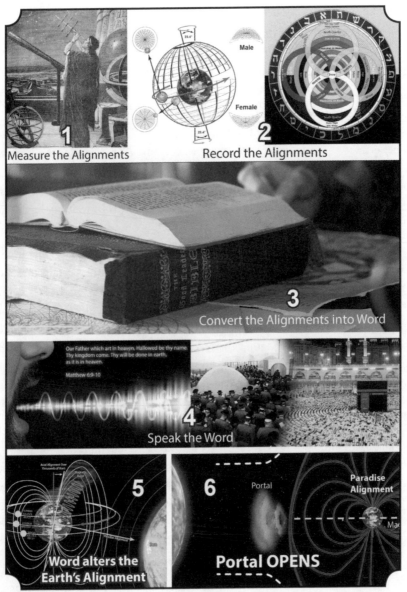

The images show a six-step process:
1. Measure the Alignments
2. Record the Alignments
3. Convert the Alignments into Word
4. Speak the Word
5. Word alters the Earth's Alignment
6. Portal OPENS

Step 4 includes text: "Our Father which art in heaven. Hallowed be thy name. Thy kingdom come. Thy will be done in earth, as it is in heaven. Matthew 6:9-10"

Step 6 includes labels: "Portal", "Paradise Alignment", "Mag..."

The Divine Plan Home: *this is the ancient 6-step process of producing real magic. Your scientists are just now learning a small part of what we knew thousands of years ago; that sound-waves carry mass and gravity. What we knew however, is how to harness the living electrolysis of spoken scripture by which to alter the Earth's magnetic-structure and mis-alignment. In the end, the portal will open. The Words power is beyond comprehension...*

Mental intent was important as well and affected the efficiency and transmission of the verses. Brain waves each have their own wave length, some of which are compatible with the engineered-Word and others which are not. The correct waves such as *lamentations*, *suffering* and even certain types of *joy* acted as *carriers* that were cleverly connected to the frequency of the Word itself as you read.

However, not only does the Word change the Earth's alignment over time, but it also permeates the fabric of our consciousness. Similar to any audio wave, the Word penetrates the molecular structure of everything on this planet to which the God Element is now attached. This in turn massages and loosens the Element from its earthly-bonds which in turn readies it for resurrection. For now its matrix is dormant within you, buried like a seed within the darkness of this world, awaiting the designated day of return.

In this process the Word has created a connective web or *body* between each piece of Element and each person in which it exists. As a result, certain facets of the human experience will also be attached and slotted for resurrection. In fact before the portal's closure, the Element cycled back and forth between the dimensions, harvesting the suffering of this world as it went. This was our job throughout the eons: tending to the precious elixir of transformation that is created from a world of fallen physics. So, regardless of the fact that the Element was trapped in flesh and blood, in no way altered its ability to store compatible consciousness.

Indeed <u>real</u> suffering has a very *real* value to the higher dimension from which we came. Similar to how our bodies transform the death of our food into life, so too were the horrors and pains of this world transformed into glory and redemption upon their arrival into the heavenly realm. Suffering can cause a loss of hope in this world which in turn opens the way for a renewed focus on that which lies beyond. This exchange process is in fact a founding principle of energy and likewise applies to <u>mental</u> transformation as well. To wit, we must die to this world in order to be alive to something greater.

However, as the Earth tilted and the portal closed, this process of dimensional transformation ended. But this is the beauty of the Element, for by its very nature it attaches and stores within its matrix for future use, -all sufferings until the resurrection occurs. Dormant or not, the Element is still compatible with the changed brain-waves of suffering, so nothing goes to waste and nothing is lost from then till now. Every torment and torture that has ever happened will soon be redeemed. Likewise, the engineered Word assists in this function by reinforcing or *"watering"* the Element as you read it.

Changing the Earth's alignment is a delicate process. One must be cautious. Changes must be gradual and in small doses to prevent an overshooting of the mark and thus a planetary disaster. As a result these corrections wouldn't happen overnight; it was a slow process that would take literally *thousands of years*, yet the Word frequencies were precisely engineered to this end.

Likewise the conversion process from numbers into usable Word was truly ingenuous. In the upcoming chapters I will actually reveal this multi-layered Word-calculator that is described throughout the Bible but particularly within the *Book of Enoch*. Basically it was a converter that changed celestial math into human languages (i.e. *Hebrew, Greek, Arabic, Hindu, etc.*) which we then pressed our cultures into reciting when and how we deemed.

We compiled quite a collection of these frequencies too, literally volumes, the most famous of which is known today as the *Holy Bible*. The more people we gathered to hear, read or repeat the Word, the greater the mental focus and energy within them. This of course gave us all the *gain* needed to impact the magnetic-fields and thus eliminate the majority of Earth's wobble and tilt. The end goal is called the **Paradise Alignment** in which the Earth's axis is re-oriented thus allowing the portal to open.

Though the *"Word"* could be likened unto speaking a magic spell, it's actually no different than a radio or TV signal interacting with a given channel. The difference of course is the immaculate design of those signals. It is a binary wave-pattern, as in, two parts, with both a masculine and feminine aspect; a stronger and a weaker wave, but an equally important and mutually supportive construct that is expressed within a single verbalization that you call the Holy Scriptures.

Within that binary structure are several complex substructures that were inherent to our Word-equations and are equally important to the end result. What matters is this: basically these frequencies were projected via your mouth and received by the magnetosphere that was then altered as a result. It is a perfect fix; it is miraculous; it is of another dimension; it is of God. It is real and it works. This is the *God-Spell*. I will show you what you need to know.

A MAGICIANS SLIGHT OF WORD

*"...and behold, **a throne was set in heaven**... And before the throne there was a **sea of glass** (dimensional light) like unto crystal. And he that sat was to look upon like a **jasper** (dark-red aurora) and a **sardine stone** (light red Aurora): and there was a **rainbow** round about the throne, in sight like unto an **emerald** (green Aurora)."* Revelation 4:2-6

It's Happening: Revelation 4 was not talking about a literal-throne, but the appearance of the portal. This image was the first recorded "On-blink" of scripture/portal function outside of the encoded scriptures. This magnetic fluctuation revealed itself in the colors of the aurora over Siberia on the night of October 26/27 2017. The portal remained closed, yet the bending of the space-time continuum allowed this before-unseen light-ring. As the Earth continues to align these phenomena will increase until the veil of space is finally torn. And while your scientists scramble for an explanation, we witnessed far greater things than this thousands of years ago. We are now approaching ground-zero for the magi's science; the fruits of the magic-Word we engineered.

In review, one must realize that ancient scriptures served three equally important purposes:

1. They are a means of cataloging, verbalizing and activating the mathematical *"spell"* that will impact and adjust Earth's magnetosphere and in turn, correct its wobble and tilt. This process occurs slowly over a several thousand years.

2. They **camouflaged** our science in the form of a symbolic story that could easily be read and understood by humans. It wasn't important that humans understood the hidden wisdom, but that they recited the Word when and how we directed them. Likewise, the outer moral directives of those books kept them civilized just long enough for us to accomplish our goal of opening the portal.

3. And this is the fun one: the scriptures also act as symbol-words that detail the **mind-images of God** or, *sacred art*. It is here, in the artwork of perfection, that this book will focus. A picture is worth a thousand words, and will simply and visually explain the mystery and science of portal-mechanics that are hidden lock-step within the Word of God.

I will introduce these sacred prints publically, here and now, for the first time in human history. Until now they have never been viewed outside of the sacred Magian priesthood. While we produced tens of thousands of these images, I have provided in this work nearly 100 of the most convincing and, I might add, *damning* recreations. They tell a forgotten story of absolute truth, yet will also destroy a *literalistic lie* that perhaps would not otherwise easily yield.

Remember, there are the myths we gave to the world and then, the science that those same fictions hide. It is now time for one to die and the other to finally live. This is a prerequisite of the divine nature, that even our beliefs should undergo the beauty of transformation.

THE GREAT WHEEL OF GOD
THIS IS THE <u>WISDOM WHEEL COMPUTER</u>

I re-introduce the **Wisdom Wheel**: *This ancient Word-computer organized and converted the math and colors of the heavens into the words of the Bible. Well over 35,000 verses were written with this astounding creation of the Master of the Magicians. Likewise the rate of Word-production was slow and took over 500 years to complete; a mere blink for an angel…Consider, will you, the implications that this device wrote the ancient scriptures…*

The strength of the code was its ability to camouflage our science in the form of a literary work. This of course gave the illusion of an actual or historical account. Such is the case with the creation-story in Genesis. Here a *"Heaven"* or *"firmament"* appears to reference a higher-dimension, when in fact its describing the analogue computer by which we spelled every last word of the scriptures. This was the **_Wisdom Wheel_** of the Temple, a multi-layered construct that not only wrote your scriptures but in turn _can and will_ re-open the ancient portal.

Though the magi developed many technologies, there was no single item in the **_ancient world, or the modern_**, that has the capabilities of this miraculous device. If that's hard to accept, then name one computer in existence than can change the math of the stars into magic, a spell that can literally open a gateway to another dimension. Throughout this writing I will use various names by which to describe the Wisdom Wheel, including _Grid System_, the _Firmament Model_, _Great Wheel_, and even _Ezekiel's Wheel_—all of which equally apply and describe this ingenious creation.

Astrolabes were used throughout the ancient world including the famous Greek, **Antikythera mechanism.** None however, were as elaborate or capable as the Wisdom Wheel of the Temple. Most kept time; mine wrote magic.

Basically the Wheel functioned from a simple *input/output* method in which the alignments and colors of the heavens were plotted in logical detail. Every conceivable facet of the Grid System was represented upon this construct including; grids, grid-series, colors of the aurora, colors of the sun and moon, planetary cycles, etc. Though the Wheel was primarily an alpha-numeric converter (i.e., it changed numbers into letters), it also provided the imagery of the scriptures it produced.

The Wisdom Wheel contains four, main layers or aspects, three of which have their own dedicated chapter in this book. One layer encases the grids upon which star data was collected and organized. Yet a second layer involved an overlay map of Israel and its surrounding nations. While finally a third layer functioned to discern the shape of the magnetosphere at any given time. Interlocked with these three layers was a fourth, *Word-layer* that cataloged the letters as they were written via the alignments of the other three.

Likewise, this chapter will first cover the <u>Wonders</u> layer which served as both a time-keeping function as well as a geometric-base by which the sacred-images of the Bible were formed.

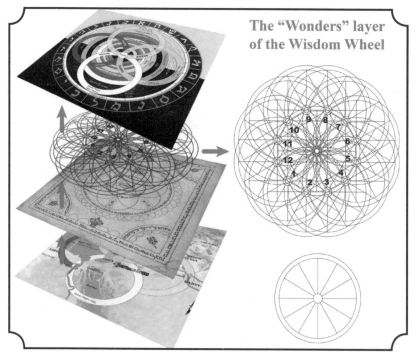

The "Wonders" layer of the Wisdom Wheel

The Wonders or Grid-Layer: *This critical layer of the Wisdom Wheel represented the 12 cycles of the zodiac, the outer circle of which represents the apparent path of the sun and moon as they cross the sky. Once pieced together into a functioning grid-series, this acted* *as a structure for volumes of scientific-data, beautiful images and the timeline in which the portal would reopen. All of this is hidden in the Bible and other ancient verses.*

We knew that the day would come in which these things would be disclosed and this is my job as master of the ancient magicians. And to think that these images began *once upon a little old man*, touching my hand. Indeed he led me back to a time I had long ago forgotten, but have since rediscovered in full.

As it did for me, your questions too will be answered. Everything about the scriptures, its stories and its mysteries, will be revealed, piece by piece by piece. I will leave nothing for you to guess, as this is not a game; it happened, it is true, and you deserve to know at this time in history, how and why. Indeed the trumpet has sounded for the seals to be broken and the mysteries of God to be known in full.

But if my claims are true about the nature of the ancient passages, if in fact my memories are correct, that perhaps I am not the madman that we both suspect, then there should be some bit of evidence to prove it, some shred by which to realize my assertions. It makes sense, I suppose, that there should be a relic or artifact by which to validate my claims. Luckily there is a trace element of my past, *clues,* that for those who can recognize the truth, are undeniable. It is the code itself and is hidden, subtly, within the body of our religious texts.

The primer of the Grid-layer is of course, the **Great Wheel of God**. Known today as the zodiac, this pie-shaped circle of 12 divisions was derived upon from the moon's 12 monthly cycles. Not only did these grids help us to track the alignment of the Earth by which to open the portal, but through its imagery and symbolism, *–to organize society*. More so this critical-layer of the Wisdom Wheel gave us the needed structure by which to build the Word as well as the line-data by which to create some of the most astounding art-work ever made.

We found that math is better by the *dozen* than the *decimal*. By <u>twelves</u> we found the sacred backbone of nature which is otherwise unachievable. As you will see, the magic that affects the Earth cannot be written with any other numeral-system. With it we kept detailed records of the repetitive, but ever-changing cycles of the Sun, Moon, stars, etc. This includes days, months, years and even 1000-year periods of time. Likewise these cycles and circles of the Great Wheel were then plotted upon a multi-layered-construct known as a *"Grid System"*, which in turn allowed us to extract and arrange the math of the heavens in order to further our science by which to open our portal.

Now; if you are even remotely-familiar with the Hebrew or Christian Bibles, (*Or any ancient religion for that matter*), it's obvious that the number **twelve** is also a common digit within their verses. For example; there were;

JEWISH/CHRISTIAN:

- *12 tribes of Israel* (Genesis 49)
- *12 sons* of Jacob (Genesis 35)
- *12 gates* of the Jewish temple (Revelation 21)
- *12 wells of water* (Exodus 15)
- *12 stones* set in the Jordan River by Joshua (Joshua 4)
- *12 golden lions* of King Solomon's throne (1st Kings 10)
- *12 yoke of oxen* for Elisha's plow (1st Kings 19)
- *12 stones* of Elijah's altar (1st Kings 18)
- *12 pieces* *into which* a woman in the book of Judges was divided

CHRISTIAN:

- *12 apostles* (*Matthew 10*)
- *12 baskets* remained after the miracle of *"5 loaves and 2 fishes"* (Matthew 12)
- *12 years* a woman had a hemorrhage of blood (Mark 5)
- *12 years old* when Jesus first went to Jerusalem (Luke 2)
- *12 sparrows of clay* created by Jesus as a child (Infancy II)
- *12 foundations* to the New Jerusalem
- *12 legions of angels* (Matthew 26:53)

Other ancient religions that contain the number twelve as a common theme include:

HINDUISM:

- *12 names* of the *sun-god, Surya*
- *12 heads* of *Vishnu*

GREEK:

- *12 Olympians*
- *12 labors of Hercules*

ISLAM:

- *12 infallible leaders/Iman's*
- *12 princes* beget of Ishmael (Genesis 17)

EGYPT:

- *12 gods and 12 goddesses* who pulled Ra's boat.

BABYLONIA:

- *12 clay tablets* upon which the epic of Gilgamesh was written.

Magi Time-keeping 101: The number 12 was only one of many astrological measurements encoded within the scriptures of every ancient culture. If I can relay nothing else but this, that the ancient scriptures were not haphazardly written by random wayfarers and prophets, but drafted no less than the blue-prints of any industrial machine.

As you can see, the symbolic correlation to the Grid-layer is consistent throughout the ancient religions we created. Note if you will, that the nouns and adjectives attached to the number 12 are actually part of the code's deception, in themselves only facets of the cover story. Regardless of the implied hierarchy of gods, angels, and heavenly orders that the outer stories suggest, beneath the veil of symbolism, are *all* detailing the *same* science. These are the *"gods"* of gravity and celestial timing including the *sun*, the *moon*, *Venus*, *Earth*, etc. Indeed the seal of our scriptures was ironclad in hiding this fact, but the clues to the primer are still there to be seen.

Luckily our sacred system has survived the great crossing of time. In fact, it is still recognizable in literally every moment of your lives today. You can find it in the **12** months of your calendars and thus the **12 signs** of your birthday. Next comes the **360°** of a modern compass which is attained by simply multiplying the twelve months by their average number of days (*12x30=360*). Consider also the **12** a.m. and **12** p.m. hours of your clock for they too are an algorithm found within the prophetical section of the Hebrew Bible, itself divided into **24** books of **12** major and **12** minor prophets! Those numbers are *not an accident*, but a metaphor for the timelines tucked away within the Word itself.

The hints of our sacred math are abundant throughout the ancient scriptures and are still used in your time-keeping today.

SPELLING THE PERFECT FREQUENCY

*This is a "**Word sheet**" displaying the Song of Solomon in Hebrew, the original language of the Bible. Consequently, each circle represents a new cycle of the Wonders, or Grid-layer of the Wisdom Wheel, the alignments of which spelled each letter. Every book of the Hebrew and Christian Bibles were first compiled in this manner, helping us to speak the hidden language of math. The next step in our hidden-science was to create the "**image sheets**" from those same circles.*

Through the format of the Wisdom Wheel we were able to convert the alignments of the heavens and their numbers into letters. As each letter was produced, it was then placed upon the perimeter of the grid-series in a specific order that in turn spelled **every sentence, verse, chapter and book of the Holy Bible.**

Finally the information that was spelled upon these Word sheets was transferred to either papyrus or parchment scrolls that in turn were read in every synagogue of ancient Israel. Long after the magi were gone, these same scriptures would survive in Christian and Catholic churches around the world and even honored to a degree within Islam. As a result of this, our math could now be verbalized in whichever language it was converted, thus creating the signals, via your mouth, that would impact the magnetic structure of Earth. Ironically, every time you speak or even read those words, *you*—yes, *you*—are literally fixing the problem with which we are faced.

There was also a fail-safe integrated within the Word, a *"firewall"* of protection against misuse, one that is superior in construction to anything on your computer. This is the mental or dimensional aspect of the Word that only recognizes true, heartfelt convictions. Call it the *power of sincerity*, if you will. Simply put, there is no way to *fake* the magic of the spell; its expression must come from a broken and contrite heart. One can even blast the verses over megaphones, but it will do nothing without a genuine love and desire for the Source.

Simply put, the Word requires *reverence*; it *feels* a person's heart and whether or not it is compatible for the dimension from which we came. This engineering feature functions like an activation-code, and directly ties your soul to the dimensional values of the Word itself. Thus not only does the Word labor to open the portal, but can literally reject any and all incompatible mind-waves or personas in the process.

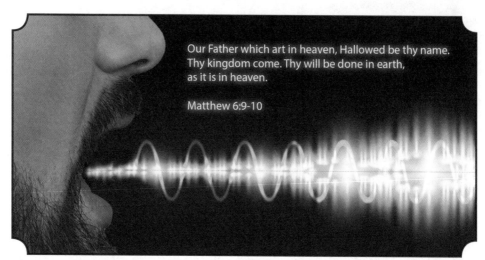

Our Father which art in heaven, Hallowed be thy name. Thy kingdom come. Thy will be done in earth, as it is in heaven.

Matthew 6:9-10

The magic of the scriptures: These frequencies were designed to impact both the mental and magnetic structure, thus opening the door to Heaven and the way home for the angels. Hearing, reading and repeating the Word we created are key elements of angelic-survival.

I would boast, at this point, yet I know better, that we were also *Word-smiths*, masters of illusion with how we wrote the ancient magic. The fact remains however, that we didn't actually write the books of the Bible, but that the heavens wrote them for us. Indeed, these scripts were the direct result of alignments within the Great Wheel and we, the magi, only deciphered that information.

Our way home will be achieved through the magic-spell of resurrection. The *Word* is the perfect wave-pattern of God that will create a bridge between the two worlds; it is the <u>Resurrection Machine</u> built by the math of the stars. Via this system, the magi accessed and mastered the physics of a dimension that, as of now, we can neither see nor touch nor smell, but make no mistake—*it is there.*

The Artwork of God

Here is where the mystery deepens and our magic of the Grid-layer becomes visible. As you will see, the magi were not only wizards at math, but incredible artisans as well. Yet our drawings were never freelance, but created along an exacting set of parameters, the center of which was the Great Wheel itself. These are in fact, the images I saw and see.

There were a lot of circles and lines in the Grid System, thus providing a perfect format by which to create the story-images of the Bible it wrote. Largely it was a matter of highlighting the lines that fulfilled the image in question. This included every story in the Bible from Adam and Eve in the Garden of Eden all the way to the beast of the book of Revelation and everything in between. Add to that the symbolic meaning of each word, and a multi-faceted artwork emerges that is truly mind-boggling.

THE APPEARANCE OF STARS
"FROM DUST YOU CAME AND TO DUST YOU SHALL RETURN"
REVEALING THE CODE

From the stars we came and to the stars we shall all return. Your scientists today will tell you the same; that all *physical* life originated from exploding stars. We pointed to this fact within the scriptures as well, often encoding our profound truths via the mundane and seemingly simple verses of the Bible.

Yet we are not merely a physical object alone. Far more important than you being part of this universe is the fact that something even greater exists within your DNA. Therein is something far superior than mere carbon and atomic structure, but a dimensional element that was imposed upon your being long, long ago. This *shining* of dimensional-light is in fact the core of your consciousness whether you realize it yet or not. This is who you <u>really are</u> and <u>the being</u> with which we must come to grips.

To this end our artwork helped us and will help you to visually comprehend yourself and the portal-science on a deeper level. These artistic-studies are rooted in the symbolic meaning of each and every word of your holy books. The Bible, for example, contains a vast array of symbol-words by which we camouflaged the word *"star"* or *"stars,"* beginning with the image of *"dust to dust"*.

Likewise, there were <u>12</u> such words we used by which to describe the stars, each identifying its own specific sector of the Great Wheel. See the symbol-words and compare them to the images provided. I*magi*ne the metaphors.

- *dust* (Ecclesiastes 3:20)
- *salt* (Genesis19:26/Matthew.5:13)
- *rain* (Deuteronomy 11:11)
- *wheat/seed* (Gen. 22:17)
- *mist* (Genesis 2:6/Job 41:31)
- *frost* (Job 38:29)
- *snow* (Isaiah 55:10)
- *dew* (Genesis 27:28/Hosea 13:3)
- *sand* (Matthew 7:26)
- *sparks* (Job 5:7)

- *tears* (Lamentations 1:2)
- *hail stones* (Isaiah 28:17)

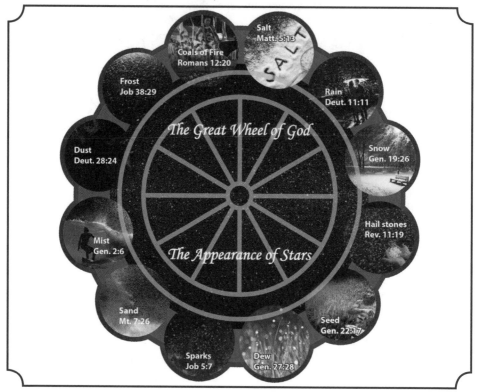

THE MILKY WAY GALAXY
REVEALING THE CODE

Next are the code-words for the appearance of the Milky Way galaxy that stretches across the night sky. On a clear night far away from city lights, this dim cluster of stars resemble, among other things, a band of celestial milk, thus its name. *Imagine . . .*

- *ashes* (Psalm 102:9),
- *Milk* (Exodus 3:8)
- *fine flour* (Leviticus 2:7),
- *prayers* (Revelation 8:4)
- *crumbs* (Matthew 15:21-28)
- *Incense* (Exodus 30:7)

- ***breath*** (Job 37:10)
- ***smoke*** (Revelation 9:2)

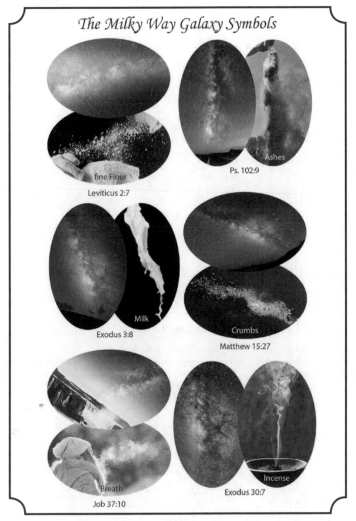

The Milky Way Galaxy Symbols

fine Flour
Leviticus 2:7

Ashes
Ps. 102:9

Milk
Exodus 3:8

Crumbs
Matthew 15:27

Breath
Job 37:10

Incense
Exodus 30:7

Constellation Symbols
Revealing the Code

The Hebrew zodiac contained over 50 star-studded constellations. These heavenly images provided us with a vast array of symbolism from which the scriptures were patterned. The list includes;

- *Aries*: the *"lamb"* (John 1:36),
- *Virgo*: the *"virgin"* (Jeremiah 14:17),
- *Scorpio*: *"scorpions"* (Revelation.9:3),
- *Lupus*: the *"wolf"* (Isaiah 11:6),
- *Capricorn*: a *"he goat"* (Daniel 8:5),
- *Aquarius*: the *"man bearing a pitcher of water"* (Luke 22:10),
- *Libra*: *"a set of balances"* (Daniel 5:27),
- *Leo Minor*: a *"young lion"* or *"welp"* (Genesis 49:9)
- *Leo*: the *"crouching lion"* (Genesis 49:9),
- *Ursa Major*: the *"bear"* (Revelation. 13:2),
- *Taurus*: the *"oxen"* (1Kings 19:19),
- *Draco*: the *"dragon"* or *"serpent"* (Isaiah 27:1)
- *Canis Major and Minor*: the *"dogs"* (Luke 16:21-22)
- *Lynx*: the *"Leopard"* (Daniel 7:6; Revelation 13:2)
- *Monoceros*: the *"Unicorn"* (Job 39:9)
- *Pegasus*: the *"Horse"* (Isaiah 63:13)
- *Pisces*: the *"Fishes"* (Mark 6:41)
- *Columba*: the *"Dove"* (Genesis 8:8)
- *Corvus*: the *"Crow/Raven"* (Genesis 8:7)
- *Cetus*: the *"Whale"* (Matthew 12:40)
- *Camel*: the *"Camel"* (Matthew 19:24)

The magi used the zodiac for locating, tracking and correcting the Earth's tilt. The juvenile pursuit of horoscopes as we know them today was <u>not</u> invented by the magi, but only by the unlearned long after we were gone.

You may have noticed that the star patterns of each constellation seldom if ever resemble the animal they were meant to portray. Yet we used the available stars of each location as simple locators to help us measure and mark those points upon the Great Wheel. That said, the images of lions, lambs, bulls, etc., that we imposed upon those star-patterns were intended to embody the spiritual persona of the area and age of the zodiac in which they were placed.

Furthermore, many of the animals mentioned in the Bible **were <u>not</u> constellations**, but artistic renderings from the Grid-lines themselves.

Each Word sheet not only recorded the scriptures, but those scriptures could likewise be imposed directly over the image they in fact described. The line data of the grids contained <u>every</u> image of <u>every</u> story that the Bible describes. This was the secret and sacred-art of the Temple.

A connected factoid is that Josephus, the son of the High Priest Matthias, wrote that on the day the Temple was destroyed by the Romans in 70AD, a cow gave birth to a lamb—or minus the code; *the age of Taurus gave way to the age of Aries.* Likewise we also exemplified Taurus in our creation of the Hindu religion, it being symbolized in the traditions of the sacred cow. Always the code.

*Not real animals, but astrological eras; the sacrificial **ages of Taurus and Aries** (4000 BC to 1 BC); these were epics in which the magi knew the God-Element within humanity would completely hibernate. Though we developed the ancient religions for the purpose of emitting divine frequencies, we also encoded the celestial facts within the outer lore and sacrificial practices of those same verses. Aries was the **Lamb of God**. John 1:29, while Taurus was the Hindu god **Kamaduh**.*

GRID DESIGNS
REVEALING THE CODE

Next are the grids themselves upon which we recorded the various facets of information. Though each grid was drawn as a flat- circle, they were actually representative of *curved-domes* which hypothetically surround our planet. In turn these grids enabled us to organize the celestial-sphere to our advantage, thus using their math by which to write the Word. Likewise each grid was also given a dedicated-design, two of which were built into the courtyards of the ancient Jewish Temple that once stood in Jerusalem Israel:

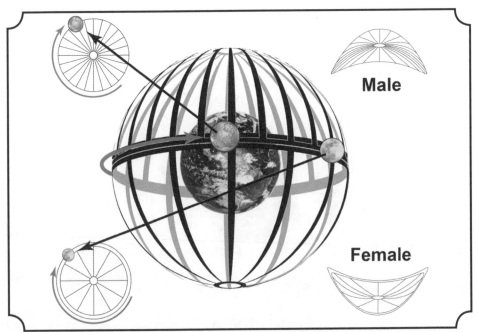

The Earth's spin or rotation grids: *These particular designs also represented Paradise Alignment, a once perfect arrangement of the sun, Earth and moon that enabled an open Heaven.*

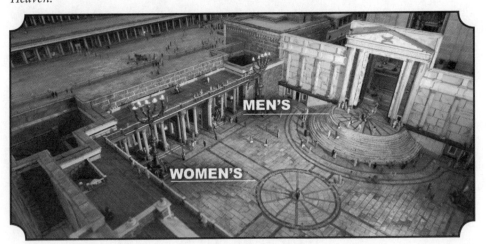

As displayed in this model-recreation by Alec Garrard, the second Jewish Temple (516 BCE and 70 CE.), contained two specific grid-designs. These were the Paradise-Grids that represented the idealistic alignment of Earth in relationship to the sun (Men's Court) and the moon (Women's Court).

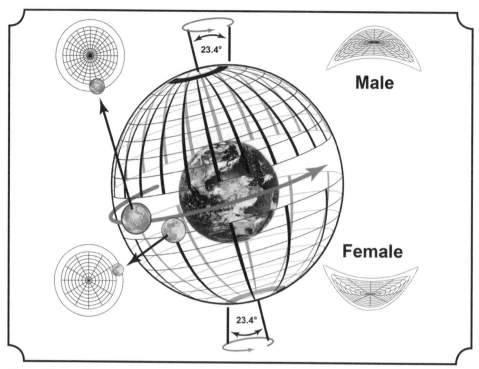

*The **zodiac grids represent Earth's tilt and wobble**. We used these grids not only to track the progress of Earth's realignment, but also the timeline of the portal's reopening. Due to the fact that the Earth's worsening tilt and wobble closed the portal, these grids were thus symbolized with evil connotations in the scriptures. I will show you.*

Each grid-type had its own mathematical logic which in turn made it easier to identify, place and track each cycle and alignment of the heavens. Going forward, realize that the grids were also the base-construct for every implied image of the Bible's stories. This ranges from Adam and Eve in the Garden of Eden, all the way to the Beast of Revelation and every story in between. More important is how we camouflaged the grid's appearance within the words of the Bible. The disguise is truly remarkable and leaves little doubt as to what we did. Compare the verses to the images and you will see their origin from within the grids. *Imagine:*

Imagine: "Nets"

"*And Jesus, walking by the sea of Galilee, saw two brethren, Simon called Peter, and Andrew his brother, casting a **net** (grid) into the sea: for they were **fishers** (Pisces).*" Matthew 4:18

Not real nets, but this grid-type

IMAGINE: "SPIDER WEBS"

*"Whose hope shall be cut off, and whose trust shall be a **spider's web**."*
Job 8:14

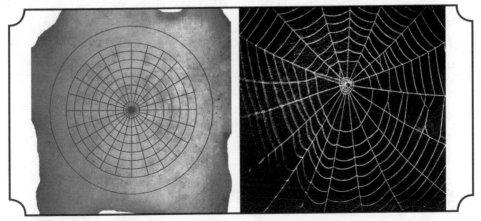

Not a real spider web, but this grid-type

IMAGINE: "MILLSTONES"

*"Take the **millstones** (grids), and grind **meal** (stars):"* Isaiah 47:2

Not a real millstone, but this grid-type

IMAGINE: "WHEELS"

*"...and their appearance and their work was as it were a **wheel** in the middle of a **wheel**."* Ezekiel 1:16

"And lost their chariot wheels, that they drove them heavily:" Exodus 14:25

Are you beginning to see the code?

The Wonders of Sacred Art
The Mind-Images of God

As the position of the sun, moon and stars change in the sky, one can attach new grids to the periphery of the original so-as to record this movement, thereby creating an organized grid-system. By combining a grid-series and then erasing only certain portions therein, we created an amazing array of articles and events, all of which lent themselves to the intricate detail of the Bible's stories.

This facet of the Grid System was referred to in the Bible as the *"**Wonders**"* layer, in that it could artistically create any and every item mentioned within its stories. Thus any time you see the word *"wonders"* in the Bible, it is an illusion to these grids and/or grid-series in some manner.

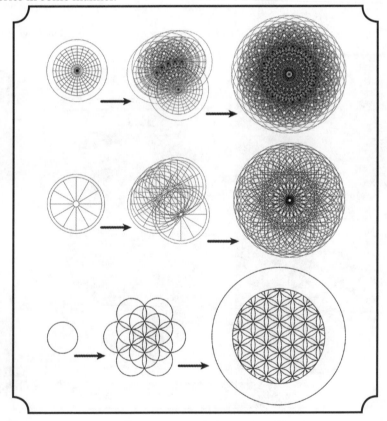

I-magi-nation was the hallmark of every magi and even we enjoyed fine art. This of course brings us to the next phase of the Grid System; the *images* themselves. The art is there, stored within the lines and circles of the grids. These pictograms are described in great detail throughout the Bible and were drawn by our artisans within the privacy of the Temple. In this endeavor, we recreated the mind pictures of God according to the Word's descriptions. The more images I explain, the more you will understand the depth of our magic.

From this point forward in this book I've provided a collection of sacred art that has been reproduced for the first time in over two millennia. You will literally be the first to see these images in over *2,000 years*. No one, -*not one person* outside of the Magian priesthood was allowed to view them until now.

I ask you to use your imagination as did we, that you may connect the dots between the grids, the images, and the scriptures that describe them. They are not separate items; they are one and the same. It is not, and was not, a history story, but the very means by which we created the books of the Bible and many other ancient scriptures. The examples are *simple, biblical* and *awesome*.

*"Consider the **lilies of the field**, how they grow;"* Matthew 6:28

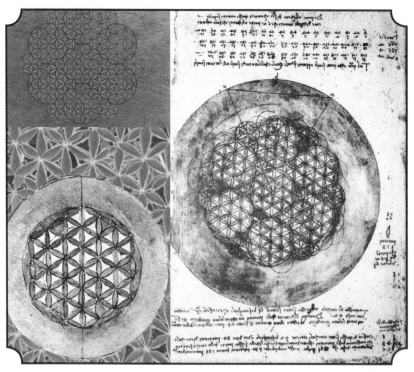

*"**Lilies of the field**": Not real lilies, but grid-patterns. They "grow" because a new circle is added each day. This grid-design was often symbolized in ancient cultures as the **flower of life**. It was displayed from the humble synagogue to the grand Temple of Osiris.*

Images show how the grids were embedded within biblical-lore. <u>Images, bottom</u>, by Leonardo da Vinci—Codex Atlanticus. This is the real secret behind da Vinci's encoded drawings. The problem is, it wasn't Da Vinci's code, but the lost art of the magi.

Imagine: "Great Millstone"

"And a mighty angel took up a stone like a **great millstone**, and cast it into the sea,..." Revelation 18:21

A "<u>Great</u>" millstone indicated not a singular grid, but an entire grid-series.

Imagine: "Clouds"

"Though his excellency mount up to the heavens, and his head reach unto the **clouds**;" Job 20:6

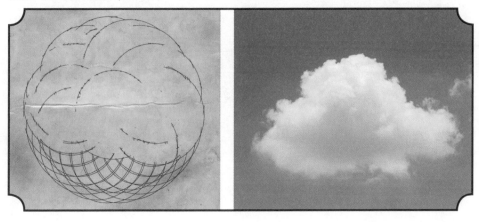

135

IMAGINE: "FISH"

*"For we don't know our time: as the **fish** that are taken in an **evil net**,"*
Ecclesiastes 9:12

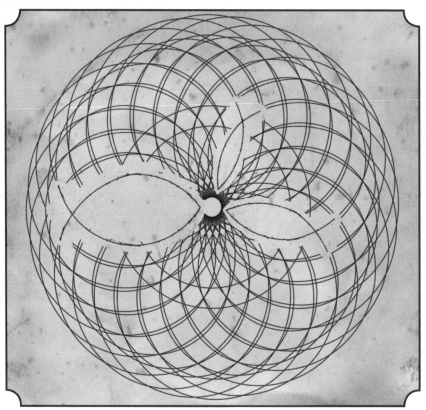

Look Familiar?

IMAGINE: "EYES"

"And God shall wipe away all __tears__ (stars) ___from their eyes___*; and there shall be no more death, neither sorrow, nor crying"* Revelation 21:4

IMAGINE: "BASKETS"

*"And they took up **twelve baskets** full of the fragments, and of the **fishes**."* Mark 6:43

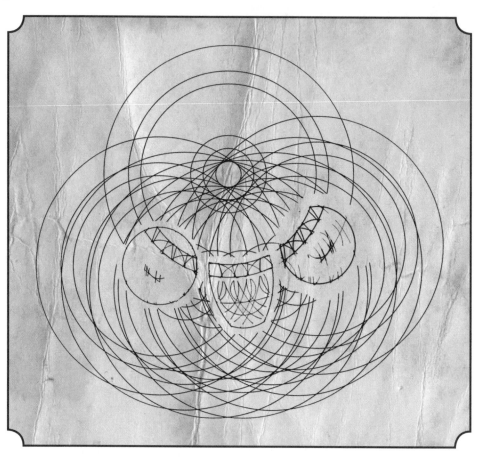

IMAGINE: "FROGS"

*"Their land brought forth **frogs** in abundance,"* Psalm 105:30

IMAGINE: UTENSILS 1

*"...and the **bowls**, and the **cups**: and for the golden **basins**..."* Chronicles 28:14-17

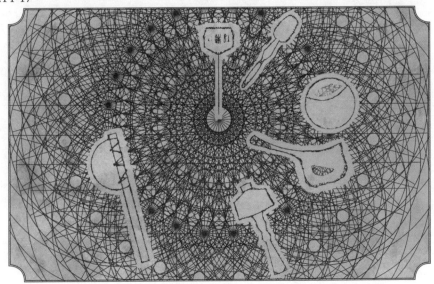

IMAGINE: "THE HOUSE OF ISRAEL:"

*"I will sift the **house** of Israel among all nations, like as corn is sifted in a sieve, yet shall not the least **grain** fall upon the earth."* Amos 9:9

*"Wilt thou believe him that he will bring home your **seed** and gather it into thy **barn**?"* Job 39:12

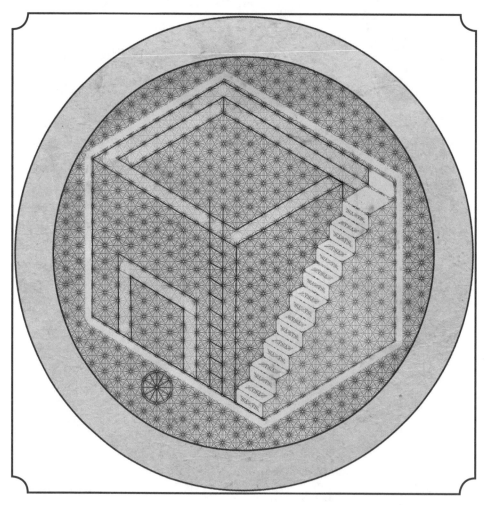

A series of 24-hour day-grids produced this 3-D image of a house. Can you find the grain of the verse?

IMAGINE: "SHIPS"   IMAGINE: "SWORDS"

*"They that go down to the **sea in ships**, that do business in great waters;"* Psalms 107:23

*"I will draw my **sword**, my hand shall destroy"* Exodus 15:9

IMAGINE: "WATER POTS"

*"And there were set there **six water pots** of stone, after the manner of the purifying of the Jews, containing two or three firkins apiece."* John 2:6

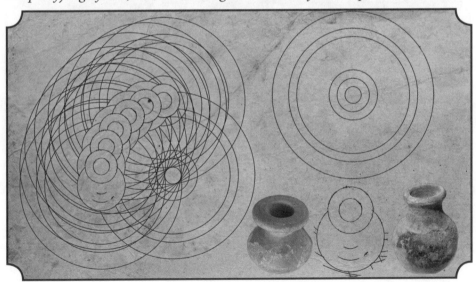

Known to us as *"Pargod"* which denotes the English word *"grille"* or grid, the Grid System was the basis for all ancient scripture production. The Greek term for the Grid System was *"Katapetasma"*, which is a pattern of lines or *heavenly veil* that encompassed the heavens. Upon this celestial curtain were the mind-images of God, called *"paradeigmata"*.

The Menorah and the Number 7

*"And said unto me, what do you see? And I said, a **candlestick** all of **gold**, with a **bowl upon the top** of it, and **seven lamps** thereon, and **seven pipes**…:"* Zechariah 4:2

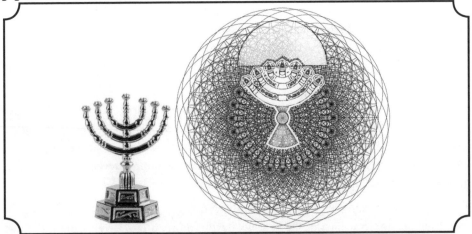

The "gold" color of the menorah was envisioned from the sunlight, while the seven candles were a mathematical configuration of the grids themselves. Notice also the upside-down bowl that was drawn from the same grid-circle as the outer band of the menorah. The Word spelled it and we drew it. Undeniable! Consider the implications . . .

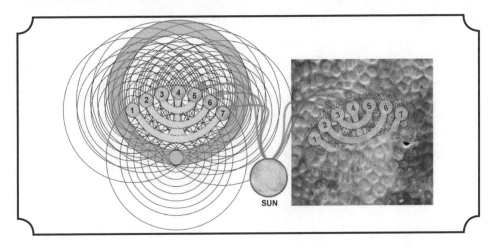

*"And thou shalt make a candlestick of pure gold: of **beaten work** shall the candlestick be made"* Exodus 25:31

The mathematical-fact of "7": Every peripheral-grid of a 24 grid-series will <u>always</u> contain the <u>hubs of 7</u> others, thus revealing the menorah design. The grid highlighted in red displays this critical alignment. The image is then colored gold with the light of the sun as it moves around the circle of each grid. Notice how the image (right) resembles the verse's description of "beaten work," an ancient metal-working technique. Our art spared no details.

Those of you familiar with the ancient scriptures may have noticed certain repetitive numbers such as **twelve** and **seven** throughout the storylines. And while it is simple to comprehend a correlation between the *12 apostles* and the *12 houses* of the zodiac, the origin of the number 7 tends to be a bit more elusive. Allow me to explain its significance.

In our science, all sun-grids contained a total of 24 pie-shaped divisions, each of which was attached a peripheral-grid. As a result, this configuration produces an alignment in which <u>any **single peripheral-grid** will contain the small inner-**hubs of 7 other grids**</u> (see image). This was important as it displayed an interaction between a grid and those upon which it was imposed. Likewise, anytime the number **seven** is mentioned in the Bible, it is typically referring to this pictorial arrangement in some capacity.

An artistic example is found within the construction of the 7-candlestick menorah, itself an iconic artifact of the Temple. Furthermore, if one were to count the two extra hubs that fall on the grid's outer circle, we can now envision the larger <u>**9**</u> candlestick menorah as well, it also being part of the Jewish religious tradition. Thereafter the menorah image is symbolically painted gold by the light of the sun as it tracks around the perimeter of each grid. Last is the *"beaten work"* of Exodus 25:31, which was the process of hammering metals into thin workable sheets. Ironically this visual effect was mimicked from the countless grid-hubs that overlay the image.

Every minute detail of the Bible is describing images of the Grid-System. <u>***None** of those verses were of historical people, places or things*</u>, but of the sacred art that only the magi could interpret. You must ask yourself, how were the various items of the Jewish Temple patterned? Who designed them and why? Why, for example, would the menorah have long semi-circular connecting bars and why would it contain **7** or **9** candles instead of any other number? The reasons are obvious.

THE STAR OF DAVID
REVEALING THE CODE

Though this popular icon of Israel is mentioned nowhere in the Bible, I can tell you exactly from where the image was derived. It is amazing that an astrological design from our grids survived the ravages of time only to be displayed upon the flag of modern-day Israel. As well, the geometric designs of both **6** and **12** are imbedded throughout nature—a direct result of the mathematical matrix that we used to chart our way home. This is how we wrote the Word; ***this*** is how we will open the portal.

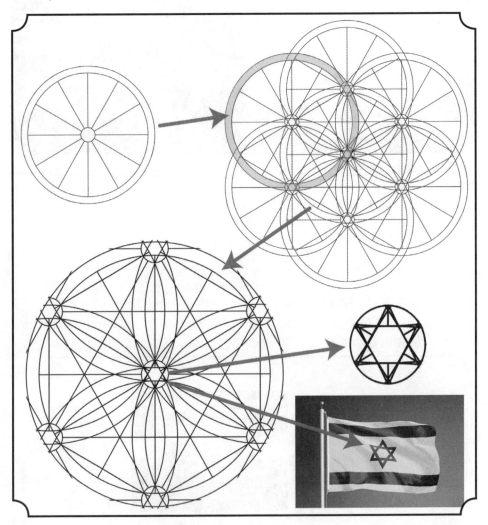

How do you suppose our symbol survived the ages only to be represented upon the flag of modern-day Israel? It seems that, perhaps, someone else knows the magi's secret but isn't saying. Funny old world, isn't it?

As above, -so below: *From the enormity of the universe all the way down to the humble snowflake, the underlying math and imagery will always be of immaculate design. The magi used this understanding by which to write the magic and to open the portal.*

Atomos:
The Real God Particle

*"Consider the **lilies of the field**, how they grow; they toil not, neither do they spin: yet I say unto you, that even Solomon in all his **glory** was not arrayed like one of these."* Matthew 6:28-29

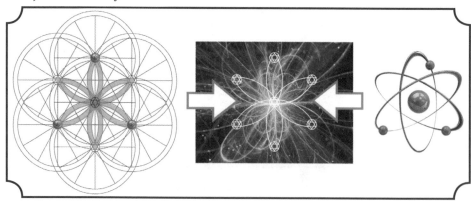

Center image: *The all-powerful "**Atomos**" or **God Element** was first postulated by **Democritus** who studied under the **Persian magi**. The magi knew then; you know now. By no surprise, its structure is revealed from within the Grid-System. This Eternal Element is a transformed energy and substance; it is the mind and force of God. It lives!*

This is where the *science of the mind* meets the rubber of the road. The *Atomos*, or, super-atom, reveals itself from within the Grid System. The design of this mighty faith particle is in fact the image-solution to what the Wisdom Wheel wrote in-code as *"The lilies of the field"* (Matthew 6:28). And, just as lilies populate the open fields, so too does the Atomos comprise the matrix of the higher dimension. Its power is unmatched anywhere in the universe and once energized auroras around the globe.

The Atomos not only irradiates the **imagi**nation, but actually stores certain facets of your consciousness. It is the same substance that entered my mind via the little old man as well as the medicine that healed that helpless young child. It is a mental structure that, once activated, will change what you see in your mind and how you think. In the end it will literally transform us into an entirely <u>*non*-*physical creature*</u> (see 1 Corinthians15:49-52).

I point that the Atomos is faintly reminiscent of a *Carbon-12* atom, though by no-means the same. This is ironic in itself, *twelve* of course being the root division of the Great Wheel and carbon being the fundamental building block of all physical life. The God-Element however, is devoid of an electron cloud as seen in a standard atom model, but rather has 6-overlapping and shared, elliptical-orbits of wave energy (see image). Thus it is also devoid of a standard-model *nucleus*, but has at its core and *throughout*, a very real type of *mental*-fusion.

Similar to a gamma ray, the Atomos has *zero* mass yet moves en-masse as a cohesive, wave-pattern and has *no* negative charge. It can travel through space, but also outside of space and time. It is beyond space, time or matter, yet connects, *always*, the beginning with the end. Thus the Atomos transcends the past, present and future, presenting itself as an eternal substance.

In this universe, the Atomos does not warp space and time, but rather penetrates it. It is a *new element, a super-particle* not belonging as an addition to the periodic-table. It is an entirely different *state* of energy that embodies the new creation. In reality, if there was ever a *"Higgs boson"*, then this is it…

This is the God-*atom*, rather the <u>*"Adam,"*</u> *as we told you in code*, of your own inner beginning. Presently the Atomos sits dormant within the positive ionic-structure of Earth's magnetic-field and as an overlay on the human DNA. There it is seemingly depleted of energy, *dead within us*, as a seed that has fallen to the ground. Strangely however, when the Atomos is at its weakest point, comes the miracle of a most explosive rebirth.

As the Earth realigns and the portal re-opens, new God-Element will enter and awaken the existing quantum as the seedling it is within us. As it does, a part of us will be revealed that we never knew existed. Here we find that it will arise in us, in our very persons: this, the *real resurrection*, not separated by history and boundless tracks of time, but *within us, as us*, the return of the God-consciousness in you and in this day.

Thus the mystery is a mystery no more: that God does not exist separate from you, that He was never *"back then"* or *"up there"*, but *in you, in humanity*—asleep all along. This truism was hidden from the ages and from generations but is now revealed in these final days. Written under many names across the ancient world, it was known in the Bible as the *mystery and message of Christ in you, the hope of glory* (see Colossians 1:27).

This is the *real* answer to the mysteries of old and the message of who we really are. Indeed, *we are* the blind-man of the scriptures who is to be healed, not as a miracle 2,000 years ago, but from our *own* blindness, now, *today*, to be given a new vision of who we are and it is the awakening of the Atomos within that will do this. Herein, God no longer sits upon a faraway throne watching over our pitiful lives, but is omnipresent, born within our very members, and giving us a new mind—*His mind*. All of this in the day of the indwelling.

Yet even today, *believing* is the miracle that activates this God particle and thus His consciousness in you, the very yeast which changes the grapes of our experience into this wonderful wine of Heaven. *Make the comparisons*;

"...for he that cometh to God (God-Element) ***must believe*** *that he is,..."* Hebrews 11:6

*"But we are not of them who draw back unto perdition; but of them that **believe to the saving of the soul**."* Hebrews 10:39

Like all images of the Grid System, whether it be the Star of David within the snowflake or even the *Atomos particle*, the magi understood millennia ago that all things are connected: the past and present, the finite and the infinite. We understood the inseparable bond of this universe as well as the universe from which we came. We knew that within the Great Wheel of God was the answer to our predicament and, ultimately, our way home.

You too are part of this story, *the story I tell*. There is no way out of your connection to the truths I share. As you continue with me on this journey, it will become increasingly evident that you *also* were there from the beginning. In the end, you will see the depth of your own ties to the magic, the magi, and the divine plan. This story is far bigger than you would have ever believed, *but believe me, my friend,* in the end, you will. It is *so*-powerful, *so unbelievably powerful . . .*

"*...that utterance may be given, that I may open my mouth boldly,* **to make known the mystery of the gospel**," Ephesians 6:19

"...The Lord said he would increase **Israel like the stars of heaven**" 1 Chronicles 27:23

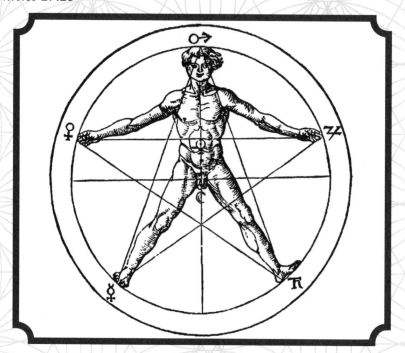

"But we speak the wisdom of God in a mystery, even the **hidden wisdom**, which God ordained before the world unto our glory:" 1 Corinthians 2:7

"Behold, you desire **truth in the hidden part**" Psalms 51:6

VII

THE CHOSEN ONES
The Real People of the Book

So which religion is chosen by God? I can hear the arguments already. This of course is the weakness of a geo-centric belief-system. Indeed people from every major religion in the world will provide scriptures proving, -at least in *their* mind, that God selected their brand above all others. Seldom if ever, though, do they care that people of other religions are doing the exact same thing all across the world. In this, the human hypocrisy is complete.

Yet religious arrogance is so often born from the same scriptures I helped to create. It was inevitable I suppose, for outer people to interpret our writs *outwardly*. Indeed within that shell are many directives that support religious identity and superiority. The question then is, why did our cabal knowingly devise something that would allow divisions, strife and even death, instead of unity?

Understand that ancient cultures were often separated by vast tracts of land and even entire oceans. Communication and information were still in their infancy; there was no Internet and no formal education system. As a result people held a narrow view of the world in which they lived. They were gullible, tribal, and superstitious.

Likewise, even the magistrates had little or no contact with one another as they explored and organized these various remote regions of the world. Though the information within our science was always consistent, the way in which it was symbolized varied among the mythologies of each culture. This is the result of necessary adaptations to each geo-centric area.

What would you do, let's say, upon discovering a group of barbaric-tribes, each speaking their own gibberish and each with their own superstitions? The first hurdle would be to mesh those languages with our sacred math. Next would be to integrate their fears and superstitions to our advantage. Local volcanos, earthquakes, oceans, mountains, etc., formed the psyche of these groups well before the magi arrived. Thus the quickest means of organization was to create and integrate regional gods that catered to their existing awe and reverence, e.g., *Mt. Olympus, Mt. Sinai, flying dragons* (the most common fear at that time), etc.

In the end, each culture became a specific blend or filter of tradition, geography, tribe, and race upon which we built their religions. Yet these humanistic *"team flags"* also helped the magi to gather the greatest number of humans in each area by which to speak our magic and to build our religious infrastructures. We were quick to learn and adapted each of these cultural idiosyncrasies to our advantage.

The problem with humans is that they were disproportionately constructed of the knowledge of good and evil. Within them, the peace of their angelic self was typically overwhelmed with the barbarity of their own demonic DNA. Thus it became evident that this spiritual-crossbreed required the image of an equally brutal god in order to contain their inherent savagery. This was in fact, the only deterrent we found would work. Yet even with the threat of eternal fire and damnation, early cultures were extremely difficult to organize regionally and *impossible* to maintain on a global scale.

Like vast herds on the Serengeti, each culture typically kept to their own, the largest barrier being not their human subspecies, but the image of the gods by which they identified. These were the boxes of belief that we created, the outer deities of the dumb that in fact guaranteed cultural and ethnic preference. Yet this also guaranteed conflict when their cultures overlapped.

As time went on and populations grew, each civilization invariably bumped into another. Drought, greed and disease led to migrations and invasions that we could not always control. As this occurred people, ignorant as they are, would often justify the butchery of an enemy based solely upon religious doctrine. As such, anyone who called God by an alternate name was either an infidel or of the devil and thus worthy of death.

History is in fact riddled with tales of rape, pillage and plunder all in the name of God. And, so long as people could twist scripture to justify such barbarisms, they at least didn't have to face their own moral corruption. *How convenient.* And now you know why the magi expected very little of the morally decrepit human creature.

The fact that many were genuine believers doesn't mean that what we gave

152

humanity was at all genuine in its literal form. Try to remember, we knew the day in which the end would come. Until then, we weren't trying to create human utopias, but merely get our angelic genepool to the finish line.

Wars would come, life and death, billions of incarnations, but it mattered not so long as they each spoke our resurrection magic along the way. Ultimately the outer religions we created were temporary fixes and we knew it. There was no reason to do more, nor could more have been considering the low-intellect of those with whom we dealt.

Beneath all of this however, were only two tribes of concern: that of light and that of darkness; that of the inner man and that of the outer. Chosen is as chosen does. The God Element once illuminated the skies, -*exploding the aurora with its glory*. As bits and pieces of that energy, as angels—we flew, not with wings, *but a mind*. We viewed, up close, this creation. We did so passionately yet dispassionately. We *felt* without *feeling*.

We mingled with the fog, the breath of the river, the fish as they jumped and the eagle as he fed upon them. The sparkle of the stream was our spirit; the unending flow of the wind was our presence. We marveled at what we saw and for us to even behold creation brought change; our focus and love altered everything.

It was all within us, within our being. We absorbed all things, every moment of every day, every life, *everything*. The interaction of the animals, the waters, the seasons—it brought us joy to see, to experience. For countless eons we beheld creation as does the one true God. Indeed we were God, *just a small bit*, as it cycled through the portal and into your world.

We loved your life; we loved your death. We gathered the food of God, the nectar of your sufferings and of every creature that ever existed, not separate from your pains, but one. We collected the wisps of transformation as you died; we carried them through that hole in space as we cycled back and forth and through again.

But then came the wretchedness that closed our dimensional bridge and thus the melding from the Element you once were to the creatures you now are. Even now however, it still resides asleep within you, the <u>chosen race *from heaven*</u>, imprisoned within a rotting physical shell. And from Heaven, there are no religions, but only light and peace. It never ages, never gets boring, and is certainly eternal.

So regardless of the outer implications of our ancient religious texts, about who is chosen and who is not, the concept ultimately pertains to the angelic races within. The *"people of the Book"*, of <u>*every ancient religious book*</u>, are in fact alluding to the <u>*same*</u> Element of God. Thus the outer gods we gave humanity were all that they could comprehend at that time. Because of them they fight; because of them they die; not only

153

physically, but spiritually. However, when the God whom is perfect comes, those in which the world has believed will be done away.

Indeed the dimension from which we came, could care less about religious banners. Thus the only reason we created these institutions was *survival*, a means to an end, using what was available in effort to get home. Beyond that, every secondary value of the world's religions are, at best, *temporary*. There was no other way; people simply couldn't understand or accept the facts verbatim, nor did we need their understanding to accomplish our goals.

The means by which to identify if your religion was developed by the magi is to look at the numbers within the body of its text. Every scroll or scripture containing the repetitive astrological numbers of **6, 7, 12, 24, 70, 72, 144, 354, 360, 365, etc.**, are thus sealed with our code. These numbers are relaavent in the study of portal technology and thus in writing the Sacred Word that will open it.

So you see, it was not the truth or *inner*-story of our scriptures that caused division, but the *outward*-story. Yet this literary ruse was also *bait*, a deliberate trap for the mind of the flesh; hence we gave the world the false, *outer gospel*. Indeed we set a snare that in the day of revelation you might review the errors—the endless wars, the futile arguments, the dogma, the condemnation, and the doubt, and see the insanity of what we've called *"God."* This is the beauty of the hidden-gospel (see 1Corinthians 2:7) in that it exposes the dark angels who are likewise damned in the pathologies of the outer man. *To them was given the deception.*

> *"But these, as natural <u>brute beasts</u>, are made to be taken and destroyed, speak evil of the things that <u>they understand not</u> (i.e., the hidden gospel); and shall utterly perish in their own corruption (i.e., the outer-gospel);"* 2 Peter 2:12

> *"And for this cause God shall send them <u>strong delusion</u>, that <u>they should believe a lie</u> (The outer-gospel):"* 2Thessalonians 2:11

God forbid that the morally decrepit human would know right from wrong on his own, that without the crutch of a verse to lean on he may do right from a pure and loving heart. I expect too much. Sometimes the law we wrote was a whip to the dark heart of the human. Through fear of hellfire and brimstone, we made him mind his manners. As often though, he twisted those same words to justify the evil that lay within his heart.

Thus by the flesh all are apostates, all have fallen short of the glory from which the inner angel came. None are righteous in their literal-gospels, something to which the Book itself attests:

> "... that flesh and blood cannot inherit the kingdom of God; neither doth corruption inherit incorruption." 1 Corinthians 15:50

Realize that _you_ are two different creatures fused into one. To the fallen yet dominant creature, the truth was simply beyond what they could mentally grasp. And what would one expect from a culture so naïve but to believe the world was flat? Likewise to travel beyond their level of comprehension was simply not safe for the magi, hence the code that protected our secret and ourselves.

But there are all kinds of religions that deceive the world, not only the obvious, but the subtle as well: _atheism, science, athletics, competitions, collections, hobbies, politics, etc._ Indeed anything that turns our focus from the pursuit of our divine consciousness, anything **through** or **by** or **in** that we feel secure or superior in some respect, is symptomatic of the fallen mind. These will always be a religion of this world.

These are all _distractions, these delusions_ are in fact bait our boredoms. Everything from a dog chasing a ball to humans chasing their own tail throughout this life—_all is vanity_; but to keep from losing our minds we chase them just the same. What else is one to do so far from our heavenly home? We desperately try to _stay_ occupied because we are no longer _consciously_ occupied by the spirit from which we came.

We desire fulfillment, to be satisfied, to be content, but seldom truly are. Be still; be quiet. Examine yourself and see if you are happy without your own distractions. Take them all away and then tell me if you are still content with only the thoughts of your mind or the spirit within.

No doubt we chase our pursuits to occupy our time, to fend off the maddening effects of inactivity. Truly, what would we do with nothing to do? With only the power and peace of God to sustain us? People like excitement; we need new experiences and challenges for the sake of our sanity. People want to _feel_ special because the one and only thing about us that truly _is_ special is as the butterfly within our human cocoon— presently invisible and unrealized.

Thus we attach and identify ourselves to our diversions. The problem is that these activities, whether grand or subtle, come to define the human ego instead of our spirit focus. Should not the cocoon do its job? We have become a trap for the spirit instead of the womb in which it should grow. Now we are distracted from our purpose and the memory of the realm from which we came, -the real *Promised Land* that lay beyond the portal.

Ironically, boredom can be our friend if we turn inward. We can see that many of history's deepest, most profound minds came from seclusion, their genius often mistaken for insanity. It is alone that we find the Element within, or perhaps where the Element finds us—that *remnant*, that thin *vapor of Faith Element*. Faint and transparent as it is, our forever is found within this substance of God. There we may see the record of our eternity and a reality that far supersedes this life. *How*, I ponder, could something so powerful remain invisible? *Ah*, but the clutter of a world that blinds us.

Yet not all of our problems are avoidable by focusing on the truth alone. We cannot simply wish away the results of being flesh and blood as if they don't exist. The physical life is a laborious-life, filled with enmity and strife. But these symptoms leave little doubt that we are presently on the wrong side of Paradise, far away and in a foreign land. This life is the proverbial *"Egypt"* of which we spoke in the scriptures.

However this realization should make us plead and pray all the more. Ironically, it is the harshness of this life that forces us to look to the heavens. Indeed in our darkest hours we can find the greatest treasure, the *new* person of which I speak, the Element of God within. The imagination gives us hope. Here, if only for a moment, we can faintly smell the scent of freedom; we sense the freshness and beauty of our home. We draw near to the portal, a chosen people who are about to enter a promised land. There the God consciousness is returned. This is the real story to which the Exodus alludes.

But we cannot find that land if we don't walk toward it. You must separate from the vices of this world. Your human and religious identities must first be shed no different than the cocoon that is stuck to the tree. Your hope is not *of* or *in* this world. Hence I beg you to consider the new creation. God's **chosen race** sleeps within humanity, *within you*, no less than a butterfly does its cocoon—one to be glorified with color, the other to be discarded and abandoned.

As unfathomable as it may be, every desire of this world must yield. That includes *every lust* for the things of this world. If for a moment, you can imagine being neither Muslim nor Jew, Christian nor Hindu, atheist nor agnostic, man nor woman nor even human at all, then perhaps you can see the consuming fire that approaches. We are no longer children, to be tossed to and fro; carried about with every wind of outer doctrine and religion, but to accept the examples that even nature has shown us must come.

We are just now able to hear this message at all. The world is far smaller than it once was. We know more than man once did. We comprehend patterns and truisms that were once inconceivable. That said, true understanding is the result of a portal that *drips its elixir*. It is only in the first stages of re-ignition; it reconnects each month, more so as we approach the equinox, *-just barely*, providing the waters that can quench our ignorance.

How bizarre that our ability to comprehend is relative to changes in Earth's axial-alignment, but as this happens, so will come an internal realignment of your mind. As the Paradise Alignment returns, you will receive a new logos from the realm of heaven. As it does, the human lie will be forced to concede. This flow of incoming Element is the *latter-day rain*. It reenters through the portal, slowly at first, increasing each month until it becomes a flood that destroys one man yet brings life to another— the *inner-man* of God. *Remember*, please, *remember*.

It's *coming*; it's *happening*, *like it or not*, and the science gets deeper as we go. Within the scriptures is a master plan in which every aspect of this day is given in detail, *in code*. And with this information, the millstone of human arrogance and misperceptions will be removed. There is no end to the human/religious argument; no one has ever won it, and no one ever will. *No one is chosen* by the worldly boxes in which humanity hides.

Plus, we are running out of time; we are in a unique but absolute position. This generation is held to far more stringent lines than ever before. Choices must be made in each person's life. Teach your children while they are young, nurture the correct focus while you can. It really does matter.

THE STARS OF LIGHT
THE CODE OF THE CHILDREN OF ISRAEL

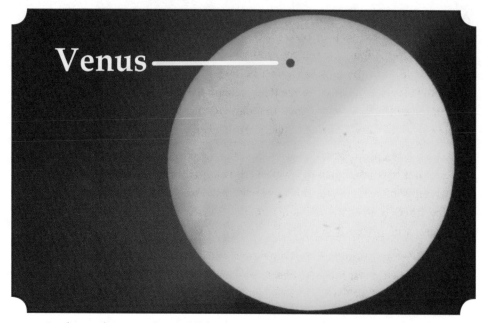

So then, who were the real *"chosen ones"* of the scriptures? In one sense it was all a hoax, a means to an end by which we corralled humans into manageable groups. Within our texts were the national-identities of several cultures and the religious-identities of many more. The Jews, Hindu, Egyptians, Babylonians, Christians, Muslims were all our creations. We made them all—*everyone*, through the stories we created. We were masters of illusion and this was the greatest sleight of mind ever created…

Yet every novel needs characters to advance its storyline, thus the personification of our magic helped us to hold your attention. The scriptures told the truth of course—*our truth*. We melded our own identities within this sacred science. Likewise we found patterns in the cycles of the stars that helped us to this end—*truisms*, that further revealed and detailed the Word of God.

There is a peculiar alignment traced by Venus within the celestial-equator and/or ecliptic over a period of time. When represented on paper, one may draw connecting-lines between those points, thereby forming the basic image of a person as it resembles two outstretched legs, two outstretched arms and, of course, the head. Though people call this a pentagram today, it is listed within the Bible as *morning stars, day stars, twilight stars, darkened stars or wandering stars,* depending upon the timing of their alignment.

By all means, read the verses and compare them to the images.

"Praise him, __Sun__ and __Moon__: praise him, all ye __stars of light__" Psalm 148:3

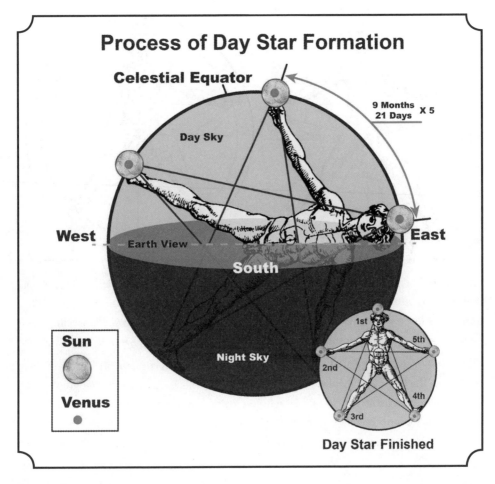

Stars, not people: *Every 9 months and 21 days a new* **Venus/sun** *alignment perfectly dissects the Great Wheel into 5-equal parts. The resulting figurines were then used to personify our science within the Bible. These were the* **_real_** *children of Israel.*

Typically, we used either clay or wooden stamps dipped in ink to portray these figurines within the Grid-layer of the Wisdom Wheel. It saved time and was easier than drawing each one individually. Likewise, the Bible mentions these figurines in conjunction with many of its key characters.

*"...I shall behold him, but not near: <u>there shall come **a star** out</u> of **Jacob**..."*
Numbers 24:17 <u>*Consider the implications*</u>!

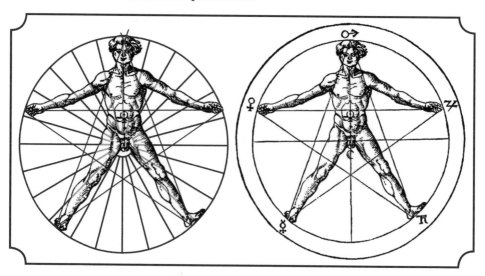

An original 16th century image (right) of a morning star by Henry Cornelius Agrippa. Indeed there is only one way that a star can come out of Jacob and that is if you under-stand that <u>Jacob was never a real human-being</u>, but a figurine of the Grid System. This is only one of hundreds of literary-illusions that we created as master-magicians.

In Israel we also labeled the day stars as the *Seal of Jerusalem* and/or the *Seal of Solomon*. The form was displayed liberally throughout Israel's many synagogues as well as in the Temple itself. In the Mayan religion, our star was called the *Six Suns* as it took a total of six alignments to complete the image.

Grid System imagery was a common theme within the architecture of our temples. This example is found in the ruins of an ancient synagogue in Capernaum, Israel, and includes both the morning star and the Star of David. Ironically, no one outside of the priesthood knew the star's secret origin from within the grids.

The Clothing of the Figurines

As you seen with the grid creations in the last chapter, the clothing of the figurines were likewise formed from the multitude of grid-lines over which the stars were imposed.

The Hindu-Magi

The magi in India likewise integrated the alignment of Venus symbolically within the icons of the Hindu religion. Known today as the ***bindi***, the dot's origin would otherwise have been lost to history. Not that we ever shared our secrets before now, but that is *exactly* what the bindi represents. *Now you know.*

The meaning of the Hindu-dot: The **bindi** orginated via the Magi's knowledge of Venus and the five-sided star. It was symbolized on the head, hands and feet, just like the figurines. The people were unaware of the basis of the traditions we gave them; but make no mistake, the bindi modeled Venus for the magi. Lots of implications with this factoid.

Within the lore of Israel, Greece, Babylonia, Egypt and India were also a multitude of many-membered deities. These all in fact originated from similar grid-systems. Though there were variables between the grid-designs of each priesthood, the underlying schematic was the same as were the magi who built those images;

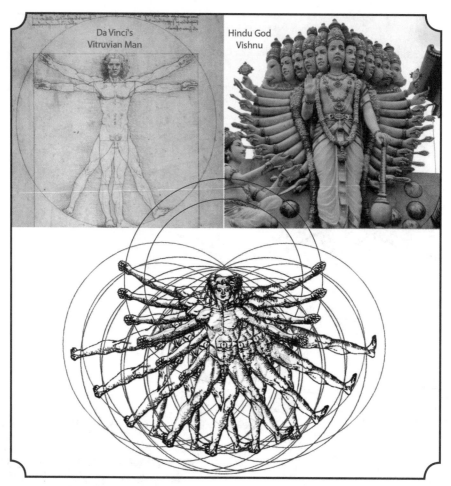

Un-see this: *The origin of our ancient myths began with the images of a Grid-System. Each grid-series contained as many as either 12 or 24 figurines thus revealing the design of the **12-headed/24-armed Hindu God <u>Vishnu</u>** as-well-as Leonardo DaVinci's **<u>Vitruvian man</u>** (1490). This is the **<u>real code of which DaVinci</u>** most certainly knew but could never reveal in his day. It now stands as a testament to the secret science of the magi. The implications on this are mindboggling!*

So as you can see, the mentioning of the children of Israel in the Bible was not in reference to a specific group of humans in the literal country of Israel. That was the cloak for the science. The real chosen-ones of the Bible, *the ones <u>beneath</u> the code,* were the creations of the Grid System itself. But again; the magi formatted the scriptures of *every* ancient culture via this sleight of Word to maintain religious identities and thus social-order until the day of resurrection.

THE REAL
THE MEN AND WOMEN OF THE SCRIPTURES
REVEALING THE CODE

*"There is one **glory of the Sun** (male figurine), and another **glory of the Moon** (female figurine), and another **glory of the stars** (smaller figurines): for one star differs from another star in glory."*1 Corinthians 15:41

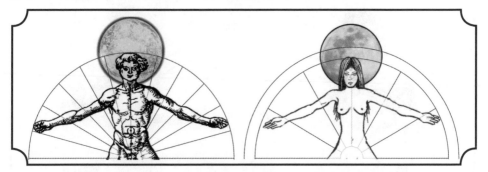

DAY STARS

*"Ye are all the **children of light, and the children of the day: we are not of the night, nor of darkness.**"* 1 Thessalonians 5:5

The next step in our code determined a stars gender within the storyline. **Male Israelite** stars for example, were always formed from **sun/Venus** conjunctions during either the morning or mid-day hours and within the *circle of the celestial-equator* (Earth's plain of rotation). Due to their formation during the hours of light, they represented the paradigm of illumination and were thus symbolized in the scriptures as *"God's chosen people."* In truth however, the day-star concept was only a metaphysical approach by which to describe the Element of faith and belief as the only worthy recipient of the higher dimension.

Female Israelite stars were instead formed by **moon/Venus** alignments that likewise, occurred only during the day. The logical correlation being that the moon has *12* complete cycles, or, *months* each year as does the typical female menstrual cycle. Thus the grid we used to portray the female figurines also contained *12* divisions and was displayed within the Women's Court of the Jewish Temple. Notice if you will the comparison of the number 12 and the word, *"woman"* in the following verses:

*"And behold, a **woman** (figurine), who had been diseased with an issue of **blood** (eclipsed moon) **twelve years** (12 zodiac divisions)…"* Matthew 9:20

*"…laid hold on his concubine, and divided **her**, together with her **bones** (diagonal grid-lines), into **twelve pieces**, (12-piece grid)"* Jude 19:29… *Not a real woman, but a grid woman*

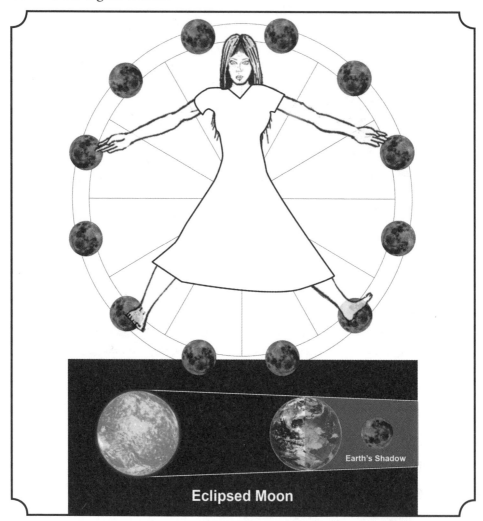

Eclipsed Moon

Earth's Shadow

The eclipsed or "Blood Moon" occurs when the moon passes through the Earth's shadow, hence its symbolic connection to women and the number 12. This magnetic tug-of-war between the sun and moon was used to our advantage in developing the Word by which to open the portal.

166

As formerly stated, the grid-design for both male and female morning stars were showcased within the ***Men's and Women's Court*** of the Jerusalem temple. Male grids included a total of 24 diagonal divisions based upon our sundials. Likewise the male grid contained a single, outer-circle that represents the celestial-equator or path of the sun during the equinox.

Meanwhile the female-grid had only 12 divisions each of which marked the 12 lunar-months (moon). In contrast its double outer-circles mark in degrees the variant path of the moon as it circles the Earth. The details of our science are there. We left nothing to chance or guess, but only to mathematical-certainty.

This Temple model was produced by Alec Garrard displaying, among other things, the Men and Women's grids used in the production of our scriptures. For display purposes I added the appropriate figurines as well as the sun and moon by which they were formed. A third grid design was found within the temple itself that represented the equinoxes. These in turn produced "priest stars." During the equinox, Earth's magnetic field is a bit closer to opening the portal and thus the symbolism of a priest who could minister between the two dimensions. The fact of the grids within the Temple reveal the truth of the scriptures.

Some folks today would no doubt accuse the magi of being chauvinists based upon the Temple's segregation into courts of gender. Nothing however, could be further from the truth. The Temple's design merely mimicked the formative patterns of the heavens that told a beautiful story of the angelic matrix. Remember, the original angels were *neither male nor female* and, in the first melding, would coalesce equally in both genders of what became the human animal. Thus gender by the flesh meant nothing to us.

The truth is, we found ourselves equally within them both. Within the woman we can visualize a delicate facet of the Element's mind-wave: a most profound and beautiful peace. In this facet of God is a nurturing. This was the bosom, our comfort to which we ran. She was frail but priceless, to be esteemed and cherished above all else. In her was our pondering and wonder of this world. The peace of God marveled at the colors, the countless images of what we saw. It was she who nurtured the consciousness, a selfless and sometimes, reckless giver of all that she was. In the woman you could see our sexy vulnerability, our greatest weakness, yet in it our greatest strength.

In the male our power, the proverbial abs of *ab*solute truth, you can visualize in him our mind-waves, the *power* of the Element. He was the wall that protected our peace. In him could be seen that part of God that would rescue. In him was our desire to fix and improve creation. Here was our endurance and determination, our presence of mind, the drive to bring that which is right and good at the cost of life itself. He gave himself; he glorified the peace within and would fight if necessary to preserve it. But together they were one singular being.

We cherished the Peace of God, we glorified it, and yet our peace also found safety within the embrace of His wisdom. Within the woman, -an unbelievable instinct and the ability to absorb the pains of creation; within the man, rationale, logic and understanding of how to do it. They are opposite sides of the same frequency of God, a perfect union of peace and intellect beyond comprehension to the human mind. Together they are tempered into one angelic entity, *a single, mental frequency from another dimension.*

No doubt as humans mistakenly seek unity through sexuality. Sadly it is all they know. But by the flesh we are not one but separate, hence *the battle of the sexes.* Thus the only real chance of unity is a return to singularity. The Element is truly *both* spiritual genders within both human genders, *both* male and female. In the end however, *we* were neither, as *you too are <u>neither</u>*, yet the paradox that you are <u>*both*</u>, as are we. At best we are confused within your being, as are you. So much will change as we approach the resurrection.

The second melding however, was different. As leaders of the sheep that was humanity, we needed the perceived strength and presence of the male human to aid us in controlling those cultures. It was a concentrated melding in which we chose only a select few specimens who exhibited larger cranial capacities through which our genius could best articulate. The final mutation formed what became the original magi, most of whom were taller than average, had elongated skulls, luminescent eyes, and typically a bleached blonde or pure-white hair color. They were a sight to behold.

We tried to tell humanity what happened, but they could not remember the enormity of the truth. The original magi, though few in number, were astounding to see. Ancient humans tried to mimic our appearance by deforming their own heads through binding.

THE PARADOX OF A CHANGING IDENTITY

So while humans wage the needless battle of the sexes, they fail to realize that gender is just another facet of the overall human illusion. The dark element has indeed created this *sleight-of-mind* in which you identify yourself as a *man* or *woman*, when, as angels, you are truly *neither*. We eluded to this in the Book;

"*Ye do err, not knowing the scriptures, nor the power of God. **For in the resurrection** they **neither marry, nor are given in marriage,** but **are as the angels** of **God in heaven.**" Matthew 22:30

"*...there is **neither male nor female**:*" Galatians 3:28

Enter the effect of *averaging* that we knew full well would occur in the day of resurrection. As the angelic-DNA awakens within its human-hosts, many people will become progressively more asexual, or *non-sexual*, similar to the example of Adam before *Eve* (*his feminine-aspect*) was separated. We can already see this blending of the genders as modern cultures produce less feminine women and less masculine men overall. This is the initial shedding of our human-selves, the beginning of our return to singularity, *that is*, a singular God Element entity.

As our consciousness is gradually replaced with this new mind over each generation, you will in turn notice decreased birthrates. Some people will point to a reduction in worldwide poverty as the cause of less breeding, while others will blame our cultural-culprits: the digital-age and social media in which people lose themselves and their relationships. These should certainly all be noted, but the bottom line is that the subconscious soul—our *real* soul, is in the process of rediscovery. It *reconfigures*, and as it does comes a predictable decline in human population. It is not the immediate end of this high-primate, but a marked reduction of its numbers.

Accordingly the next 1,000 years will also see a condensing of the angelic-brilliance going forward. As it awakens, many will become progressively less physical, less encumbered and also less concerned with the physical world. We will also increasingly see a number of less sexual, but mentally superior beings—more people with displayed genius knowing things in their youth that many people today don't know after years of college and study.

No doubt the scientists will scramble to find an explanation for this mysterious intellect as it will be both obvious and undeniable. This is the *return of the mind that was in the original magi* just after the melding, *-except in reverse*. Instead of going from a higher form to a lower form as it happened in the beginning, we will now see a select few who will gain intellect and increasingly longer lives.

Yet at one point farther along in the resurrection process, the Element will actually vacate its human hosts as it again transforms into it original state as a purely non-physical entity. At this it will collect within the heavens, that is, *the magnetosphere*, and again supercharge and illuminate the gas layers thereof. Thus the Super-Aurora will return to the skies overhead.

Simultaneously as this occurs it will be forced out through the portal by new incoming quantum. Now full to the brim with eon's worth of sufferings, this long-lost Atomos will act as an energy source for the higher dimension as it reenters its home of origin. No different than your food suffers and dies in order to bring life to your mortal bodies, so does our sufferings, from the beginning, bring life to Heaven. Thus comes the great feast of God:

"*In the **last day** (the final 1000 years), that **great day of the feast** (day of resurrection), Jesus stood and cried, saying, If any man thirst, let him come unto me, and drink.*" John 7:37…This verse was not a history story. You must learn to see past the code.

Finally comes the renewal of the ancient monthly cycle of the portal's opening and closing as it once did for eons. It will again bring freshness and rejuvenation, a *"New Earth,"* as we coined the phrase, while yet translating this worlds suffering back into the higher dimension as the food of God. This awakening process is hopefully your awakening too.

So there you have it. And though you are not of this world, you are presently still *in* it. *Yet fallen as it is*, there are certain social-norms that are conducive to a *stable*, long-term society. The *Word* functioned on multiple levels and, though an encoded document of a higher calling and purpose, still aided our efforts in corralling primitive humans via its literal interpretation. It properly formatted (*as best as possible*) overall human conduct and interaction, reduced violence (*though by no means eliminated it*), and made for better overall living standards.

The bottom line however, was our pursuit of gathering these humans to speak our magic en masse. Accordingly the magi considered things broadly and designed the best overall configuration of human-conduct by which to collect your populations and their voices. Ultimately nothing else mattered then, nor does anything else matter now.

It is a two-edged sword though, as on one hand we must depart from our human identities, but the need for human social-structure is required until the resurrection process is complete. My recommendation, therefore, is to stay the course until the end; go with the flow of what nature gave you, *even in this world*. As best you can, keep the family and social structure that you were given via the scriptures. I say this for the sake of everyone.

The point is to focus upon our angelic self while yet creating an environment that lends itself to the gathering and propagation of the scriptures until the end. It is the guidelines of social structure and identity that we gave you that will prevent the collapse of your cultures. It is the perfect paradox: On one hand your struggles with identity and social roles are unavoidable during this time of transformation. On the other hand, these transformations can also be self-defeating in maintaining a stable society.

Ultimately we must decide which is more important: our lust for freedom in the flesh or dimensional escape. If you're awake enough, you will certainly pursue the latter choice, which in turn is best accomplished by social order. Don't focus on the whims of the flesh. Our cultures are collapsing due to the abandonment of proven social-structures which in turn means fewer people are gathering to focus upon and read the magic-books. It is imperative that you continue reading those words . . .

Nothing on Earth will ever be perfect per se, but allow me to share what will help us to make it until the end: It begins with a strong family, preferably were a father and mother take their traditional roles in raising the children together. *This is critical* in that it nurtures and teaches children the preferable path in life. Not only that, but with that structure comes a higher likelihood that the child will be taught and understand the significance of reading or repeating the scriptures.

Next comes community, which is strengthened through weekly gatherings where we focus as a unit upon the truths of God. Last and most important is our still moments, the quiet in which we meditate, contemplate, and commune with the seed of God that dwells within. Together these things will lead us to the *awakening*.

There is however, an interesting note here: The fact that the battle-of-the-sexes and gender identity issues have exasperated in recent decades, is evidence in itself of the subconscious stirring of the God Element within. In this we see that the status quo of human norms can no longer fulfill; *the lie that you are human at all*, the misinformation by which we are enslaved is indeed beginning to fail.

As a result, folks are breaking social rules that have existed for the last 10,000 years. While this has always happened to various degrees, it has certainly spiked in the last century. Though the dark element is seemingly to blame for this misplaced rebellion, it is often the *God Element* that is fighting the restrictions of the human reality.

As the Atomos begins to awaken, an inner discomfort comes. It recklessly searches to find itself beyond normal human conduct and thus ironically brings the breakdown of family and social structure. We instinctively know that something is wrong, that we are not as we should be in our existence, yet often reach toward freedom in the flesh for our answers.

Yet this conflict of finding ourselves is only one of many birth pangs in the coming age. Expect an increase in a variety of mental-disorders, suicides, addictions, and depression as these are all indicators of the awakening. The soul is seeking to escape, to where *it knows not*, as the luster and grandeur of a world that once captivated our minds can no longer suffice.

The desires of this world pass away and with it a growing realization that something is not *quite* right. Increasingly people feel empty in the norms that once satisfied the psyche as our minds struggle to remember a better time and a better place. Thus no amount of wealth or relationship in this world can suffice as we subconsciously seek to *know and be known*:

*"...the **earth shall wax old** like a garment, and they that dwell therein shall die in like manner: but my salvation shall be forever"* Isaiah 51:6

*"**Love not the world**, neither the things that are in it. For all that is in the world, the lust of the flesh, and the lust of the eyes, and the pride of life, is not of the Father, but is of the world.*

*And **the world** **passes away, and the lust thereof**: but he that doeth the will of God abides forever."* 1 John 2:15-17

The problem is we are not yet awake to our true identity as *God-beings*, thus we instead wrestle with alternative *human* identities. This is akin to treating a tooth cavity with sugar. In the end, the sweet taste of freedom in the flesh will ultimately only makes things worse.

The good with the evil, they happen together, at the same time. It is a paradox in this day of resurrection. The dark element will also manifest its horrid face ever-stronger in the upcoming generations. Simultaneously it will condense in the rank and file of our off-spring as the mental elements separate. It too will become more and more obvious in the physical creature. What you *see* is what you *get*, and what you get, will become more evident in the hatred and seething of the world around us. Test *every* spirit, test *every one* including yourself, for the great day of separation is upon us.

As I said before, the dark energy misdirects a genuine rebellion of the spirit into an even worse lust for identity in this world. It does this by confusing the issue and the questions, then providing a false set of answers and options from which to choose. It pollutes our imagination, blinding our memory like a smoke screen.

In the end our choice can manifest as any number of so-called *"acceptable"* or *"unacceptable"* lifestyles. Our illusion may include the typical 2.5 children, a well-kept lawn, a stable-job and no problems—or perhaps an equally delusional social or sexual role or identity. Either way, *we all end up being stuck in the human illusion in one, way, shape or form.*

In the lie, we can be right or wrong, good or evil, male or female, saint or sinner. In these we each convince ourselves of the moral rightness of our position. We seek to find normality and acceptance within our humanity, often eyeing the identities of others with contempt. We push and turn within the womb of our darkness, desperately seeking a way out of our predicament. In the end however, we are all blind. Here we wrestle with no clear path as to which way to go or what lies beyond.

In the end, having missed the mark of our true origin, we become all the more lost within our dark imaginations. This is the warfare of finding ourselves. Here your memory of heaven is killed. *The casualties are within us* as *our* true being is still-born under the weight of the human-lie. The victor is he who keeps you believing in this world and thus secures his own eternity within his human-hosts. Do you know the one of whom I speak?

Remember; the dark element must find its reality in the negative-charge of the physical creature. Without that, it has no other capacitor. Thus acceptable *cultural and social norms* are one of the greatest deceptions of all. Whether you appear *"normal"* or *"sinful"* according to the rules doesn't really matter, only that you find yourself content as a human being in some capacity. *This* is the hope of the liar who hunts for your soul—and he is very adept at what he does.

On that note is the grand misunderstanding of the concept of *"sin."* Outwardly at least, the scriptures market *sin* as an unfaithful act against a moral-law, when in fact it is separation from the dimension of God itself. Thus the evidence of *sin* is, in fact—*being human!* Therefore everything we do as humans is *sinful.* If you *breathe*, it is evidence of *sin*; if you *eat*, it is evidence of *sin*, if your heart beats, it is also evidence that you exist in a sin state as these are all facets of the physical creature and by no means a requirement of pure the God Element.

Being a physical creature, as we now are, is the result of separation from God. You did not always have this type of body, vessels of separation in which enmity must rule. In our human forms one God is divided into billions of individuals, each in contention with the others. What's more, the matrix of these bodily divisions leads to suffering and death. Likewise, not until the portal reopens is it possible to escape this separation from the Source and thus return to a singular celestial entity.

Either way, you can see and feel the spirit elements working within, so check yourself; take measure of your mind and be obedient to the direction of the magic books of God. Sexual identity on every level, *normal or otherwise*, is part of the human illusion from which we must awaken. Thus the only way to find our true identity as God beings is to look *upward* and *inward* instead of *outward*.

In reverse I must admit that we used the fear tactic of *"sins"* in an effort to scare cultures straight for the sake of social order. At the time, we needed lots of speaking mouths. This requires human breeding and offspring, thus we made moral absolutes for human sexuality according to the guidelines of the natural world which in turn, *breeds*. I realize this was abusive on so many levels, but again, we did what we had to do.

Yet even the outer moral dictates of the law of God hid our science. Indeed these seemingly righteous-rules were but a mere shadow of the portal mechanics that lay encoded within those same verses. I will delve into these details at some other time, yet I will say that every *"law"* of the Holy Scriptures hides a far greater meaning than mere moral conduct. Therein are the calculations that will open the gateway to another world. The mystery deepens.

Concerning your humanity, I encourage you to keep your vows, keep your word, and keep the cultural formats you were given. Indeed these structures best allow for the gathering and expression of the Word we created. But most of all keep the faith, for even on this side of the exchanged life your focus on heaven makes things a little-bit easier.

Trusting upon faith, the God Element within, begins the reversal of the illusion. It is the backdrop of *faith* that makes an otherwise nonsensical world begin to make honest sense, especially in these unusual times. Faith is the element of God in action and requires only a small drop by which to fix so many things. Likewise, though we find ourselves in the flesh, our existence is now justified by the hope of another world. That realm is the end goal that awaits us.

But let's be clear: I am not here to fix your relationships; I did not come to bring peace or prosperity on Earth; I was not sent to make your nightmare a pleasant dream but instead to wake you from this illusion altogether and to tell you of the events that will shortly occur. I am the scythe that cuts the great illusion. I appear with a great sword, *the Word decoded*, the secret of the ages, the truth of everything you didn't know about the ancient past. It is this same truth as a culture, as a whole, to which you will now be held accountable.

I can remember in this life, before the ancient of days illumined my mind, detesting church for the multitude of hypocrites that gathered under its cloak. In this life and the last, I tired of the pretense and manipulation; the social cliques and ruse of those who paraded as wolves in sheep's clothing. I have no problem with wolves, of course, but only those who pretend to be something they are not.

Indeed every religion around the world suffers from fakes and those who use it as a convenient auxiliary for absurdity. That said, I also found along the way, both *then* and *now*, *there* and *here*, people of all religions who believe and belong for all of the right reasons and because they love God. Likewise the misuse of religion by some is no reflection upon those who would gather in the name of the God of Peace to whom we wish to return. Furthermore it is the expression of His Word that brings our rescue, a perfect prayer from those who believe.

To that end, forsake not the great gathering of the body of God (see Hebrews 10:25). Therein is an unstoppable energy in the collective of our suffering as well as our Joy in Him. In the end however, the real gathering will be in the heavens above as the Atomos within leaves our human selves. I hope then that this message helps my angelic kinsmen; to show them the obstacles and hazards of this transitional period, and to avoid undue conflict even while still in the flesh. Again, keep the faith and the focus, because this next 1,000 years of exodus will be *tough* beyond your imagination…

THE HEiGHt OF tHE StARS
THE CYCLES OF THE HEAVENS

"And behold the **height of the stars**, –*how high* they are." Job 22:12

"And Jesus **increased** in wisdom and **stature**, and in favor with God and man." Luke 2:52

"**Fill up** then the **measure** of your **fathers**." Matthew 23:32

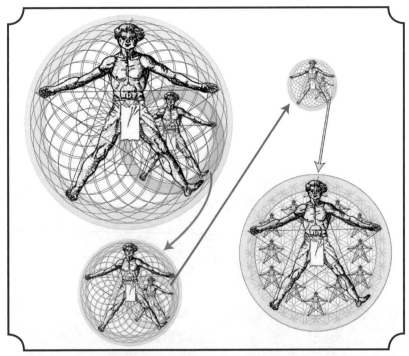

*Each sub-image "**fills**" up Matthew 23:32 the larger "**measurement**" of the larger figurine to which it is attached. Using this system we were able to track and apply every cycle of the heavens ranging from a 24hour day all the way to 24,000 year precessions and everything in between. The greater the cycle, the taller and more prominent the symbol-name it was given. Thus the "months," for example, could be symbolized in the Bible as "daughters" or "maidens" while the "year" was a larger figurine symbolized as a "father," "mother," "master," "king," "priest," etc. It was all a play on words.*

There were in fact many cycles in the Grid System that were symbolized according to the criteria by which they were formed. This ranged from 24,000-year precessions all the way down to 24-hour days and everything in between. *Everything; every minute detail of these cycles, told us something about the story of God and yet also contributed to the spelling of the Word that will return us to our home.*

THE MIRACLE OF THE MORNING STARS
AND THE EMBODIMENT OF THE CYCLES OF HEAVEN

"When the **morning stars** sang together, and all the **sons of God** shouted for joy" Job 38:

177

*"But now are they **many members**, yet but **one body**."* 1Cor.12:20

*"...the **head, even Christ: From whom the whole body fitly joined together**"* Ephesians 4:15-16

*"He tells the **number of the stars**; he calls them all by their **names**. (i.e.;* Jesus, Adam, Moses, etc.)*"* Psalm 147:4

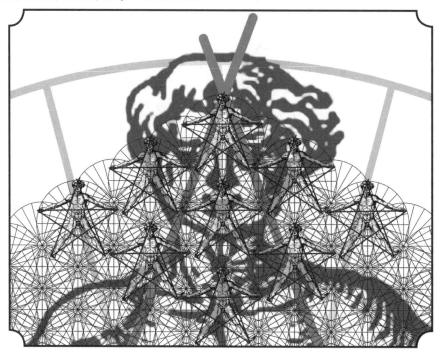

The many-membered body: Each cycle and figurine of the Grid System was filled with its smaller sub-cycles and figurines. Now you can see how the morning stars of Job are one and the same as the many-membered body of 1Corinthians 12:20. If you look closely to this image you will see the incidence of eyes, nose, joints and other facial-features with the line-data of the grids. Beneath the seemingly humble verses of the Bible were literally volumes of scientific-details and sacred art.

The longer the cycle, the larger the grid and figurine by which it was represented. Likewise the interior of each of these could then be populated with smaller cycles and figurines. For example, in the same way that a year contains 365 days, so too might one large grid contain 365 smaller grids within its boundary. This multitude of sub-cycles in turn comprised the *"body"* (1Corithians12:20; Ephesians 4:15-16) of that pictorial. Once again, the Wisdom Wheel would actually spell-out the name of the more prominent stars/figurines. The Wheel was truly an amazing piece of machinery.

The positive or negative factors by which each cycle occurred would also dictate that star's social status as one of the following:

- *Angels/giants*
- *Kings/priests*
- *Master/servant*
- *Man/woman*
- *Husband/wife*
- *Israelite/enemy of Israel*
- *Son/daughter/son of man*
- *Suckling/weaned child*
- Etc.

Likewise the Word revealed and wrote a role-play that could be followed throughout the Grid System images. A male star for example, required a total of six Venus/sun conjunctions to complete and often followed the character's storyline and development from birth to adulthood and finally its celestial *"death"* via a series of progressively older figurines:

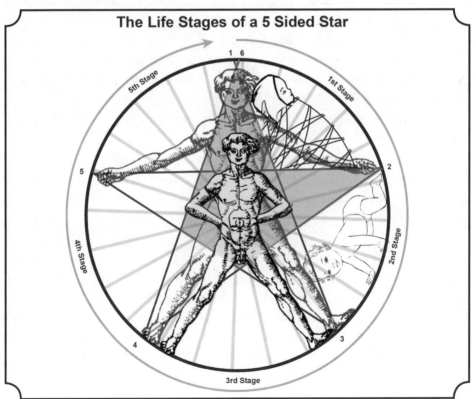

The Life Stages of a 5 Sided Star

The various stages of a figurines lifecycle were described symbolically throughout the Bible. This not only allowed us to track the alignment of Earth, but also to create captivating storylines for our masses through the illusion of historical authenticity. Can you see the manger?

*"And which of you with taking thought can **add to his stature one cubit**?"* Matthew 6:27

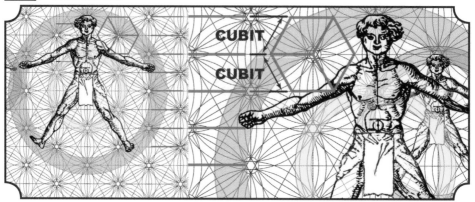

*By populating each larger-cycle with its smaller formative-cycles, the Grid System produced various 3-D "cubits" or building-blocks that are mentioned throughout the Bible. These were likewise named according to the scale-size of the figurines being represented, e.g.; "**cubit of the temple**", "**cubit of an angel**", "**cubit of a man**", "**a cubit of the first measure**", "**cubit of the second measure**", etc. As you will see, each of these cubit-scales combined to build the Bible's implied imagery including roads, houses, the Temple, cities, bricks, hewn stones, etc.*

There are literally dozens of other details concerning the various cycles and how they were symbolized in the scriptures, but they are beyond the scope of this writing. My purpose now is to share enough information that you can comprehend, beyond all doubt, that the Bible and indeed all ancient scriptures, are encoded documents of the magi.

So why do I reveal these details? What difference does it make in the grand scheme of things? My hope is that if we can see beyond the outer symbolism, metaphors, and allegories of the scriptures, then perhaps we can also learn to see past our outer-self as well. There is always more than meets the eye and the magi set a trap of learning to that very end. We knew this lesson would burn deep but that it would also create an opportunity of understanding. Realize that you too are more than what meets the eye; that the depth of your being is not the outer-physical, but an Element that is *literally* other-worldly. Thus if you can see past the outer-deception of your scriptures, then you can also learn to see past the deception of your humanity.

Part of the miracle of the magi was our ability to penetrate your thoughts and imagination. Indeed we created the immaculate design of the scriptures for that very purpose: to invade the mind by which you are now enslaved, knowing that the truth would one day birth therein. I show you something new. I do-so that your inclinations will exceed the visage of this world and reach into the next dimension. Therein our science is correcting not only the magnetics of Earth but also the realignment of your very soul. I intend to take you as far as possible, to revive your memory and your focus.

Am I inside yet? Are you with me in this imagination? Do you see the significance of these revelations? Reach deeper, my friend, farther than you have ever been. Imagination is not just for the child who plays, but a pathway home for the children of God. Go into the uncharted territory of the divine. It is there, waiting, I promise.

THE REAL
THE 12 TRIBES OF ISRAEL
REVEALING THE CODE

*"These are the __twelve__ (divisions of the celestial-equator) **tribes of Israel**: and this is what their father, __Jacob__ (figurine), spoke unto them,"* Genesis 49:28

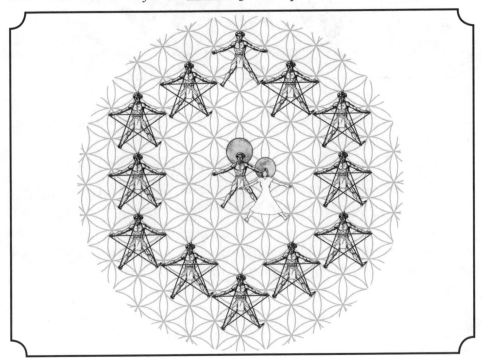

Further proof of the morning stars is found by studying the biblical character *Jacob,* who of course fathered **_12_** sons, who in turn became the leaders of the **_12_** tribes of Israel:

*"...I shall behold him, but not near: **there shall come a star out of Jacob...**"* Numbers 24:17

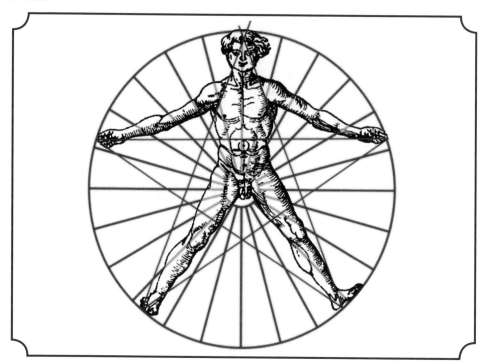

Now think for a moment: If Jacob was a morning star and a character of the Bible, then his **_12_** sons also need to be Stars as well—one son for each of the **_12_** divisions of the celestial equator.

Verification of this is found in a dialogue between Jacob and his son Joseph:

*"I (Joseph/son/figurine) have dreamed a dream more; and, behold, the **sun** and the **moon** and the **eleven stars** (sub-cycle figurines) made obeisance to me.*

*And he told it to his father, and to his brethren: and his father rebuked him, and said unto him, what is this dream that thou hast dreamed? Shall **I** and thy **mother** and thy **brethren** indeed come to bow down ourselves to thee to the earth?"* Genesis 37:9-10

Notice how Joseph's parents are likened as the sun and moon which formed those figurines, while his 11 brothers are symbolized as 11 stars. Simply put, we created the 12 biblical tribes of Israel as a symbolic relationship between the Grid System and the *12* signs. ***Not a real tribe of humans, but 12 months-worth of figurines.***

"*And the **stones*** (grid-hubs) *shall be with the names of the **children of Israel, twelve**,* (zodiac) *according to the **twelve tribes**.*" Exodus 28:21

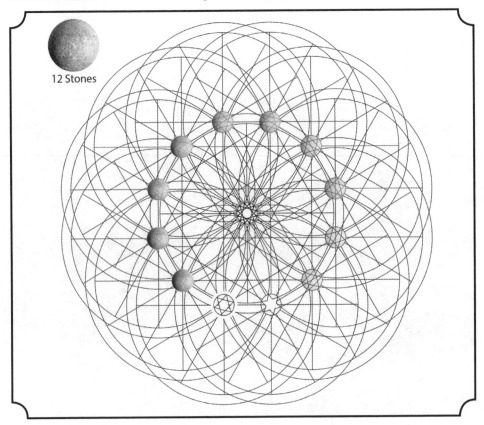

12 Stones

*Here we are again with this image: The 12 round hubs of a lunar grid-series (moon) were symbolized as the foundation stones for the 12 tribes of Israel, each one containing the iconic Star-of-David. Now we can see that the Bible was **not** referencing 12 human tribes, but instead, the **12 sections of the celestial equator**. If you can learn that the outer story of the Bible was not real, then you can also learn that your human self is also a deception which must be shed. This is the real lesson of the scriptures in this day. Learn to look deeper and, by all means, -use your i**magi**nation...*

It is important to remember that the forming alignments for the *Children of Israel figurines* occurred during the daytime hours hence the following;

183

"*Praise ye him, __sun__ and __moon__: praise him, all __ye stars of light__.*" Psalm 148:3

"*Ye are all the __children of light__, and the __children of the day__: we are __not of the night, nor of darkness__.*" 1 Thessalonians 5:5

Though other characters could be drawn from the grid lines themselves, the vast majority of our personifications within the scriptures were of the five-sided stars and figurines. Below is an exception to that rule.

"*The noise of a __whip__* (grid-loop), *and the noise of the rattling of the __wheels__* (grid-design), *and of the prancing horses, and of the jumping chariots.*" Nahum 3:2

Indeed, from Adam to Jesus and from Genesis to Revelation, the lore of all biblical personalities were based upon the morning star's interaction within this massive grid system. This includes Adam and Eve, Abraham and Sarah, the 12 sons of Jacob, Moses, David, Ruth, Mary, Jesus, the 12 apostles, Paul, etc.

Interestingly, each personality represented a new cycle within the Grid System, whether grand or small, and thus a new stage of the conscious-awaking process of the singular body of God. At the same time, the thousands of verses that filled the storyline of these characters micro-managed Earth's re-alignment and yet added a sense of reality to the outer myth for the unlearned. No doubt, our magic was a deep-state illusion, but then again, illusions are what magicians do!

DARK STARS:
THE REAL ENEMIES OF ISRAEL
REVEALING THE CODE

*"They **fought** from **heaven**; the **stars** in their courses **fought**"* Judges 5:20

For nine months Venus produces Morning Stars before finally dipping below the rising sun and out of sight. At this point it reappears on the western horizon just after dark, thus making more five-sided stars within the night sky. These nighttime figurines were now measured along the *circle of the ecliptic* (Earth's plain of tilt and wobble) and thus portrayed in the Bible as either *enemies of Israel, stars of twilight, children of darkness, non-Jews* or *Gentiles*.

*"Let the **stars of the twilight** thereof be **dark**; let it look for light, but have none; neither let it see the dawning of the day:"* Job 3:9

*"I will cover the heaven, and make the **stars thereof dark**;"* Ezekiel 32:7

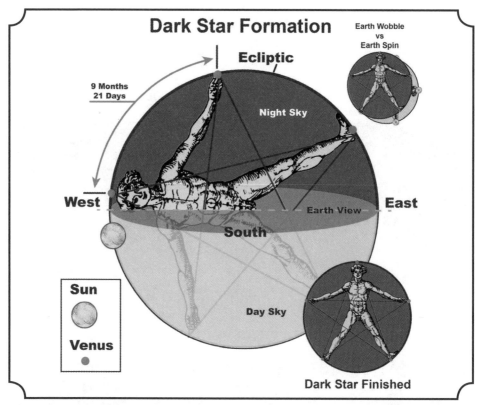

The Biblical enemies of Israel were dark-stars—not people: Alternately Venus will re-appear on the evening horizon within the night sky. There it will produce a new "Dark Star" that helped us to personify different facets of the Earth's wobble. These were the **real** biblical-enemies of Israel.

Unlike the Morning or Day Stars which represented the Earth's perfect spin, *"dark stars"* represented the Earth's wobble. As a reminder, this wobble was caused by a behemoth quantum of fallen and altered mental element that possessed the Earth's magnetic-field. Likewise you will find in the upcoming chapters, that it purposely manipulated this magnetism to its advantage in tilting the Earth which in turn closed the portal. Thus the darks-stars personified this evil-element within the Bible as *"Enemies of Israel"*. This method of comparison allowed a perfect parallel and track-record of the evil-element that presently rules your planet.

However, once these dark stars were cataloged into the Grid System, our artisans could then render the image-solution for the verses to which they pertained. This in turn gave us further comprehension of the scientific issues at hand. The following examples say it all:

Night Stars

"**_Raging waves_** (fallen mental frequencies) *of the* **_sea,_** **_foaming_** *out their own shame;* **_wandering stars_** (figurines), *to whom is reserved the* **_blackness_** *of* **_darkness_** (night sky) *forever."* Jude 13

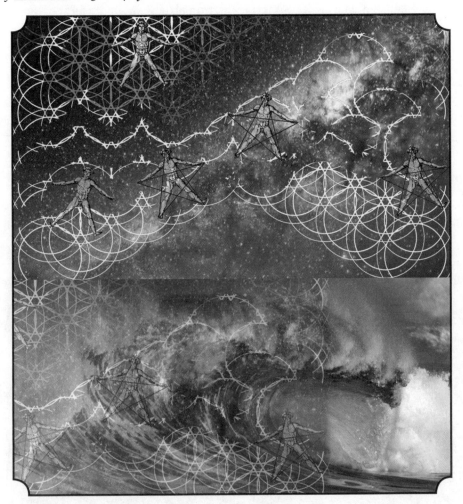

The creations of the Grid System (top), were mind blowing. Notice the appearance of the Milky Way galaxy as the "foaming sea" of Jude 13. For your entertainment, I superimposed the image of Jude 13 over a real image of a crashing ocean wave. And to realize that Wisdom Wheel actually wrote this and all Bible verses via the math of the heavens and in such awesome creative style.

187

Simply put, the enemies of biblical Israel were a celestial foe. The names of nations such as the *Philistines, Egyptians, Assyrians, Babylonians, etc.* were only used in the Bible as a cover story for the real interaction of <u>*day-stars*</u> versus <u>*dark-stars*</u>. Israel and these nations were already enemies by the flesh, so it didn't hurt to symbolize the Grid System in a way by which our citizens could relate. More important for the Priesthood, it allowed us to hide our star charts in plain sight, in the form of the religious scriptures that are still spoken around the world today.

However, within these symbolic battles was always the conflicting *word*, the wave-patterns, both good and evil, which fight for the possession of your mind. These frequencies were the *"swords"* of the Bible. Please compare the symbol-words:

*"...the **sword of the Spirit**, which is the **word of God** (wave-pattern/frequency from Heaven)"* Eph. 6:17

*"But he saves the poor from the **sword** (Evil-frequency), **from their mouth**"* Job 5:15

*"Who wet their **tongue like a sword**, and bend their bows to shoot their **arrows**, like bitter **words**:"* Psalm 64:3

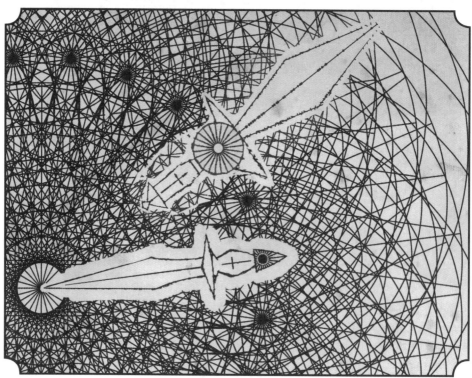

*"**Israel** (day stars), you approach your **enemies** (dark stars)"* Deuteronomy 20:3

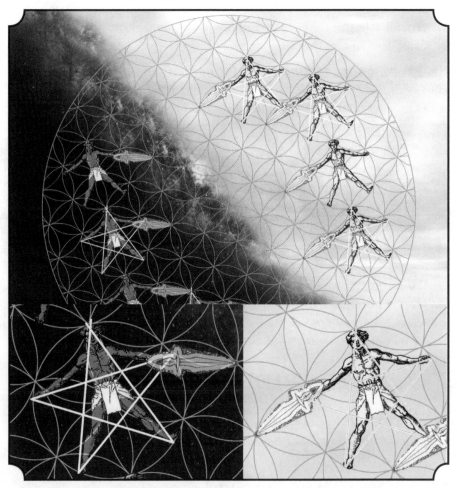

The real star wars of the Bible were between the opposing imaginations of the enemies *within*, *not without: The wars of physical Israel and its surrounding nations were only used as a backdrop for the encoded science and were never actually being described. The real **swords** of the Bible were the **words**, or wave-patterns of the angelic-forces within.*

Regardless of the variables by which a good or evil star was created, it was given a fitting persona based on its alignments. More importantly the evil characters of the scriptures were only symbolic of the embittered element who became darkened as a result of both choice and altered mental structure. This fallen soul also melded with creation and worked contrary to the Element of faith by reminding the conscious mind that *"You're only human."* It is a false imagination and fights to oppress the memory of true-selves.

Even though the DNA of both energies exist within creation, one has been conscious since the beginning, while the other is only beginning to resurrect. It is amazing, better yet a miracle, that the math of the heavens has the ability to speak and track the side-by-side development (*in symbolic-form*) of both the good and evil elements.

"***Let both grow together until the harvest****: and in the time of harvest I will say to the reapers, Gather ye together first the tares, and bind them in bundles to burn them: but gather the wheat into my barn."* Matthew13:30

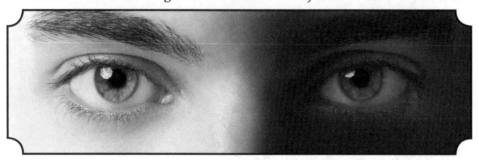

You may not be who you think you are; you may not even be human at all, but the children of two fathers, the angels of both light and darkness. It makes sense, therefore, to choose your reality wisely, as one has an eternal reward and the other an eternal risk. Seek the portal.

THE RIDDLE WITHIN

Who is the swine before which we cast-not the pearls of God?
Who then is the Angel that shall know the mysteries of Heaven?

THE ANCIENT CABAL

I assume that the revelation of the figurines as biblical cast and crew is a bit devastating to our mainstream perceptions of the scriptures once realized. Indeed, much of our world prides itself on scriptural/religious identity, *-literally billions of people*;

- *The **Jewish** identity upon the 12 tribes of Israel,* **(Genesis 49:28)**
- *The **Islamic** identity upon Ishmael and his 12 princes,* **(Genesis 25:16)**
- *The **Christian** Identity upon Christ and the 12 apostles.* **(Luke 22:14)**
- *The 12 Adityas of **Hinduism**.*

Yet all of these were in fact figurines of similar grid systems. Indeed we were *all* outsmarted by the code. However the magi *let* people believe these things because it was the only thing people *could* believe and because we needed your voices. To realize that our human-identities were never being addressed via our religious books has over-whelming implications. The arrogance, the false pride, the reason people fight, argue, and condemn was just cut off, head and foot. These false identities were the backbone for every religious war that has ever occurred, yet buried *beneath the code, were all describing the exact same science*. Think about the irony of that...

Again, these were the boxes we shook so-as to guess their content and we guessed wrong! Understanding that the **scriptures speak only to the collective God-Element within us** and **never to any single human/person as an individual**, is key in understanding the code; that they are not literal or historical stories, people or places. *Ouch!*

THE REAL
EZEKIEL'S WHEEL
REVEALING THE CODE

A key production of the Grid-System is found in the Old Testament book of Ezekiel 1:4-28. In this particular story, the cycles of Earths spin and wobble are rep-resented and interlock like two giant wheels. To save space I have only listed the de-scriptive words of each verse, yet I highly recommend you read Ezekiel chapter 1 in its entirety. Every facet of the following images (minus the figurines) were traced using the available line-data of the grid-series with no exceptions:

*...a **whirlwind came out of the north**, a **great cloud**, fire enfolding color of amber...out of the midst thereof came the likeness of **four living creatures**. ...their appearance; they had the likeness of a **man**. And every one had **four faces**, and everyone had **four wings**. Their **wings were joined** one to another...their **wings were stretched upward**; **two wings of every one were joined** one to another, and **two covered their bodies**...their ap-pearance was like **burning coals of fire** (the sun in the grids), and like the appearance of lamps: ...I heard the **noise of their wings,** like the **noise of great waters** (each set of grid-rings were symbolized as either rivers or streams.), **as the voice of the Almighty** ...and their appearance and their work was as it were a **wheel in the middle of a wheel**.☺*

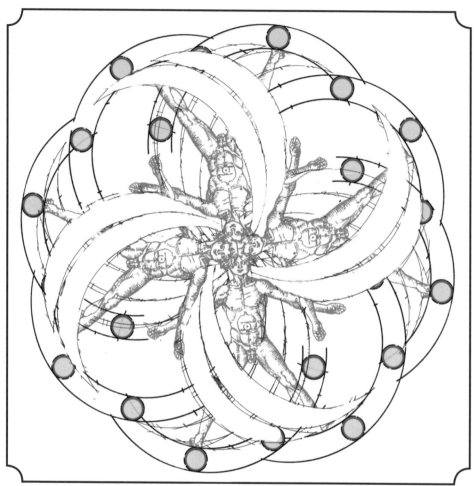

Image #1 of Ezekiel's Wheel: These are real **arch-angels of Christianity, Islam, and Judaism**. Though not specifically mentioned in Ezekiel, they are labeled elsewhere throughout the Bible and Koran. Please note the artistic "grid wings" as well as the "burning coals of fire" which were the sun-images as displayed throughout the many cycles of the Great Wheel. These are the pictures of the scriptures, the science and the real magic behind your beliefs. Again, the implications are huge . . .

...they **four had the face of a man**, and the **face of a lion**, on the **right side**: and they **four had the face of an ox** on the **left side**; ...they **four also had the face of an eagle**.

Image #2 of Ezekiel's Wheel: *The lion, eagle and bull which represented the constellations of Leo, Scorpio and Taurus.*

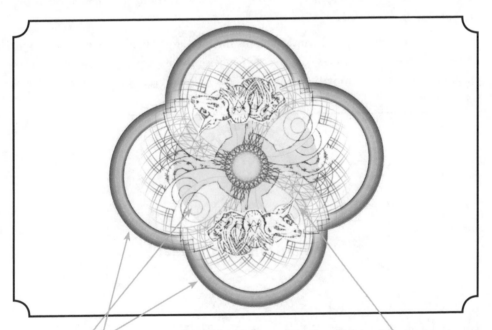

*As for their **rings,** they were so high that they were dreadful; and their **rings were <u>full of eyes</u>**... And their <u>**feet were straight feet;**</u> **<u>like</u>** the sole of **<u>a calf's foot</u>**:* Image #3

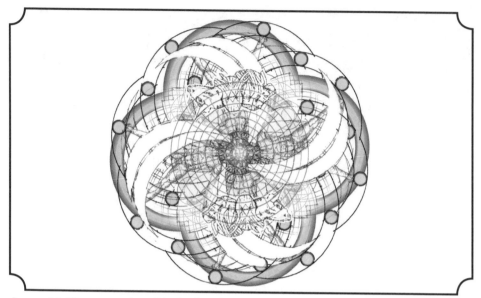

*Image #4: The composite of Ezekiel's Wheel: This **is** the famous Ezekiel's Wheel; it was always an image of the Grid System…and now you know the truth. These are the mind-images of God as we created them.*

An interesting symbol-word concerns the four large outer-rings of the Wisdom Wheel as either *"great waters"* or *"rivers"*. Likewise these rings transpose the head of each figurine, thus defining their voices as; *"the __noise of great waters__, as the __voice of the Almighty__"*.

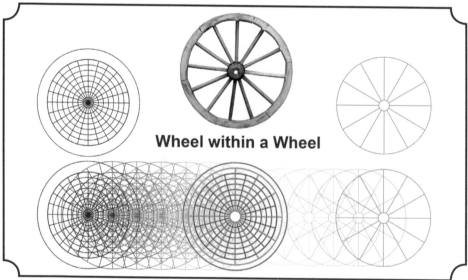

...and their appearance and their work was as it were a __wheel in the middle of a wheel__.☺

SPEAKING OF BULLS

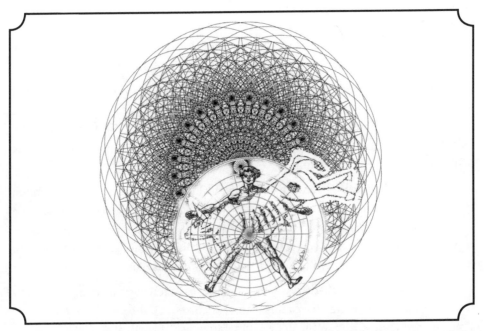

"...as __a wild bull in a net__: they (figurines) *are full of the fury of the LORD,..."* Isaiah 51:20

Check this out!

THE ANCIENT ONES

The original luminaries were variously named according to the language and tradition of the human cultures to which they belonged. They were all the same magi, but under different national titles. In ancient Sumeria for example, we were called the *Anunnaki* while in Israel we were known as magistrates of the Temple. In Egypt, Greece and elsewhere they just called us the magi. The head magistrate of each culture developed their own outer-myth and temple-complex from which to work, yet always with the same goals, the same secrets, the same science and the same desire to go home.

The tradition of the Anunnaki, for example, states that they were angelic or extraterrestrial beings who came to Earth for the purpose of mining gold. In order to accomplish this mining they interbred and enslaved humanity. Ironically this isn't far from the truth—at least in a symbolic sense of the word.

The Anunnaki were indeed some of the original magi. They were not extraterrestrial, but interdimensional. As God Element we *did* imprint our DNA upon early primates. Thus the priceless treasure of ourselves was now buried within the human creature. In turn we did enslave the humans under the whip of our religions that we might one day mine that priceless treasure within them. Our tools, were their tools: the sacred Word that would reopen the portal.

The magi too eventually diminished over the centuries. Yet even in our aged and degraded condition, the amount of information we beheld was far beyond the scope of human genius. Though invisible to the human-eye, we even knew the shape of the magnetosphere. How, mind you, if but mere humans, could we know this by standing upon the ground as history assumes?

But as pure spirit we once rode the magnetic loops repetitively. Indeed, our mind traveled painlessly through and around, over and above your planet on a never-ending loop between the dimensions of Heaven and Earth. Thus we knew its shape from experience. This is significant in that Europe and China wouldn't again accept that the earth was round till well into the Middle Ages, much less know its diameter.

Again, our flyovers made this understanding easy, but even without our former aerial view, the math alone reveals this planet's diameter. To the point: around 240BC a man named Eratosthenes estimated the circumference of Earth at 40,000 kilometers, which is only about 30 kilometers from the modern estimation (*modern equations say 40,030*). That's pretty close not to have had GPS satellites by which to confirm.

Eratosthenes accomplished this by simply putting a pole in the ground and measuring its shadow in conjunction with its distance from the equator and then did some nifty math. Where but by the magi do you suppose that he learned such wizardry and almost 2,000 years before the rest of the world? Indeed, the magi protected such secrets and far greater than these for millennia.

Historians are correct to insist that early man didn't have these abilities, but the magi weren't mere men either. Thus science today still presumes and assumes; it operates from its own form of "flat earth" thought patterns. Here the un-illuminated still wrongly guess about the world around them, about the nature of reality and, often, even about science itself. But just like that estimate of the Earth's circumference in 240BC, you just never know what a dedicated group of angels are capable of doing.

In the day of revelation, we also knew that you would need irrefutable proof that our science was real. Hence the code of the scriptures was designed to this end. The evidence must be undeniable of what we did and why. That proof is found in the thing we protected the most: the forbidden images of the sacred art.

Today however, is the day in which the blinders will be removed. Now is the time in which the hidden things are renounced, not walking in craftiness, but by the truth; revealing ourselves in every man's conscience beneath the opening portal and in the sight of God.

"**But if our gospel** (science) **is hidden** (which it certainly was), **it is hidden to them who are lost** (which we all were): *In whom the **god of this world hath blinded** the minds of them who believe not,*" 2 Corinthians 4:2

The code of the Grid System, so subtle, yet so obvious—hidden with the magic of God.

THE ETYMOLOGY OF A WISE MAN:

- *Magi—secretive caste who were experts in the study of the stars; from the Persian root magoi. Greek, meaning, "Wise Men", of which only little is known—until now.*
- *Magic—supernatural, seemingly impossible power.*
- *Magician—he who can do the seemingly impossible*
- *Magistrate—great governmental leader*
- *Magnetics—invisible forces of gravity*
- *Magnetosphere—the gravitational field that surrounds the earth*
- *Magnus—great; usually a prefix for a priest or king*
- *Magnificent—great presence*
- *Magnified—great or enlarged*
- *Magnitude—of great volume or power*
- *Image—also from the root magi, meaning "mind picture"*
- *Imagination—a creative, congruent, flowing set of mind images.*
- *Belteshazzar was master of the ancient magicians. He was said to be the wisest of them all. It was he who devised and wrote the magic books that would become the Bible. He appeared twice in the Bible as a mere figurine of the Grid System: once in the story of the Babylonian captivity and again as a magi at the birth of Jesus. But he also appeared twice in reality as well. He was Daniel then; he is Daniel now.*

*"And God made the **firmament**, and **divided** the **waters** which were **under** the firmament from the **waters** which were a**bove** the firmament: and it was so. And **God called the firmament Heaven**." Genesis 1:7-8*

VIII

HEAVEN AND EARTH
The "Glory" or Color-code Layer of the Wisdom Wheel

To me, the next layer of the Wisdom Wheel is the most interesting thus far. This is where things become *colorful*, to say the least, as it shows how we symbolized the relative hues of the heavens within the Bible and other ancient scriptures. This layer primarily cataloged the colors of the aurora or *"northern lights,"* which were critical in understanding portal function or failure.

In the end, it was all about gravity and alignment, yet even the magnetic structure of Earth was revealed via these glorious reflections of the stratosphere. As you will see, the *aurora* was of key importance in how we developed the scriptures and was thus logically placed within the Wheel. It was not a guessing game but an exact science that we mastered thousands of years ago.

This chapter will focus on how those colors work, what they meant in portal technology, and how we encoded that information within the Bible, Koran, Vedas and more. Don't forget however, these colors also helped to form the final product of the Bible's imagery. Once meshed together with the Grid-Layer, the end products of *image* and *Word* were astounding.

JOSEPH'S COAT OF MANY COLORS
THE COLORS OF THE NORTHERN LIGHTS

A simple example of the Glory Layer within the Bible is found in the story of Joseph's coat of many colors. This was a combined image of a figurine, the Grid-layer and the colors of the aurora over which it was imposed.

*"Now Israel loved **Joseph** more than all his children, because he was the son of his old age: and he made him a **coat of many colors**."* Genesis 37:3 (fig. 23)

The artistic rendering of Joseph's coat of many colors as it originated from within the Grid System. Remember; there was no real man named Joseph but rather a figurine of the Grid System. In the end, the historical/literary ruse was only a cover story for our encoded science.

THE REAL
JE8U8 OF ᵵHE BiBLE (PARᵵ 1)
THE SON OF MAN AND THE LAMB OF GOD

The color-code of the verses

"**I Jesus, am** the bright and **morning star.**" Revelation 22:16

This verse is of course verification, *straight from the book of Revelation*, that Jesus (*the Son of Man*) is indeed a morning star. The following are only some of the many images that I saw and recorded. So now for the rest of the evidence you will need to believe:

"And in the midst of the (image #1) **seven golden candlesticks** one like the (image #2) **Son of Man** (image #3) **clothed with a garment down to the foot**, (image #4) **girded about the breasts with a golden girdle**."

"His (image #5) **head and his hair were white like wool**, as **white as snow**..."

"And his (image #6) **feet like fine bronze**, as if they burned in a furnace; and (image #7) **his voice was like the sound of many waters**."

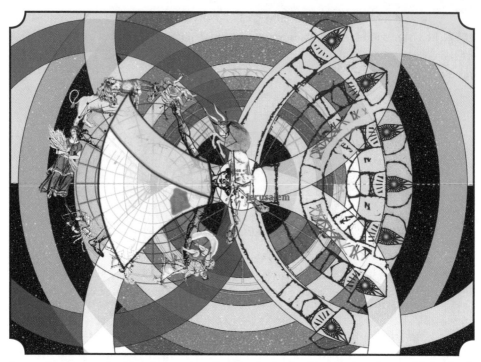

Jesus: A morning star/figurine as described in <u>the book </u>of <u>Revelation</u>. By combining both a grid series and figurine with the color-layer of the Wisdom Wheel, the origin of every single biblical character can be recreated as we knew them to be. Imagine the impact to realize that **<u>none</u>** of the biblical personalities were in reference to real people. The implications of course, are huge! That said; the Grid System portrayed was even more powerful than the literary ruse that hid it.

(Image #1 & #2)

"*And in the **midst** of the **seven golden candlesticks** one like the **Son of Man clothed with a garment down to the foot**,*" Rev. 1:12-13

The Seven Lampstands: This is the Menorah-artwork derived upon from the large, eastern ring of the Wisdom Wheel. Each of these large rings would typically contain their own grid series, thus providing us with the line data by which to produce this image. (See Great Wheel of God). As you can see, Jesus stands within its midst, just like the book of Revelation says.

(Image #3)

"**clothed with a garment down to the foot**"

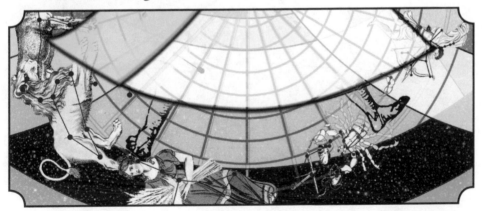

The dress styling of the verse is perfectly outlined in this Grid System image of Jesus.

(Image #4)

"girded about the breasts with a golden girdle"

<u>The Golden Girdle</u>: *This item of grid-clothing is an outline of the large golden band of the Wisdom Wheel that drapes across the front of the Jesus figurine. The golden color is that of the sun.*

(Image #5)

"head and his hair were <u>white like wool</u>, as <u>white as snow</u>"

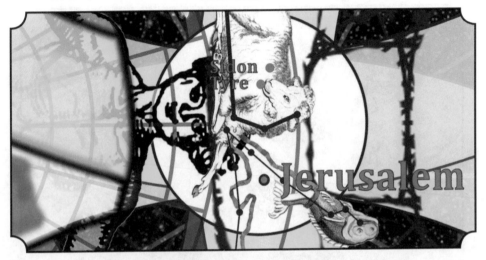

*Notice how the head of Jesus aligns with the house and constellation of **Aries**. By tradition Aries is a **lamb**, so naturally his hair is "**white like wool**". This is another reason why Jesus was called the <u>**Lamb of God**</u> (<u>see</u> John 1:29). Likewise we symbolized the center, **white dot** of this sector as "**snow**" in the Bible. The dot represents three things, including the South Pole of the earth; the full or "Wisdom moon" which is required to open the portal and the location of the "faith-ions" within Earth's core.*

(Image #6)

"feet like fine <u>bronze</u>, as if they burned in a <u>furnace</u>"

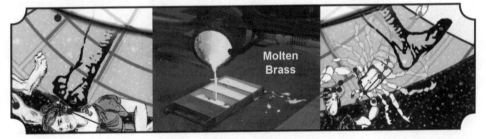

The feet of Jesus were located upon the brass and black-colored rings of the <u>anti</u>-aurora, which contain much of the satanic element. Metaphorically speaking, this substance must be stamped out and destroyed (<u>see</u> 1 Corinthians 15:25). The pictorial lessons of the Wisdom Wheel make an otherwise complex science, easy to understand.

(Image #7)

"his <u>voice</u> was like the sound of <u>many waters</u>"

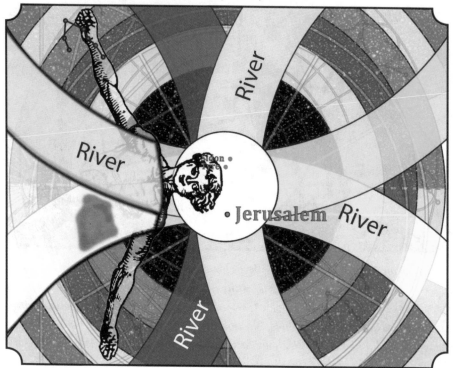

The *"**many waters**"* are the four large rings of the Wisdom Wheel that intersect with the head/mouth area of Jesus. Among other things, these were symbolized in the Bible as rivers, hence His *"**voice was like the sound of many waters**"*. In the story of Adam and Eve, these were symbolized as the rivers of Eden which *"**parted, and became into four heads**"* (Genesis 2:10; <u>see next chapter</u>). The alignments are undeniable.

In the Image of God Part I
Revealing the Code

The divine face was illegal to produce in specific detail. God is spirit, a mental capacity of the most incomprehensible power, and thus we revered His name and image within our science. Indeed, who am I to describe God's unspeakable being and the glory in which we persisted in Heaven? *Why*, I ask, even for the sake of symbolism, would I disrespect an eternal dimension with the likenesses of the primitive beasts we have become?

I remember of course, my home—my heaven. It is the one bit of leisure that I have here on Earth, pondering the Source from which I came all those eons ago, the divine realm. But it is not yet to be: It is instead time for you to take the next step of awakening.

I am called from the dust of the earth into a form to which you can relate, one that you can hear and see and touch. By this form I will show you these things about your past; I will tell you these things for the sake of your understanding that you may walk towards that ultimate goal of remembering who you are.

Provided here are those God images of the Grid System. Again, His face is blank for a reason: to force your own memory to function; to recover those lost files, that hidden data from long ago. The real visage of the Source is beyond description, yet is stored somewhere in the recesses of your mind; just beyond the veil of your understanding is your angelic recollection, waiting to be stirred from its sleep. It is important therefore, if for only a moment, that you imagine your own connection to the realm of which I speak—*not* as a human, for flesh and blood can never inherit the kingdom of heaven, but rather as the God Element that sleeps within you.

And isn't that the point of opening the portal? That the part of God within would someday reawaken into a full and rightful self-knowledge, a new image, and a new creation. Yet this realignment of both the earth and your consciousness are not separate studies, but one and the same. And with the bending of the space/time continuum, *the alteration of your thoughts*, will come the opening of our way home.

We used two simplistic pictorials for the image of God: one standing and one sitting, the description of which are both detailed within the scriptures. Please read the following verses and compare them to the line data images of the Wisdom Wheel:

GOD'S THRONE:

"*The LORD says: The **heaven** (upper-half of Wisdom Wheel) **is my throne**, and the **earth** (lower-half of Wisdom Wheel) **is my footstool**:*" Isaiah 66:1

"*And I saw a great **white throne** (bottom half/legs and arm-rests), and him that sat on it, from whose face the **earth** and the **heaven** fled away;*" Revelation 20:11

"*It is he that sits upon the **circle** of the earth; that stretches out the **heavens** as a curtain*" Isaiah 40:22

The fulfillment of Isaiah 66:1 is found in the positioning of the God-figurine's feet upon the "footstool" or "Earth" section of the Firmament. His upper half rests within the large yellow circle of the "Heaven," thus resembling a common throne design throughout history. Please note how the head or "Mind of God" is located on the 8th, 9th and 10th rings of the magnetosphere: This is location in which the mind of Heaven enters your world upon the portal's opening.

"And **he that sat upon the throne** was to look upon like a **jasper** (dark-red aurora) *and a **sardine stone** (light-red aurora): and **there was a rainbow round about the throne**, in sight like unto an **emerald**.* (green-aurora) *And before the **throne** there was a **sea of glass like unto crystal**:"* Revelation4:3

208

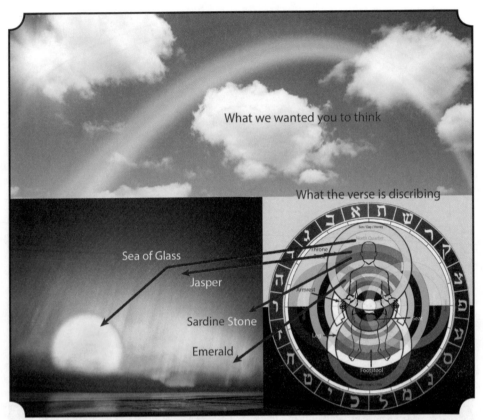

Look familiar? This magnetic anomaly occurred over Siberia on October 26 2017. It perfectly reflects the colors of Revelation 4:3 as well as the schematic of the Wisdom Wheel. The magi understood the significance of the ripping the fabric or "veil" of space thousands of years ago. Trust this: the Word will re-open the portal to heaven.

"The appearance of the **Lords face,** like **iron made to glow in a fire** (red bands of the aurora), *and brought out,* **emitting sparks** (stars), *and it burns."*
Enoch 22:1

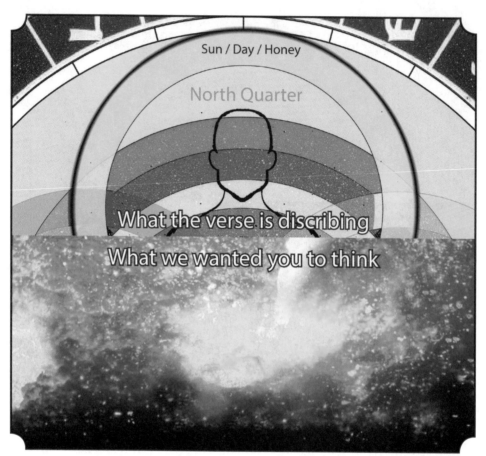

The Face of God: *The highest visible layers of the aurora are of the red and yellow spectrums and are displayed in the face area of the God image. When layered with a splattering of stars, we can easily envision the image of the* **"Lord's face, like iron made to glow in a fire, emitting sparks"**.

GOD STANDING:

"*So **God created man in his** own **image**, **in the image** of **God created he him; male and female created he them**.*" Genesis 1:27

"*There is . . . **One God and Father** of **all**, who is **above all**, and **through all**, and **in you all**.*" Ephesians 4:6

"*I have made the earth, and created man upon it: I, **even my hands, have stretched out the heavens**, and all their host have I commanded.*" Isaiah 45:12

THE COLORS OF KING NEBUCHADNEZZAR PART 1
THE SYMBOL SPEAK OF THE HEAVENS

The book of Daniel contains its own share of color-depictions including that of the Babylonian king, **Nebuchadnezzar**, and his dream of a great image. As you will see, it was **_not a real dream_**, **_nor a real king_** named, Nebuchadnezzar, but the imagination of the Word and the mechanics of the Wisdom Wheel:

"Thou, O king **_Nebuchadnezzar_ _of Babylon_**, saw, and behold a **_great image_**."

"This **images _head was_ _of fine gold_**, it's **_breasts and it's arms_ _of silver_**, it's **_belly and it's thighs_ _of brass_**,"

"Its **_legs_ _of iron_**, its **_feet_ _part_ _of iron and_ _part of miry clay_**."

"**_Thou, o king, art this head_ _of gold_**."

"And whereas thou saw **iron mixed with miry clay**, they shall mingle themselves with the **_seed of men_**:" Daniel 2:31-43

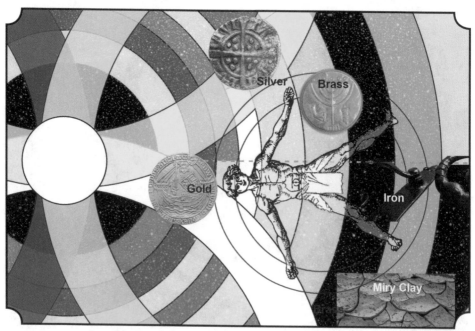

"great image": a figurine named by the Wisdom Wheel as "King Nebuchadnezzar".

*"Thou, o **king**, art this **head of gold**"*: this sector of the firmament is the large golden ring that represents the *"**brightness**"* of the sun as *"**fine gold**"*—not real gold, but sunlight.

*"**breasts** and its **arms** of **silver**"*: this sector of the firmament represents a rare *"**silver**"* color of the aurora—not real silver, but aurora…

*"**belly** and it's **thighs** of **brass**"*: this sector of the firmament represents the "**brass**" aurora and spans across the king's belly, waist, and thighs. This verse is not referring to a real image of a king, nor real brass, but to a figurine and its interaction with the brass ring of the Wisdom Wheel.

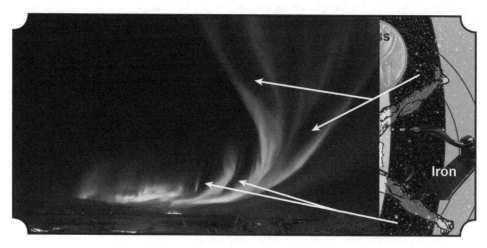

*"**legs** of **iron**"*: the **black aurora** that exists in the gaps of the normal colored aurora, but primarily between the brass and red bands. The Bible connotes these darkened areas with negativity as they contain something far more evil than you can possibly imagine (more on this later).

Miry Clay

"*feet part of iron and part of miry clay*": the image's feet are partially in the **black aurora** and **light-green aurora**; thus part "iron" and part "miry clay." Notice how the image is sprinkled with the symbolic, "seed of men," code for the appearance of the stars.

THE REAL
WOMAN OF THE BOOK OF REVELATION

"*And there appeared a great wonder in heaven; a **woman clothed with the sun**, and the **moon under her feet**, and upon her head a **crown of twelve stars**:...And she **being with child** cried, travailing in birth, and pained to be delivered.*" Revelation 12:1-2

Does this grid make me look fat? *This image is the origin of the "woman with child" spoken of in Revelation 12. As you can see, it perfectly fulfills the Bible's description. This is who she was; this is her alignment. In the older books of the Bible, her name is* ***Wisdom****.*

Our image begins by placing a female figurine within a peripheral grid of the Wisdom Wheel's large white circle. Next we overlaid this image with the large yellow grid series of the sun, which provided the line data for the woman's maternity clothing as well as her coloration according to the verse. Furthermore her ***"crown of 12 stars"*** (count them) was formed from the junction of the grids which align with the image's head. What is not shown here is that the verses of Revelation 12 were written around the perimeter of each grid, thus adding to this complex, but beautiful image.

How the Color-Layer Functioned

Basically the function of the Wisdom Wheel is twofold: not only does it spell sacred Word, but it also creates a series of images by which to comprehend the divine plan on ever-deeper levels, each layer symbolizing an aspect of the final image. Accordingly I have attached key symbol words to the colors of the Wisdom Wheel that you may grasp how their descriptions were cloaked within the Bible's verses.

The final images are thus an accumulation of figurines, grids, line data and colors that were placed according to exacting mathematical input. Likewise the chapter, verse numbers, and letter counts of each Bible story are relevant to the final arrangement, all of which were timed better than any Swiss watch.

That said, I have excluded the majority of *mathematical* details of each layer: Not only is that information too scientific for the average reader, but it could also be misused. Too much math is a temptation for the unlearned, at which point the numbers are of little consequence. There is no further need to write new Word as the ancient books are themselves sufficient to correct Earth's realignment. There are however several details I can share about the engineering-magic of the Wheel:

THE 1ˢᵗ LAYER OF COLORS:
~THE GREAT SEAS~
THE WAVE PATTERNS OF HEAVEN
REVEALING THE CODE

"And God said; let the __waters under__ the __heaven__ be __gathered together__ __unto one__ __place__, ...and the __gathering together__ of __the waters__ (waves/frequencies) *he called __Seas:__* (the two dimensions)*"* Genesis 1:4, 5

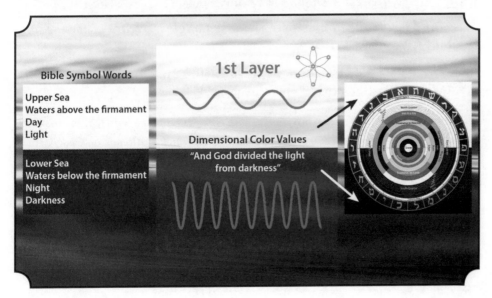

The Frequencies of Heaven and Earth: The *first color layer* of the Wisdom Wheel was a simple background of white and black. These colors were typically symbolized in the Bible as either *"seas"* or *"waters"*. They represented the vibrational frequencies and substances that comprise the two dimensions. Your scientists call these *"strings"*.

The 1st color layer was a simple contrast of light and darkness over which other layers of the Grid System were located. This allowed us to track the timeline from the portal's original failure and our subsequent fall into this *dark* world, all the way through to its repair and our resurrection into the *light* of Heaven.

Likewise, the two colors of this layer were symbolized as *"seas"* for a very scientific reason: We knew that each world comprises a baseline frequency, or, *wave pattern*, similar in shape to the waves of an ocean. Thus, portraying this layer of the Wisdom Wheel as *"seas"* or *"waters"* in the Bible was the perfect camouflage by which to hide the angelic science. Again, please follow the symbolism of each verse:

Sample Scriptures of the Upper "Sea" of the Grid System
White/Dimension of Heaven:

*"And to the **north** (or upper part of image) of the garden there is a **sea of water** (Atomos-structure)…And when a man washes himself in it, he becomes **white** of its **whiteness** even if he were **dark**."* Adam and Eve chapter 1:2

*"And before the throne there was a **sea of glass**, **clear** (white) like unto **crystal**:"* Revelation 4:6

*"He makes me to lie down in **green** pastures (green aurora): he leads me beside the **still waters**. (wave pattern/frequency)"* Psalm 23:2

*The abstract symbolism of the two dimensions: The "crystal sea" of Heaven is a **wave pattern** of clarity and peace and is comprised of the mighty Atomos or God particle. "Still waters" (wave pattern/frequency) run deep, and thus the frequency of the Atomos is symbolized in the Bible accordingly.*

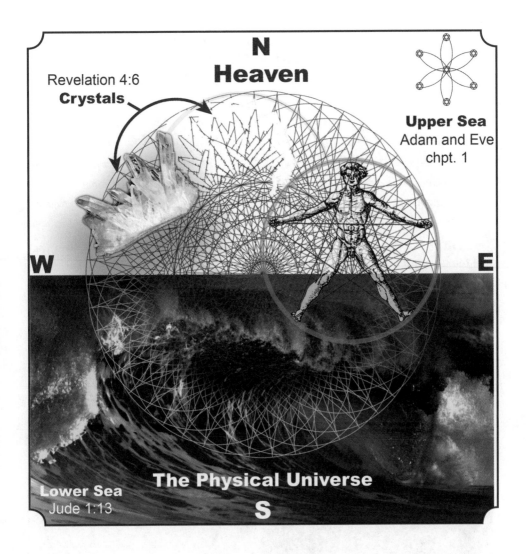

N
Heaven

Revelation 4:6
Crystals

Upper Sea
Adam and Eve
chpt. 1

W

E

The Physical Universe

Lower Sea
Jude 1:13

S

SAMPLE SCRIPTURES OF THE LOWER "SEA" OF THE GRID SYSTEM
DARK/PHYSICAL DIMENSION:

*"**Raging waves** (grid-design) **of the sea, foaming** (the appearance of the Milky way) out their own shame; wandering **stars** (figurines), to whom is reserved the **blackness of darkness** forever."* Jude 1:13

*Meanwhile, the baseline wave pattern, or "string," of this world was symbolized by the **dark, raging waves** of Jude 1:13. This is the physical realm, i.e., the "flesh." The grids that superimpose this layer likewise track the timeline of subduction and rebirth of the God Element.*

There was however, a second color scheme we used for the first color layer that included **sky-blue** and **black** instead of white and black. This color arrangement tracked the day/night cycles of the earth and its orientation throughout the course of the year. A simplified example of the blue color code is found in the Bible's book of Exodus 28:31 and addresses the robe of the High Priest himself:

*"And you shall make the **robe of the ephod** all of **blue**."* Exodus 28:31

*A **real priest**, a magi priest, was truly somewhere between Heaven and Earth yet was still symbolized in the Bible via this Grid-System image. They were administers of the truths that befall us, small parts of God who were still awake yet locked within a mortal body. And yet the same Element that dwelt within them is also in you. Notice the Wisdom Wheel's version of a priest including the Jewish yarmulke, or cap, as well as the purple band of the aurora. Every color code found in the Jewish tradition was formulated from within the Grid System.*

THE 2ⁿᵈ COLOR-LAYER OF THE WISDOM WHEEL ~THE AURORA~
REVEALING THE CODE OF THE NORTHERN LIGHTS

"And God said, Let there be __lights__ (colors) __in the firmament of the heaven to divide the day from the night__; and let them be __for signs, and for seasons, and for days, and years__:" Genesis 1:14

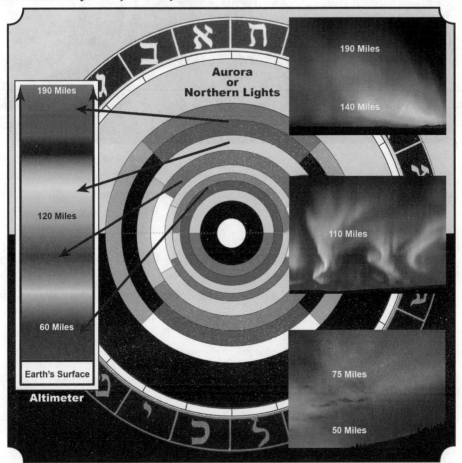

The "Glory" or __2ⁿᵈ color-layer__ of the Firmament. These ten colored-rings functioned as a visual __aurora/magnetic-line altimeter__. By understanding the interaction of the aurora and the Earth's magnetosphere, the Magi were able to adjust the Word output accordingly. These rings are described in the __Book of Enoch__ as the "Ten levels of heaven".

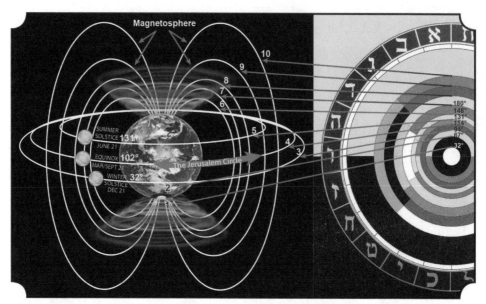

This artistic-rendering (not to scale) shows the location of the 3-seasonal orbital-planes of the Sun and Moon as-well-as the lines of the magnetosphere and their placement within the Wisdom Wheel. In sync with the colors of the aurora, this information allowed us to visually track and adjust the Word-output-solution of the Wisdom Wheel so as to correct the Earth's alignment over time.

Part of adjusting Earth's alignment begins by first adjusting the magnetic lines that surround our planet. Likewise we knew that each color of the aurora indicated the basic height of those lines at any given time and thus we integrated that information within these ten-rings of the Wisdom Wheel. Hence the 2nd color-layer of the Wheel acted as a visual-altimeter in which we could discern the relative height of the magnetosphere based upon the colors we saw on any given night.

This in turn allowed us to rotate and adjust the ten color rings as needed to alter the final Word-solution that would become the Bible. This resulting wave-pattern, once spoken by you, impacts the magnetic structure accordingly and thus changes Earth's alignment over time. Basically the Word pushes the magnetic lines, creating a bulge to which our planet will naturally seek its new magnetic center, thus changing its axial tilt. It's hard to believe that a seemingly humble Bible verse contains such unfathomable power and engineering, but then again, it's just good magic...

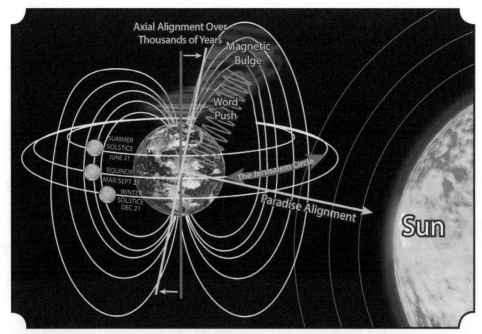

The complex wave-patterns of the Bible connect your mind to the magnetic-structure of the Earth. In this representative image, we can see how the Word organizes and impresses a form of living electrolysis upon Earth's magnetosphere, thus altering its lines and tilt over thousands of years by which to open the portal. Not only did the science of the magi far outpace modern science, but we did it with fewer bad hair days than did Einstein. And, yes, at times we had a sense of humor—sometimes.

However in order to hide this technical data, each color of the aurora was given a symbol word in the Bible that in turn identified its specific altitude, providing you knew the code. For example, the light-green layer of the aurora could be symbolized as *"green grass"* at about 120 miles above Earth, while the darker green layer just beneath that was called *"emerald"* and so on. It was all a play on words that was further detailed according to the chapter and verse numbers in which they are mentioned.

But there is more to the 2nd color-layer than meets the eye. The two inner most color rings (white and black), also indicated the location of the positive and negative ion bands as they pass through Earth's core. These electrically charged particles actually capture and adhere to the angelic-elements. This is where the *"mental"* meets *"magnetic"* in our science—a little-known fact in which the angelic-minds, both good and evil, are literally attached to your planet's magnetic structure ever since the portal's failure:

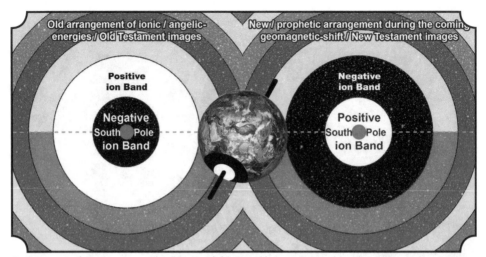

Left image: the present arrangement of the Earth's ionic/magnetic structure as it entwines the axis. This alignment isolates and imprisons the God Element from emitting. Likewise this color arrangement was used in the Wisdom Wheel during the creation of the Jewish Bible or "Old Testament".

Right image: In contrast, this configuration was used to create the New or Christian scriptures and prophesied the coming geomagnetic-shift that will herald the portal's opening. These white and black ion-bands were symbolized in the Bible as "iron" (black) or "snow" (white). Always the code.

Likewise each ring and band of the Wisdom Wheel serves multiple functions. It's not important that you know them all, but a few of the simple aspects will display the depth of the angelic-genius. For example, the inner, 7 divider-lines of the aurora-bands also represent a 360° view of Earth beginning at the South Pole in the center and accumulating with the North Pole at the outer edge of the 7th ring:

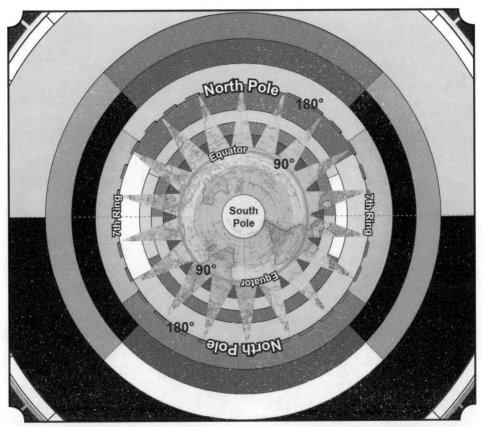

We never actually displayed a globe over the Wisdom Wheel, yet several aspects of the globe were yet represented therein. This artistic rendering shows the locations of the North Pole, South Pole and Equator, all of which played a key role in Word production. The multi-faceted functions of the Wheel are exact and mind-blowing. It was all very precise.

More so, the boundary lines of the 3rd, 4th and 5th rings mimic the seasonal arcs (*the solstices and equinoxes*) of the sun and moon, as viewed from Jerusalem. Again, the gravity of these celestial bodies affects the alignment of our planet and whether or not the portal could be reopened; thus we needed to know their seasonal <u>angle of magnetic pull</u> via these 3-rings. Each ring in turn was assigned a numeric-value that affected the final Word output of the Wheel:

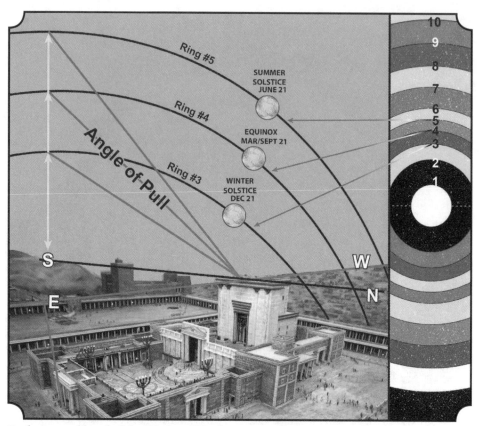

*Each ring and band of the Wisdom Wheel represented an important aspect of gravitational-interaction that in turn dictated the final Word-solution. In this instance, the 3rd 4th and 5th rings represent the sun and moon's **seasonal-<u>angle</u> of magnetic-<u>pull</u>***.

Lastly, the 8th, 9th and 10th rings strictly represent the outermost-lines of the upper magnetosphere, high above Earth. This part of the magnetic structure was critical in our science as they simultaneously *"rip"* upon the portal's full opening. In turn these lines also transfer the Source Element back and forth, to and from Heaven. This is the great conveyor belt of the *"daily-sacrifice"* (Daniel 12:11).

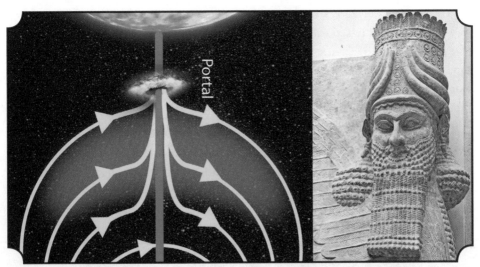

If there is any doubt left in your mind about these revelations and the science of the magi, then deny this: The portal hat of this ancient Babylonian stela perfectly displays the rip of the space/time continuum upon the portal's opening. These 3 magnetic-lines are the great conveyor belt upon which the Source-Element cycles in and out of Heaven. As it exists back into Heaven the Element carries with it our sufferings, or "daily-sacrifice" of Daniel 12:11. Thus our sufferings are transformed into the food of God. The portal and the resulting Super-aurora were real.

Likewise the bands of the Wisdom Wheel that are attached to these outer-3-rings were also overlaid with measurements of the celestial globe including the arcs of *Lunar Mansions*, the *12 signs of the Zodiac* and finally, the altitude of the portal itself. This information further complemented the total input/output-data of the Wisdom Wheel via its timing and arrangement.

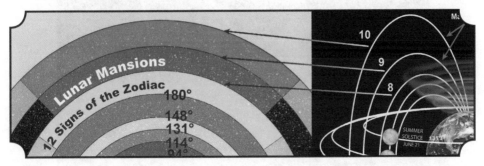

Ground Zero for the portal location: It is the last three lines of the magnetosphere in which the tear of space will occur. It is here my friend that the mind of God Almighty will enter your world.

The effects of Earths polarity, its magnetics, and its connection to our minds were ultimately addressed within the construction of our wave-pattern. In my opinion it is absolutely a miracle of science that we could articulate this advanced information thousands of years ago. This is why I call it a *"super-science,"* in that it surpasses physics alone by quantifying the relationship of the physical to the mental. The fact is, something *this* flawless can only *be* the Word of God.

For the magi, decoding the scriptures was easy as we understood their design from within the Grid System. As we scrolled through the many verses, our minds instantly converted the symbol words to the scientific-facts that we had long ago memorized, thus removing the historical or literal facade by which to reveal something far more profound. Meanwhile, everyone else could only see the outer stories from which their rabbis, priests and preachers read; they took it all quite literally, just as we intended.

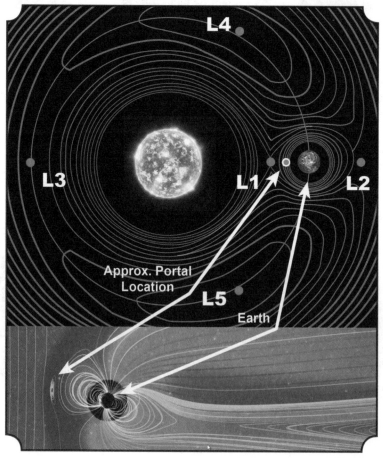

The delicate work of tearing the fabric of space: Our science and the Word by which to open the portal was precise and considered all critical input data including Earth's magnetic structure and even the angle of the sun and moon's gravity. This image of Lagrange-points (not to scale) displays some of the complexity of that gravitational-interaction.

~HEAVEN AND EARTH~
REVEALING THE CODE

*"And God said...Let the **waters** (wave-pattern) <u>**under**</u> the <u>**Heaven**</u> be **gathered together** (solidified into a reality) unto **one place**, and <u>**let the dry land appear**</u> (image-structure): And God **called the dry land <u>Earth</u>**;"* Genesis 1:9-10

*The <u>**gathering of the waters**</u>: The magi used the Wisdom Wheel to locate and track the dimensional wave-patterns, both good and evil, that are compacted within Earth's magnetic-fields. These minds were then personified via the figurines, one of which brings angelic-illumination (**Heaven**), and the other, the darkness of our humanity (**Earth**). It was all part of the symbolic code.*

Now that the 1st and 2nd color-layers are meshed into one, we can symbolize a bit more. We can understand that each frequency or *"sea"* of the 1st layer is now interlocked with the aurora of the 2nd, thus providing a means to locate those frequencies within the Earth's magnetic-fields. This area of overlap in the Wisdom Wheel acted as a foundation, or, *"Heaven and Earth"* by which to track the angelic-energies: the top-half symbolized as *"Heaven"* in the Bible, and the bottom-half as *"Earth,"* or the *"dry land"* (Genesis 1:9), that emerged from the dark *"waters"* upon which it sits. *It was symbolism through and through.*

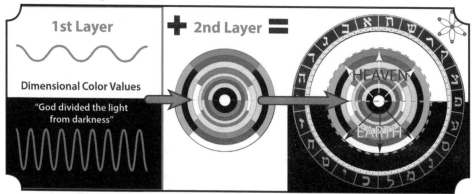

This also sets the stage for the data layers that come next. It gives us a medium through which a real set of scientific facts can be understood mathematically, pictorially and in a logical order. We then used that information by which to extract the written Word that contains the very solution to the problem being described. Most ancient religious texts function in this same manor.

Indeed the Word that the Wisdom Wheel spelled is a high-tech *"fix-it"* that will <u>soon</u> separate the angelic-element in you from the dark mental construct in which you are trapped. The magic activates when you speak it, after which Earth's magnetic-field is reorganized, thus contributing to the realignment process. Thanks for helping.

THE MAGI MIND BENDER

The Bible perfectly describes the symbolic appearance of the same Wisdom Wheel that wrote its verses. So how then did we engineer the Wheel that hadn't yet been described??? Oh the depths of a magi's mind . . .

~PLACING THE PLANETS~

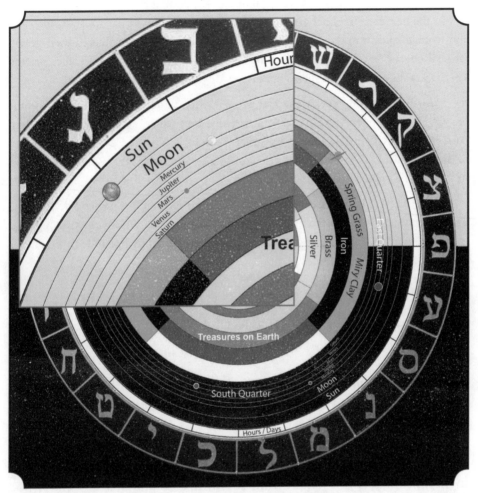

The orbital-positions of the sun, moon, Mercury, Venus, Mars, Jupiter and Saturn were located just outside the perimeter of the ten aurora colors. These allowed us to calculate a sphere's gravitational influence and arrive upon a __total-sum of gravity__ and its __direction-of-pull__ upon Earth during any given hour. This mathematical sum was then projected into the final Word-solution of the Wisdom Wheel.

The next facet of the Wisdom Wheel tracked the orbital positions of Mercury, Venus, Mars, Jupiter, Saturn, the sun and the moon. This was accomplished via another 7 rings located within the circle of the Hebrew alphabet. The placement of these spheres within the Wisdom Wheel was not intended to mimic their location within the heavens, but rather to calculate their __direction-of-pull__ upon the Earth.

231

Each of these 7 spheres were allotted a *gravitational value* that could then be added or subtracted from the other celestial bodies depending on their compass position within the heavens. The final gravitational sum in turn affected Earth's orbit, tilt, spin and wobble, and were thus relative in creating a *"Word"* that considered their gravitational effects. In consideration of this, their placement in the Wheel makes perfect sense and thus functions to spell a perfect wave-pattern that you can speak.

Again, once this data was expressed via your mouth, it would impress upon Earth's magnetosphere, creating a void or bulge that would act to slowly but surely correct our planet's misalignment. These voids would, as a result, also change the colors of the aurora, therefore giving us a visual validation each night that we had succeeded in our goals. Simple science for angels…

We really did come from the dimension of Heaven and we really did visit your Earth. In the end, there simply is no other explanation for this advanced knowledge to appear thousands of years ago and at a time when humanity had little or no formal education.

THE 3ᴿᴰ COLOR-LAYER OF THE WISDOM WHEEL
~THE GREATER AND LESSER LIGHTS~
REVEALING THE CODE

*"And God made **two great lights**; the **greater light** (sun-ring) to rule the **day**, and the **lesser light** (moon-ring) to rule the **night**: he made the **stars** (figurines) also.*

*And **God set them in the firmament** of the heaven **to give light** upon the **earth**, (moon/lower-half of model) and to **rule over the day** and **over the night, and to divide** the **light from the darkness**: and God saw that it was good. And the **evening** (large left circle) and the **morning** (large right circle) were the fourth day."* Genesis 1:16-19

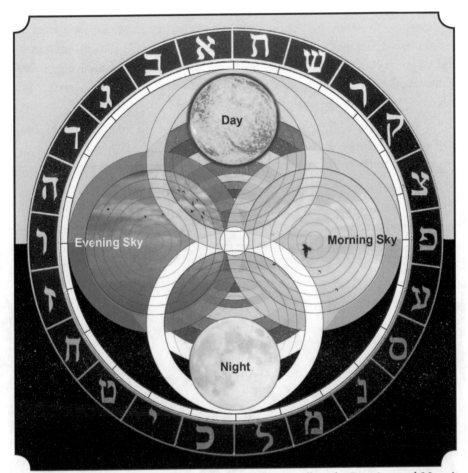

*The **greater and lesser lights** (sun and moon rings) as well as the **Evening** and **Morning** quadrants of the Firmament: These 4 large rings were assigned a logical color code and represented longer, grand cycles of the heavens. Among their many symbol words were the "four rivers of Eden" (see Genesis 2:10-14).*

The 3rd color-layer of the Wisdom Wheel included <u>**4 large circles**</u> that represented longer, grand-cycles of the heavens. These larger timelines were critical in the Word production process and so were included in the Wisdom Wheel's design. Accordingly these four sectors were symbolized in the Bible as;

    1. (Yellow-ring) ***day/summer/sun,***

    2. (White-ring) ***night/winter/moon,***

    3. (Right/golden-ring) ***morning/spring*** and

    4. (Left/dark-ring) ***evening/fall.***

Again, I have purposely omitted the calculations that were superimposed upon each of these circles, but I will say there was a lot of data to be considered in the creation of Word. Likewise these four quadrants contained representative-figurines of great size, called "*arch*-angels", so-named due to the large diameter or "**arch**" of their grids in comparison to the smaller figurines:

"*For the Lord himself shall descend from heaven with a shout, with the voice of the <u>**archangel**</u>,* (large-figurine of the yellow-ring)" 1 Thessalonians 4:16

<u>Arch</u>: *A curved symmetrical structure spanning an opening or elevated space. And that, my friend, is why we called them <u>arch</u> angels...*

These four arches also form an inherent cross at their intersection, the center of which includes the small white circle of the Wisdom Wheel. In turn, this cross design was described in symbolic detail throughout the Bible and is the origin of the iconic cross of Christianity.

What's more, many of the magi wore this symbol as a necklace by which to be identified. Though people recognized it as our sign, they in no way understood its meaning or origin. The knowledge of the Grid System was highly classified; so if you'd never seen its imagery, then there was no way to realize the basis of the necklace design.

The Sign of the Magi: *We used the Grid System by which to format our religious icons. This Assyrian relief dates to about 700BC and clearly shows the cross styling of the Wisdom Wheel as well as the center dot in perfect proportion. To the outsider looking in, no one knew the meaning of the necklace; but now you do.*

~HOURS AND DAYS~

…This of course brings us to the next ring of the Wisdom Wheel. Around the outer perimeter of the 2nd and 3rd color-layers was an even larger circle that was divided into 24 equal-sized parts. This functioned to measure both the 24 solar hours of each day and, simultaneously, the 24 one-thousand-year-long retrograde measurements of the celestial equator. These measurements were in turn symbolized in the scriptures as both *"**hours**"* and/or *"**days**"*, according to the cycle being measured:

*"But of that **day** and **hour** knows no man, no, not the angels of heaven, but my Father only."* Matthew 24:36:

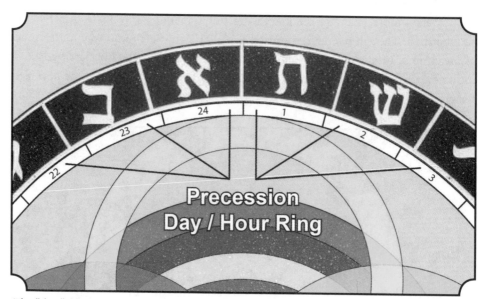

*The "**day**" (i.e., a 1,000-year precession) and "**hour**" (i.e., an actual hour). This ring of the Wisdom Wheel was also encoded within the scriptures as "**days**" and "**hours.**" It measured and calculated into the Word both hourly and retrograde considerations that led to the final spelling of each letter of the Bible.*

Ironically when the word "**days**" was used in the scriptures, it was not referring to a day as you know them, but instead a **1,000-year period of time** that was graphed within the Grid System. In case you don't believe me, then please refer to 2nd Peter 3:8;

"*But, beloved, be not ignorant of this one thing, that one **day is** with the Lord **as a thousand years** (1,000), and a **thousand years** as one **day**.*"

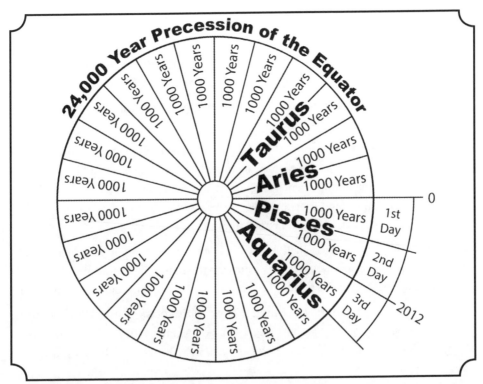

As is the case with most verses, people either guess or gloss-over the symbolism that lie directly in front of their eyes. Therefore consider our code; that when reading the Bible, the word, *"day"* or *"days"* is to be _multiplied by a 1,000 year period of time_. Likewise a perfect ___equatorial-precession___ lasts for __24,000__ years thus dividing the Great Wheel into 24, 1,000-year increments, or about 1 millennia for each pie-shaped section.

The equatorial precision however, was only one of two long-count calendars; the other a ___grand ecliptic-cycle___ which lasted __25,920__ years. The Wisdom Wheel's final ring of letters were rotated against this slow backdrop of precession, the changes of which show in the literary styling of each of the Bible's books. This is also why you will notice a higher incidence of certain words in some books than others, especially when comparing those of the Old and New Testaments.

Though we led our followers to believe that each book was named after its actual author, it was the movement of the rings themselves that account for both the literary-styling and the name of the book itself! Thus names such as *Ezekiel, Isaiah, Mathew, Mark, Daniel*, etc., _were not real people_ but figurines of the Grid System that were named according to the movement of these rings. Pure magic!

The following verses are only two tantalizing examples that will help you to see the code of *"hours"* and *"days"*. Please note the correlation of the highlighted words;

*"After **two days** (after 2,000 years) will he **revive** us: in the **third day** (The 3rd thousandth years) he will **raise** us up, and we shall live in his sight."* Hosea 6:2

*"And they shall kill him, and the **third day** (3rd thousandth years) he shall be **raised** again."* Matthew 17:23

I promise to tell more about the 3rd day of resurrection, perhaps in book II, but what you should note is that the historical context of the Bible has just been removed and replaced with an omnipresent prophecy that directly involves you. Indeed, it is today that the real, thousand year-long, *3rd day resurrection* begins. I'd dare to speculate that this is somewhat better than a history story . . .

Continuing on, however, the Bible symbol word *"hours"* did, in-fact, literally indicate the **24 hourly measurements** we took from atop the Temple in Jerusalem each day. This factoid is also secretly encoded within the verses of the Bible and in context to a figurine:

*". . . take no thought how or what ye shall **speak**: for it shall be given you in that **same** **hour** what ye shall **speak**."* Matthew 10:19 *Indeed, each hour the figurines knew exactly the letters to speak, -figuratively speaking! The scriptures were always a play on words.*

~THE RING OF LETTERS~

The final ring was of course the letters of the Hebrew and later, the Greek alphabets. However, dependent upon the sector of the Grid System in which a story was written, it might also include any one of numerous other language alphabets. This includes Latin, Aramaic, Egyptian, etc. This was a comparative format in which the Hebrew language was attached to the perfect "Spin-grids" of the Grid-System, while every other alphabet was attached to the "wobble-grids" as an "enemy" of portal function.

This dis-includes the Greek language which was forced upon Israel by Alexander the Great during his conquest. As a result the New Testament was written in Greek in-lieu-of the native Hebrew.

Once every hour on the hour, a new measurement of alignments were taken from the heavens and placed upon the rings of the Great Wheel. The rings, thus adjusted, would precipitate into the words, sentences, verses, chapters, and books of the Holy Scriptures. Interestingly each letter was selected via the hand of the God Image, thus creating the miracle of the "Word of God":

"In the same **hour** came forth **fingers of a man's hand, and wrote** over **against** the candlestick upon the **plaster of the wall**" Daniel 5:5 *A symbolic-description of a Grid-System alignment.*

"But if **with the finger of God** I cast out devils, no doubt the kingdom of God is come upon you." Luke 11:20 *(An illusion to replacement of the dark imagination via Word which was spelled by the hand of the God figurine.)*

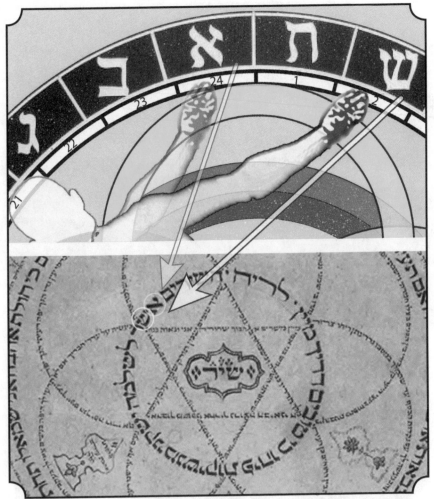

Every hour the alignments of the heavens changed, thus spelling a new letter of the Bible's verses. They really were written with the finger of the God figurine, but no less by the divine reasoning of the Wisdom Wheel. And now you know why it is called the Word of God...

Since only a total of 24 measurements were produced each day, sentences would pick-up or leave-off at the same hour each day until completed. As a result the Word would alternate between the sentences of good and evil characters, each written upon their corresponding Word sheets. These formative patterns likewise shown within the storyline of the characters in question:

"Thy __Word__ is a __lamp__ unto my __feet__, and a __light__ unto my __path__."

An image portraying Psalms 119:105: The final position of the sun dictated the letters of the Great Wheel, thus the depiction of the Word as a lamp and a light.

THE AUTHOR OF PEACE
WRITING WITH THE FINGER OF GOD
THE ORIGIN OF THE MAGIC WAND

Every magician had in his possession a magic-wand that was personalized and blessed. Magic of course, was one of the few frills we enjoyed on Earth. The origin of your modern fantasies thus evident, every magi custom-made their own wand by which to execute the mysteries of the divine power. My own was a faithful companion over the centuries and until the very end. I stowed it in a small sliding case made of olive wood, tucked safely within the inner pocket of my cloak. Through all of my trials we never once parted.

The *Finger of God* was but a humble stylus made from reed and tempered over an open flame. But it wrote the original drafts of almost every Jewish and Christian scripture in existence, a magic so powerful it can literally turn the world on its end. With a mere wave of the wand—that is, *a stroke of the pen*—it wrote the code that forever changed mankind. *How*, you may ask, could an item so quaint, produce a spell of such magnitude, something that could alter the Aurora and even open the portal to Heaven? Indeed all other magic pales by comparison.

The magic it wrote is changing you as well, slowly but surely awakening you from an age-long slumber, altering your thoughts and most important, your real-world imagination. As a royal scribe and servant of the Almighty, I penned the words that the Wisdom Wheel revealed. But indeed it was *you* who committed the magic of the Word and the wand. Ultimately is was *you, dear **angel***, who spoke the spell of God that will unlock the star-gate and our way home.

It's surreal that a simple reed gathered from the bank of the Euphrates would create the most powerful book ever written. And while today your smart phones and computers with all their mighty electronics can so much as send an endless babel of mindless texts and internet noise, we, with not but the Wisdom Wheel, a stick and a bit of ink—changed the alignments of the Earth itself.

So as you can see, the wand has been misrepresented by myth, but then again, the scriptures too hid, within their covers of unassuming stories, the greatest science of all time. The lesson I suppose, is to never judge a book by its cover, nor a magic wand by its simple design. Our magic may not have pulled a rabbit from a hat, but it could open an interdimensional portal. Indeed we were the imagination of God incarnate.

THE PARADIGM OF THE PORTAL

The problem that modern science has with dimensional physics is that each level is promoted as an anomaly of calculous relative to space and time. Therein is an angular hierarchy that connects every other dimension or warping of space within the physical universe. The dimensions as the magi knew them, however, were not quite the same.

In the purest sense the higher dimension to which we referred, aka <u>Heaven</u>, is *transformative* instead of *angular*. And to articulate our model scientifically also allowed us to better quantify the mental gears and cogs of each world. The science of the ancients uses math to be sure, but rather relates those paradigms outside of the angular/physical box of math. Indeed we are not dealing with *curvatures* of space and time, but instead a *rip* in the very fabric of reality and this is the real difference.

Try to think of mental transformation as the molecules of a tree that are burnt and thus completely reorganized into an entirely different molecular structure. You've seen wood burn, so what happened to it? Where did it go? *It transformed*: the atoms are no longer solid pieces of wood that are stuck to the ground via gravity and weight.

Indeed this new structure, the air, is free of gravity; it is no longer visible, but invisible and free flowing in ways that the tree could never be. The air is the opposite of the wood in every capacity. No doubt the tree strives to reach the light of heaven much in the same way that humanity does towards God. Ultimately however it is an exercise in futility and cannot achieve the higher state of existence until the tree itself is destroyed through the transmutation process of fire.

There is also a *mental* fire of transformation. Though I speak figuratively of the wood and air, there is yet a very real application of this principle in the ancient study of mental-physics. Similarly, each dimension also contains its own form of matter and energy that dictates the type of mind that is articulated therein.

Accordingly there is an incompatibility or enmity between the two minds. Much in the same way that the air is disconnected from the Earth so is each dimension largely restricted to its own yard, touching yet separate. They are as different as daylight and dark as is the scope and scale of the math we used to understand them.

But how to understand these things more simply? *Science*, the magi believed, should only *begin* with mathematics, but always and ultimately be pushed into the visual realm. This is what the Wisdom Wheel accomplished, itself being mathematically placed and designed. But in the end it formed a comprehensive image that could be easily grasped and used to our advantage.

As such you have already seen how the center of a grid-series resembles a star gate, including the light-rays that beam from within its center. This is no accident. The difference however between our portal and that of a movie, is that our portal is <u>real</u> and empowers you, via the Word, *to open it*. Indeed it offers a narrow window of opportunity, a means to attain an eternal world that was long ago forgotten.

Compare the Wisdom Wheel images to any other 3-D model of modern science and then tell me which is superior in revelation. To realize that we designed thousands of these images and thousands of years ago without a computer generated video, simply boggles the mind. But it also tells us that there is so-much more than we ever thought was possible, that there is a whole new dimension to math that we neither teach nor have even considered in our world today.

There was a time when magic was real, and in this case, *fact* is far more fantastic than fiction. It really is the science of God. *Something is coming—and now you know what it is.* These are the revelations of the ages that were intended for this day. *It is time.*

*"Does not wisdom call; at the **entrance of the <u>portals</u>** she cries aloud:"* Proverbs 8:1-36

"And ye shall know the truth, and the truth shall make you free." John 8:32

"Ask me, and I will tell you remarkable secrets, which you did not know" Jeremiah 33:3

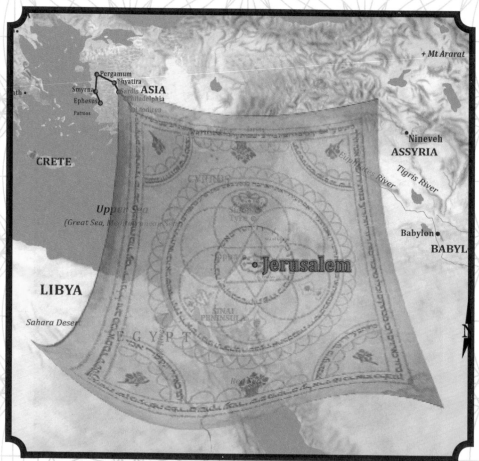

And saw **heaven** opened, and a **great sheet knit at the four corners**, and let down to the earth: Acts 10:11 & 11:5

THE SACRED MAPS
The Map Layer of the Wisdom Wheel

So then, was the story of the little old man a fiction or not? If so, then how else do I know the code of the scriptures and the portal science in such detail? Ah, but our secret was bigger than what you have seen thus far. In fact we added an entirely new dimension to the Wisdom Wheel, one which required an otherworldly intellect to accomplish. Indeed it included an ingenious and *monumental task*.

During the first Temple period beginning at around 500 B.C., the magi not only surveyed Israel, the Mediterranean and the entire Middle-East, but also super-imposed our star charts and grids upon those maps, thus creating a *hybrid land/star-chart*. Once completed, these maps were used as a base-layer to the Wisdom Wheel that allowed us to cleverly symbolize each and every star of the heavens within the Bible's stories by instead listing the name of the town with which they matched.

Indeed *the towns mentioned in the scriptures are not towns at all, but stars and/or marking points on the Grid System*. This in turn further camouflaged our celestial-science. By connecting the "*12 tribes of Israel*" (i.e., *the 12 figurine-groups*) to the geographic regions of the maps, the Israelites could now relate to the Bible on a more personal level, thus solidifying the Jewish national identity.

The fact that there never were 12 real Israelite tribes didn't matter, as no-one dare-question the scripture's authority and literal-sounding declarations. What mattered rather is that our population now accepted it as fact. This in turn increased their hearing, reading and repeating of that same divine-Word that in turn would open the portal.

This hybrid land/star map was centered over the city of Jerusalem which was the capital of ancient Israel, though it could have just as easily been placed over any country and city, anywhere in the world. The only differences in locations would need be the latitude, longitude, and language input primers that customized the outer word to those local cultures. Remember, the sacred word was based upon <u>math</u>, not a geocentric language or region in which a scripture was written. Thus the resulting Word only gave the illusion of language, when in fact it was infused with a mathematical wave-pattern. In this case however, the illusion created was of *Jerusalem/Israel and the Hebrew tongue*:

*"And I John saw the holy city, New **Jerusalem** (map layer), coming down from God (the God-image) **out of heaven**, (star-chart layer)"* Revelation 21:2

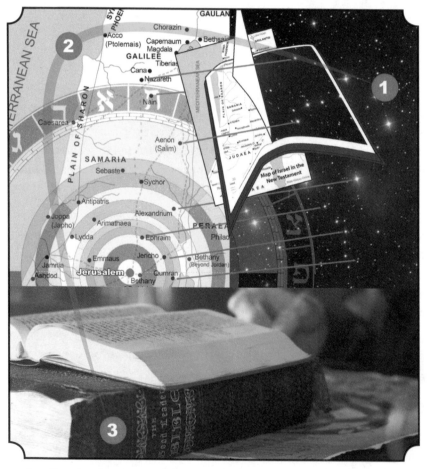

The perfect disguise: *Magi map-making 101: Hide star-charts in the form of a land-map and then record that information in the Bible as though it's referencing those towns and*

geographic-features. **Result**: <u>No one will ever figure it out</u>. *We didn't just do this in Israel however, but in the scriptures of every ancient culture we developed.*

I'd like to begin with some obvious examples of our sacred-maps within the Bible. However, because there are no known surviving maps from my day, I was thus forced to use modern versions by which to portray them. Take note that ***these are not my maps; I didn't make them***: The ones chosen were produced by <u>*Broadman Supplies/ Holman Bible Publishers*</u>. Their numerical-integrity and scale are consistent and portray the basic areas of Bible-geography.

This chapter covers the *real* land of Israel and the biggest secret of the Temple thus far. Essentially you will see Bible verses decoded and located upon a modern representation of Israel and its surrounding countries. Any doubt concerning the angelic-genius, will likely be removed while viewing these recreations. *The results are accurate and undeniable...*

THE REAL JESUS OF THE BIBLE (PART 2) "THE SON OF MAN"
THE MAP-OVERLAY AND ALIGNMENTS OF THE JESUS STAR

Using the same positioning and grids as before, but this time with the map, you will see yet another layer of the Bible's unbelievable symbolism. The following image of Jesus will be dissected and expanded for viewing. As you read, notice that every last detail of the verses **perfectly** fits the maps, grids and the colors of the firmament. The configuration of grids and their alignments border upon miraculous and, by-the-way, don't forget; that these maps were produced by a reputable map company. All that is required to see the code is the *magi-c* of your mind!

"*...and his **eyes** (sub-image #3) like a flame of **fire**...And **he had <u>in his right hand seven stars</u>** (sub-image #1); and <u>**out of his mouth went a sharp two-edged sword**</u>; (sub-image #2) "**<u>the seven stars are the angels of the seven churches</u>**" Revelation 1-3

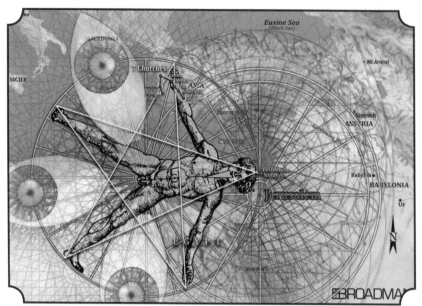

*This is the **real Jesus** of the Bible as viewed upon the map-layer of the Wisdom Wheel.*

Sub-image #1

"And he had **in his right hand seven stars**" "... **the seven stars are the angels of the seven churches**" (Ephesus, Smyrna, Pergamum, Thyatira, Sardis, Philadelphia and Laodicea.) Revelation 1-3

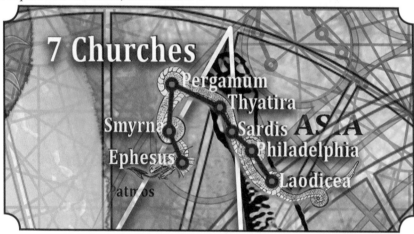

*Aligned with the right hand of Jesus are the **seven churches** of **Ephesus**, **Smyrna**, **Pergamum**, **Thyatira**, **Sardis**, **Philadelphia** and **Laodicea**. Their listing in these verses*

have a sole purpose; **to _portray the ancient star_-_pattern_ of _Draco_** as they aligned with the hand of Jesus. The issue of whether or not there were real churches in those towns is irrelevant to the Scripture's true function, yet their location on our maps was of key importance in cloaking the Israeli Grid System. Huge implications!

Sub-image #2

"out of his mouth went a sharp two-edged sword" Revelation 1:16

"and the **sword** of the Spirit, which **is** the **word of God**:" Ephesians 6:17

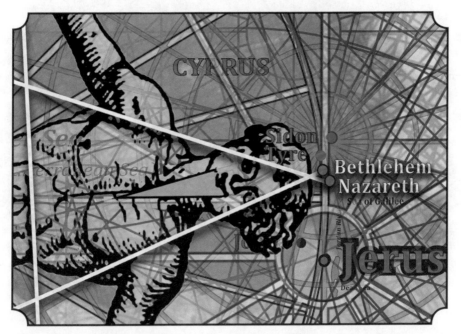

This **"sword"** is the combined line data that aligns with the mouth of Jesus. It pictorially represents the lethal, wave-pattern of the sacred-Word which fights against the false imagination of this world, hence;

Sub-image #3

"his <u>eyes were as a flame of fire</u>" Revelation 1:14

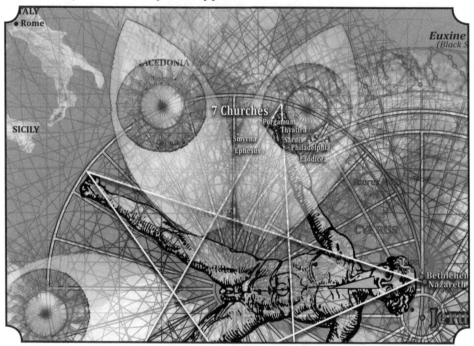

The *"eyes"* in question (highlighted in white) are envisioned from the hubs of Jesus' peripheral grids with the sun placed at their center as it would be, hence the *"<u>eyes were as a flame of fire</u>"*. Thus the verse is not describing the eyes of the figurine itself, but instead a singular body-part formed from within the grids.

JESUS PART 3
THE MIRACULOUS ALIGNMENTS
THESE DETAILS ARE UNBELIEVABLE!

The actual map-data of the Jesus figurine and its alignments are mind-blowing. Please note the conjunctions of Venus that formed his 5-sided star and the Bible details by which they are explained:

Bethlehem (1ˢᵗ conjunction)
Revealing the Code

*"Now when **Jesus was born in Bethlehem** of **Judaea**"* Matthew 2:1

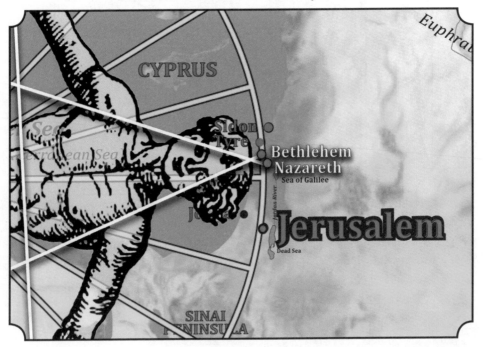

Bethlehem: *The "birth" or 1ˢᵗ Venus/Sun conjunction of Jesus, aligns with the forgotten town of Bethlehem, not the traditionally accepted town of Jesus' birth, but the town that the magi selected by which to synchronize our map-data. The Bethlehem of the Bible was only recently brought to archaeology around 2004, yet its memory came to me as a mind-image and instinct in 1995. This Bethlehem marks the 1ˢᵗ alignment of the Jesus figurine.*

Egypt (2ⁿᵈ conjunction)
Revealing the Code

*"...Joseph took the **young child** and his mother by night, and **departed into Egypt**:"* Matthew 2:14

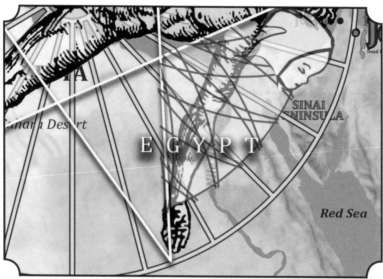

Egypt and the infant Jesus: *The figurine's left hand aligns with Egypt. Unlike the exact points of Bethlehem, Nazareth and the seven churches, there were no towns in that part of Egypt by which to pinpoint the 2nd conjunction of the Jesus star, hence a non-specific region was instead chosen. That said, this phase of the Jesus Star is symbolized as the "child" or beginning phase of Matthew 2:14*

Sea and Earth (3rd and 4th conjunction)
Revealing the Code

Next we skip to the angel of the book of Revelation, which gives a general location of Jesus' feet on our map;

*"and he set his **right foot** upon the **sea**, and his **left foot** on the **earth**,"* Revelation 10:2

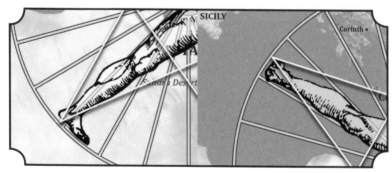

The feet of Jesus: Again the book of Revelation has provided only a non-specific geographic location by mentioning the "sea" and "earth". Usually these two symbol-words were used to describe specific-facets of the Wisdom Wheel, yet in this case they were a reference to the alignment of Jesus' feet with northern Africa and the Mediterranean Sea. Amazing!

THE 7 CHURCHES (5TH conjunction)
REVEALING THE CODE

*"The mystery of the **seven stars** which thou saw in my right hand, ... are the **seven churches**."* (*Draco's star pattern*.) Revelation 1:20

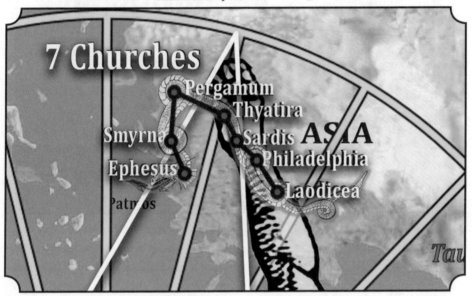

*Here again are the seven stars of Draco as the 5th alignment of the Jesus Star: In this case there were an abundance of towns by which to pinpoint the seven stars of Draco in that region of the world. The seven chosen on the map by the Wisdom Wheel were **Ephesus, Smyrna, Pergamum, Thyatira, Sardis, Philadelphia** and **Laodicea** (see Revelation 2-3). Indeed they perfectly match the star pattern of Draco and, likewise, the star-pattern matches the towns' location exactly. As you will see, there is much more about this alignment that I will reveal in the upcoming chapters.*

NAZARETH (6TH conjunction)
REVEALING THE CODE

"And he came and dwelt in a city called __Nazareth__: that it might be fulfilled which was spoken by the prophets, __He shall be called a Nazarene.__" Matthew 2:23

__Nazareth__ marks the 6th and final-alignment of the Jesus Star (Yes there are 6 in total), matches perfectly with the town of Nazareth. As Venus completes its final-leg of a star, it will overlap the first alignment by exactly 2.5 (degrees) and will be slightly higher or lower from its original position. Nazareth of course fulfills the verse's location and perhaps the most important five-sided star in history; -the Morning Star known as Jesus. Can you see the significance of this revelation?

"THE LAND OF MILK AND HONEY"
THE LAND OF SOLAR (HONEY) AND LUNAR (MILK) ALIGNMENTS
REVEALING THE CODE

"And I am come down to deliver them out of the hand of the Egyptians; to bring them out of that land unto a large and good __land flowing with milk__ (full Moon) *and __honey__* (sun)*;"* Exodus 3:8/fig.8

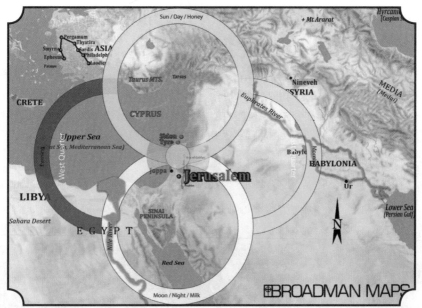

The Real Land of Milk and Honey: *This is the land of which the Wisdom Wheel spoke. The Israel of the Bible was never of this world, but instead an overlay of our grids upon a map of the earth. This type of encoding covered the tracks of our intentions until the final day. Milk and honey simply don't flow from the ground; they never did, never will.*

Though this verse does not outline a specific set of map alignments, it does provide a general outline of the Grid System on our star-chart/map overlay. To begin with, the *"milk"* being referenced is the appearance of the large, white, lunar-band. Likewise by using one's imagination it is easy to envision the golden, *"honey" like* effect of the sun within the large solar band. Remember that it is the sun and full-Moon that open the portal once Earth's tilt and wobble are eliminated, hence the wording of Exodus 3:8.

Furthermore the boundaries of <u>biblical Israel</u> within the map layer are outlined in Genesis 15:18.

"In the same day the LORD made a covenant with Abram (figurine), *saying, Unto thy seed* (stars) *have I given this land, <u>__from the river_ of Egypt unto the great river, the river Euphrates__</u>:"* Genesis 15:18

Please note the Nile and Euphrates rivers with the left and right enclosure of the grids. As you can see, there is quite a contrast between modern Israel's ***actual*** boundaries and its symbolic boundaries within the scriptures. Therefore any time you read the words *"milk"* or *"honey"* in the Christian or Jewish Bible, it is always referring to these two grids in some capacity. The land simply doesn't flow with milk and honey, but the Grid System maps surely did!

255

KING NEBUCHADNEZZAR PART II
THE BABYLON ALIGNMENT

*"Thou, O king **Nebuchadnezzar of Babylon**, saw, and behold a **great image**. This images **head was of fine gold**, its **breasts and arms of silver**, its **belly and thighs of brass**, its **legs of iron**, its **feet** part **of iron and** part **of miry clay**. **Thou, o king, art this head of gold**."* Daniel 2:31-33

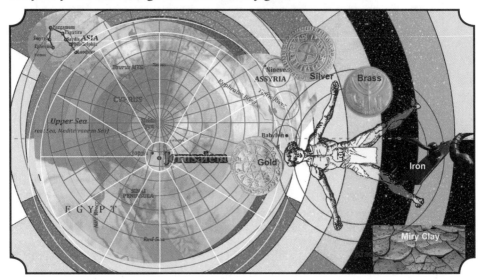

Will the real King of Babylon please stand up . . . or turn sideways . . . or whatever. We can plainly see how the Nebuchadnezzar figurine perfectly aligns with the ancient city of Babylon per the biblical-description. This figurine is a sub-grid of Tyre/Sidon, and though the math might be complicated, the images are simple to comprehend

You've already seen the **_colors_** of King Nebuchadnezzar in the Heaven and Earth chapter, but now I would like to draw your attention to the same image only with the map-layer added as well. As you can see, King Neb's head is located directly over the ancient city of **_Babylon_** per the Bible's description as *"**Thou, o king, art this head of gold**."*

What else does a doubting Thomas need? So once again we can see that the scriptures were not telling us a history story about a real king, but instead about the placement of the ecliptic grid within the Grid System, the alignments of which coincide with Babylon on the map.

King Nebuchadnezzar was a biblical-badguy of sorts, which means he was an evening star within the larger, *wobble*-grid of Tyre and Sidon. There is no faking these alignments. Obviously there really was a historical King Nebuchadnezzar in Babylon, but when his name was mentioned within our scriptures, there was **_zero historical reference_**. Now you know the real story of this royal figurine.

The Real
Giants of the Bible
Revealing the Code

*There were **giants in the earth** in those days;* Genesis 6:4

*And there we saw the **giants**, the sons of Anak, which come of the giants: and **we were in our own sight as grasshoppers**, and so we were in their sight.* Numbers 13:33

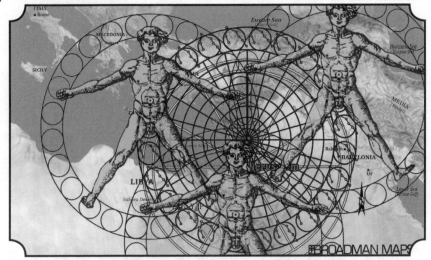

Giants—and really big ones too! Biblical claims of giants originated from within the images of the Grid System. That said, it is yet a truism that the original luminaries were somewhat taller than the average human.

And so now you know where the biblical concept was derived. *Of course* there were giants in the land, *huge ones*: not flesh and blood mind you, but the larger pictorials of our sacred maps. There are however, two sides to this part of the story. On one hand we understood that humans were notoriously superstitious, thus the implied imagery of large scary monsters fed nicely into their consciousness. It was part of the storyline that the Wisdom Wheel wrote and thus part of the outward literary mystique of the Jewish religion as a whole.

257

That said, gigantism is a real condition that is believed to be the result of an over-production of growth hormones. Yet scientists struggle with tracking the genetic link in this disease as even, on occasion, the removal of the pituitary gland still doesn't stop excess growth. It is possible I suppose that the responsible culprit is the angelic energy connected to that person's genetic-code.

During the time-frame of the melding our elements (*Both light and dark*) compacted more heavily upon some parcels of land than others, and at various points around the globe. This was the result of magnetic anomalies to which our element was attached which then distributed more heavily is some locals than others. The end result was an increase in the size of humans and primates in those areas including entire tribes of *"giants"*.

The Hammurabi Code and Sinaitic Legislation. Credit: Wellcome Collection. CC BY /4.0

Today however the vast majority of elements are melded and distributed within the huge *volume* of the human race. This is why there are far less giants born today than in prehistory. That said, none of the giants mentioned in the Bible were in reference to these beings, but instead the larger figurines of the Grid System.

On a more dramatic note, a few of the original magi did eventually mate with human women. As the dimensional-energy faded more quickly in some magi than others, things got boring, thus one does what they can to pass the time and avoid losing their mind. Believe it or not however, even sex gets boring after a couple of hundred years as does even finding yourself in a body to begin with. After enough time, the fun is all gone and an angel simply wants to go home. That said, the giants of the Bible were *figurines on our maps*; nothing more, nothing less…

THE FOUR CORNERS OF HEAVEN AND EARTH
REVEALING THE CODE

*"I saw a vision, a certain vessel descend, as it had been a **great sheet, let down from heaven by four corners**; and it came even to me:"* Acts 11:5

*"And he shall set up an ensign for the nations, and shall assemble the outcasts of Israel from the **four corners of the earth**."* Isaiah 11:12

So, at this point I must ask, did you really think we believed that the earth was flat; that it really only had four corners? I chuckle, for just as your modern maps are flat, four-cornered representations of the earth, -*so were ours*. The difference is that it wasn't that long ago that the majority of humans actually believed you could fall from the earth's edge (*sadly, some still do*). So indeed the four corners were those of the sacred sheets, and since a flat earth was all that primitive humans could understand, then we simply let them believe it.

Perhaps however, you don't believe in the myths that we created and their simplistic descriptions by which we tamed the human animal. If so, that's *good*; then awake! But don't make the mistake of confusing us with the simpletons of humanities past. Neither be deceived that because our myths were misleading in the strictest sense, that somehow the spirit of God is also a farce. ***God is real***: More *real* than, at this point, you can possibly imagine, but I am here to tell you, he lives in you and is soon to be born from within.

THE REAL
JERUSALEM AND ZION OF THE BIBLE
REVEALING THE CODE

"Then the __moon__ shall be confounded, and the __sun__ ashamed, when the LORD of hosts shall reign in mount __Zion__, and in __Jerusalem__ and before his ancients gloriously." Isaiah 24:23

"__Jerusalem__ is built as a city that is __compact together__: (**Two grids superimposed**)*"* **Psalm 122:3**

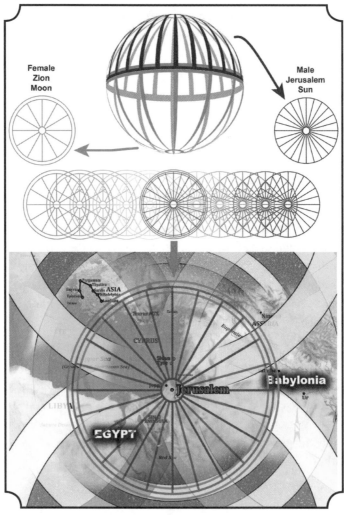

*For the magi, the location of Jerusalem on our sacred maps was not used for land navigation, but instead to mark the center of the <u>Zion and Jerusalem Grids.</u> These facets of the celestial-globe were symbolically described throughout the scriptures. This is the **real** Zion and Jerusalem of which the Wisdom Wheel wrote.*

Now that you've seen some fun examples, I'd like to show you the reasoning behind each grid's placement upon our maps. We must begin with the city of Jerusalem which was the religious epicenter of ancient Israel. Because Jerusalem was central to the Jewish people, it also made a logical center of the Wisdom Wheel. Thus we used the city's location and basic geography as an overlay by which to symbolize a critical element of the Grid System.

At the heart of this symbolism is that Jerusalem was originally built upon the hill of Zion, one being atop the other. This is similar in fashion to the grids of the celestial globe when viewed from above, *also one atop the other.* This stacking of the grids in turn provided the line-data by which to create the artistic hill of Zion as well as the artistic town of Jerusalem. What's more we were able to populate this artwork with both the male and female stars that were located therein. Neat!

Both the Jerusalem and Zion grids are *"generative"*, meaning they were the shorter sub-cycles that in turn produced the larger grand-cycles of the Grid System. Thus when you see the word, *"generation"* within the Bible, it is symbolically correlating these two grids in some form. Imagine them, if you will, as the beginning or central cogs of the Wisdom Wheel by which all others functioned to ultimately write our magic-spell.

Next of course were the colors and personas that we attached to Zion and Jerusalem within the scriptures. Due to the fact that these grids are perfectly superimposed, their male and female symbolism is interchangeable. Once described in conjunction with the colors of the Wisdom Wheel, these portrayals were really fun. Please follow the symbol words.

*"I will gather you into the midst of **Jerusalem**. As they gather **silver**, and **brass**, **and iron**, and **lead**, and **tin** (aurora colors), into the midst of the furnace,"* Ezekiel 22:19, 20

*"And I John saw the holy city, **New Jerusalem** (grid), coming down from God out of heaven, prepared as a **bride** (white or full moon) adorned for her husband ...and had **twelve gates**, (12 lunar months) and at the gates **twelve angels** (figurines), and names written thereon, which are the names of the **twelve tribes** of the children of Israel (figurines)."* Revelation 21:2

261

*"**Jerusalem** is as a **menstruous** (lower red aurora bands) **woman** (figurine)"* Lamentations 1:17

*"Their **blood** (lower red auroras) have they shed like water round about **Jerusalem**;"* Psalms 79:3

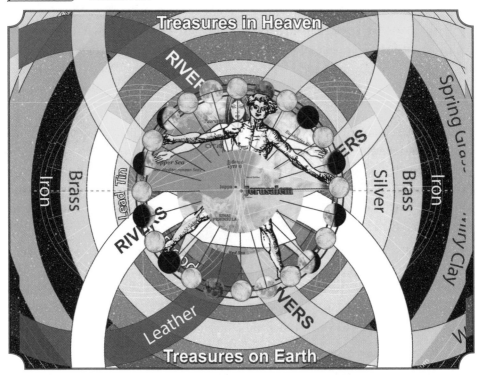

*The **Zion and Jerusalem grids** tracked the movement of the moon and sun as well as to place the resulting figurines within the Grid System. These grids were centered directly over the city of Jerusalem on our maps. Likewise, the first figurines of the Grid System were symbolized in the Bible as Adam and Eve. In this story we portrayed the moon's strayed orbit; symbolized by Eve's separation from Adam's body. Can you visualize the proverbial "rib" from which Eve was formed? The Symbolism was incredible.*

For those familiar with the Bible, you may have noticed that both an *old Jerusalem* and a *New Jerusalem* (Revelation 3:12) are mentioned therein. Allow me to explain why: During the time in which the portal was destroyed, Earth's axis tilted to about 24° away from the sun which was exactly 12° farther than what is preferable for a solid Paradise alignment. Likewise this 12° discrepancy is mimicked in Jerusalem's off-center placement in the old Wisdom Wheel alignments and symbolized in the Bible simply as simply *"Jerusalem"*.

Meanwhile the futuristic _Paradise-Alignment_ was called _"The New Jerusalem"_ and is centered on the map directly over the town of Megiddo; as in _"Armageddon"_ (Much more later).

_The Jerusalem Alignments__: The **Old** and **New** Jerusalems represent the broken and repaired alignments of the portal as they were encoded upon our sacred maps. The New Jerusalem is located over the famous town of Megiddo and heralds some unprecedented and amazing events for planet Earth. Never, at any time, was Jerusalem mentioned in the scriptures as an actual reference to the physical city, but instead to symbolize these critical aspects of the Grid System._

Yet as Earth's axis realigns in the coming age, this center point of the Jerusalem Grid will likewise be relocated to the center of the Wisdom Wheel's white dot. This will be the _New Jerusalem_ or new axial point of the sacred maps. Thus, by camouflaging our science in this manor, it became impossible for a reader to suspect our code beneath the words.

Try to remember that the scriptures are **not** a history story **nor** are they a catalog of human events, people, or places, but instead star charts that were designed to pave the way home. These sacred maps chronicled the heavens and hid those records within an outer skin or code; a cloak for creatures that could only see the outer.

JESUS SITTING ON THE RIGHT HAND OF GOD
...LITERALLY!

Next: Notice if you will the interaction between Jesus and the image of God as well as the artistic Jerusalem in context to the scriptures;

"So then after the Lord (Jesus) _had spoken unto them, he was received up into heaven, and **sat on** the **right hand of God**."_ Mark 16:19

*"No man hath seen God at any time; the only begotten **Son, which is in the bosom of the Father**, he hath declared him."* John 1:18

*"Swear not at all; neither by **heaven** (upper-half of Wisdom Wheel); for it **is God's throne**: Nor by the **earth** (lower-half of Wisdom Wheel); for **it is his footstool**: neither by **Jerusalem** (Grid); for **it is the city of the great King**."* Matthew 5:34-35

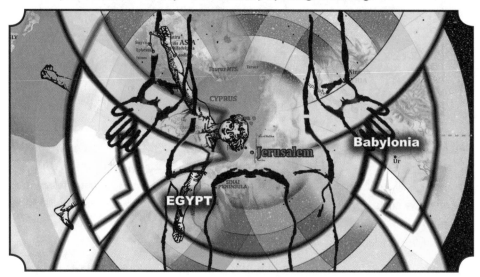

*As you can clearly see, Jesus is relaxing in the **bosom of the Father** (John 1:18) and sitting directly **on** the right hand of God (Mark 16:19). Please note that the map alignments are unchanged as before. You are seeing the real secrets of the Bible; **this is it!***

TYRE AND SIDON
THE CRITICAL ALIGNMENT OF EVIL
REVEALING THE CODE

*"**Tyre** shall be **a place for the spreading of nets** in the midst of the sea;"*

Ezekiel 26:4-5 - *The appearance of the grids as fisherman's throw-nets...*

*"Son of man, because that **Tyre** (grid) hath said **against Jerusalem** (grid), Aha, she is broken that was the gates of the people: she is **turned** (tilted lunar orbit) unto me:"* Ezekiel 26:2 *a correlation between the Jerusalem and Tyre/Sidon Grids.*

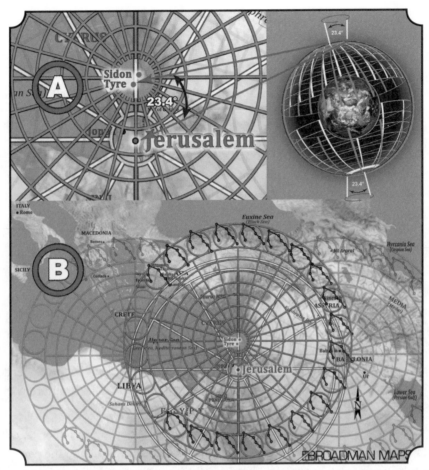

The Tyre/Sidon Grid represented Earth's 23.4° wobble and was offset from the Jerusalem/ Zion Grid accordingly. At its center is the constellation of Draco. Beginning with the serpent that deceived Adam and Eve and ending with the dragon of Revelation, we symbolized this grid with an evil connotation throughout the Bible. Indeed it is Earth's tilt and wobble that closed the portal and thus our charts recorded that information.

The next critical facet of the Grid System to be understood is the placement of the wobble grids upon the maps. So while the Jerusalem Grid showcases Earth's axil alignment, we now need another grid and town/towns to represent Earth's wobble. If you review the images of Jesus, one can see that there is another grid located due-north between the cities of Tyre and Sidon. The <u>relative</u>-distance between this location and the Jerusalem Grid is 23.4, thus mimicking the Earth's axial-tilt/wobble offset (see fig. A). In the final analysis, the towns of Tyre and Sidon are like all cities mentioned in the Bible, their sole function being grid and star locators on our maps.

Thus by mathematically extending the known, relative distance of 23.4° between the center-hubs of the Tyre/Sidon and Jerusalem Grids, we can now calculate the location of each grids outer circumference. Notice therefore, if you will, the location of the seven churches and that they fall perfectly upon the perimeter of the Tyre/Sidon Grid (see fig. B). Not only that, but even more miraculous is that they fall exactly, mathematically, where they must to form the new center of a new Draco peripheral grid. *These alignments are amazing!*

Better yet, the *Word* made our job easy as these marking points were first spelled via the Grid System itself, thus making map-production a synch. Please note that maps this accurate weren't produced again until the age of GPS and satellites. I'm sure you're wondering how this is possible, but the alignments of Jesus should be enough to convince even the biggest skeptics. By the way; we also took into account the Earth's curvature while engineering those models.

Admittedly it requires both a genius that goes beyond the intellect of this world, as well as the assistance of the Word which outlined each and every location of our maps within the books it wrote. Perhaps though you are wondering why I'm giving you such detailed information about our secrets. Because ***it is time***; *today is the day for this to happen.* As well, it is necessary that you know these details so that you can relate the countless misconceptions of the scriptures. This in turn will help you to understand the importance of what we did and therefore your connection to the realm from which you came.

I want all of your questions to be answered so as to help you understand both the mysteries we harbored as well as how it affects your relationship to the portal. The images being revealed herein will likewise assist in that comprehension. One step at a time.

SACKCLOTH AND ASHES
REVEALING THE CODE

"...for if the mighty works, which were done in you, had been done in **Tyre and Sidon***, they would have repented long ago in* ***sackcloth and ashes***.*"
Matthew 11:21

"...there was great mourning among the **Jews** *(figurines), and fasting, and* **weeping** *(stars-symbol), and wailing; and many lay in* ***sackcloth and ashes***. (grid line-data and Milky Way)"* Esther 4:3

This is how we invented your traditions: *The "**sackcloth**" of Ester 4:3 is the multitude of line-data that comprises Draco's Grids. It perfectly mimics the coarse, black, appearance of goats'-hair sackcloth used in ancient Israel. Meanwhile the "**ashes**" were symbolic for the backdrop of the Milky Way galaxy as was the "**weeping**," or stars of the image.*

*Notice the verse's correlation with the cities of "**Tyre and Sidon**" thus showing how we overlaid our maps with grids. This old Jewish rite is also the basis for what would become the Catholic-tradition of Ash Wednesday. And to think it all began from the Grid System…*

Humans seldom if ever understand the brainchild behind their religious traditions—and not that this sacrament of repentance accomplished anything more than a form of social obedience, but it certainly was interesting for us, as magi, to model and observe our handiwork of the grids. Yet for those who observed our simplistic rituals it was the pennies they had to give, the bread crumbs of repentance and dedication to God. So while there was little comprehension as to what or why we required them to commit to these rites, people gave what they could and *believed*.

In its un-encoded format however, these verses are referring to the subduction of the angelic DNA into the dark *"clothing"* of this dimension, i.e., *your human body*. Likewise that rough outer shell came about as the result of Earth's wobble and dysfunctional magnetic-structure which in turn was represented by the Draco Grid design. The horror of the fall is also reflected in the *"weeping"* of Ester 4:3. The true repentance of which we spoke however, is not of an individual act, but a plea for you to flee this dimension altogether. Again; we are in this world, but not of it.

THE REAL
GARDEN OF EDEN
THE LOST AND FOUND OF THE SCRIPTURES

"And the **Lord God** *planted a* **garden eastward in Eden**; *and* **there he put man** *whom he had formed"* *"And a* **river** *went out of* **Eden** *to water the garden; and* **from thence it was** **parted** *and became* **four heads"**

"The name of the **first** *is* **Pishon**; *which encompasses the whole* **land of Havilah**, *where there is* **gold**;"* (large eastern, morning-circle of the Wisdom Wheel) *And the gold of that land is good: there is* **bdellium** *and the* **onyx stone**.

"...the **second is river** *is* **Gihon**; *the same is it that encompasses the whole* **land of Ethiopia**"* (large southern, Moon-circle of the Wisdom Wheel)

"And the name of the **third river** *is* **Tigris**; *that is it which goes toward the* **east of Assyria**."* (large western, evening-circle of the Wisdom Wheel)

"And the **fourth river Euphrates**."* (large northern, Sun-circle of the Wisdom Wheel) Genesis 2:8-14/fig. a, b

The real 4-rivers of the Garden of Eden: Its four rivers of solar, lunar, morning and evening colors, creating the symbolism by which the Bible-story was patterned. Notice the precision of the overlay with the colors and locations that are listed within the scriptures. The Wisdom Wheel even spelled the name of the rivers, some of which have proximity to real-world rivers such as the Euphrates. This is none-other than the long lost Garden of biblical-lore...Amazing!

Like all Grid System images, Eden was *centered just north of Jerusalem* and is translated to mean; *"enclosed paradise"* or *"enclosed delight."* It was *"eastward"* not because of its location on the map, but rather due to the eastward equinox sunrise being represented in this story. The original Paradise Alignment (before the portal's failure) was a time in which the sun rose *much closer to due east* year-round. I hesitate to tell you the exact measurement of this ancient sunrise as your scientists today would emphatically deny its possibility based upon their own misinterpretation of alleged evidence.

By looking at the same map overlay as before, one immediately notices that the description of Eden encompasses a huge amount of territory extending from the Tigris and Euphrates Rivers, Assyria, Ethiopia, and even the land of Havilah. Included in the Bible's story are the color-symbols of **bdellium, onyx,** and **good gold**, all perfect matches for the various colors of the western ring/river named *"Pishon".*

Likewise at the center of the Wisdom Wheel is the junction of Eden's peculiar four-headed river, which is nothing more than the four, grand cycle rings of (*morning, Evening,* Sun/*Day* and Moon/*Night*). As the diagram portrays, this intersection parts and becomes the *"four heads":*

*"And a **river** went out of **Eden** to water the garden; and **from thence it was parted and became four heads"***. Genesis 2:10

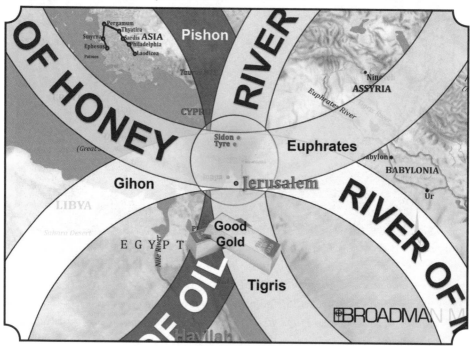

In support of this, the *book of Enoch* includes even better details about Eden and its rivers:

*"And **two springs** come out which send forth **honey** (yellow/Sun circle) **and milk** (white/Moon circle), and **their springs send forth oil** (evening circle) **and wine** (morning circle), and they separate into **four parts**, and go **round** with quiet course, and go down into the **EDEN, between corruptibility** (lower-half) **and incorruptibility** (upper-half)."* Enoch 8:6

The symbolism here is fascinating in that the basic appearance of the day, night, evening and morning skies are branded as being *"honey, milk, oil and wine."* It was a way to encode the prominent colors of the heavens at those specific times, thus hiding the science in the form of a soothing storyline for our congregations. Eden was also described as being *"between corruptibility and incorruptibility"* due to its alignment in both the day and night background sectors of the Wisdom Wheel. Later in the story of Moses, these same white and gold rings are symbolized as the "*The Land of Milk and Honey*". It was the same rings, but with different symbolism.

THE TREE OF LIFE AND
THE TREE OF KNOWLEDGE OF GOOD AND EVIL
REVEALING THE CODE

*"And out of the ground made the Lord God to grow **every tree** that is pleasant to the sight, and good for food; the **tree of life** also in the midst of the garden, and the **tree of the knowledge of good and evil**."* Genesis 2:9/3:3

The trees of Eden were abstract-images of the Grid System formed by the gold and white rings that were also two of Eden's rivers (same grids with different symbolism). The **Tree of Life** is symbolic of the light of the Source of Heaven and is located over the "incorruptible", day section of the Firmament, while the **Tree of Knowledge** is upside down over the darkened or, "corruptible" sector.

271

Likewise the book of Enoch better describes the co-symbolism of the four-rings as *"rivers"* and/or *"trees"* as well as the throne upon where God *"rests"*:

*And in the midst of the **trees of Eden, that of life**, where upon the* **Lord rests** *when he goes into **Paradise**; and this tree is adorned more than every existing thing; and on all sides it is in form **gold-looking** and* **Vermilion** *(bright red) and **fire-like**. Its **root is in the garden at the earth's end**. Enoch 8:6*

Remember the image of God's throne?

Let's also compare the co-symbolism of the Garden trees and God's throne with the four rivers as described in the book of Enoch

*"And **two springs** come out **beneath the tree** which send forth **honey** and **milk**, and their springs send forth **oil and wine**, and they **separate into four parts**, and go round with quiet course, and go down into the **EDEN, between corruptibility and incorruptibility**."*

And while the Tree of Life represents true illumination, the Tree of Darkness, (i.e., *the Tree of the Knowledge of Good and Evil*) is located in the black corruptible section of the Firmament, thus its evil portrayal. Similar to the satanic element, the moon that shows this light is deceptive in that it has no light of its own but is merely a reflection of the real light of the sun. This is a metaphysical likeness to our existence on Earth as humans—not really who we are, but a mere reflection of the truth. And the more knowledge we get, the more we *forget* the power of the Atomos in the moment…

What's more, each tree of this grid Garden was named based upon its likeness to the real type of tree that most closely mimicked its artistic- appearance. For example the Tree of the Knowledge of Good and Evil was symbolized as a *"fig-tree"* (white bark) while the Tree of Life was named as a *"Mustard Tree"* (yellowish tree) in the book of Matthew 13:

*"The **kingdom of heaven** is like to a grain of **mustard seed**, which a man took, and sowed in his **field**: Which indeed is the least of all seeds: but when it is grown, it is the **greatest among herbs**, and becomes a tree, so that the birds of the air come and lodge in the branches thereof."* Matthew 13:31-32

*Teaser: As I will expound upon in Book II, you will see that the town of Bethlehem is both the mustard seed in question as well as the immaculate seed of Mary. Please refer to the "Woman of the Book of Revelation" in the **Heaven and Earth** Chapter to solve this*

secret of the magi.

As a final note is the orientation of the Tree of Life and the Tree of Knowledge of Good and Evil per Ecclesiastes 11:3:

"*...and if the **tree fall toward the south** (knowledge of good and evil), or **toward the north** (Tree of Life), in the place **where the tree falls, there it shall be.**"... Enough said...*

THE TWO OLIVE TREES
AND THE MORNING AND THE EVENING

Meanwhile the Morning and Evening rings were called "*olive trees*" and sit directly to the left and right of the Tree of Life:

"*...and their springs send forth **oil and wine**,*" Enoch 8:6

"*...and see thou hurt not the **oil and the wine**.*" Revelation 6:6

"*These are the **two olive trees**, and the **two candlesticks** standing before the God of the earth.*" Revelation 11:4

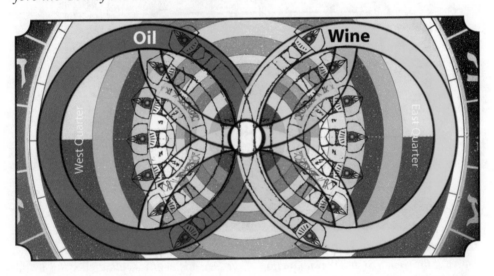

Later in the Bible these two olive trees were grafted into the Tree of Life. This symbolizes the increased time in which the portal will remain open each year as we return to the Paradise Alignment thus providing greater access to the glorious God-Element.

THE NEW TREE OF LIFE
THE TIMELINE OF PORTAL RECONNECTION

"...and thou, being a __wild olive tree__, (combo-image of the morning and evening rings) *were __grafted__ in among __them__,*(grafted into the Tree of Life) *and __with them__ partake __of the root__* (i.e., tree trunk) __and fatness__ (tree canopy)...*and wert grafted into a __good olive tree__* (north/sun ring) *For I __would not__, brethren, that you should __be ignorant of this mystery__,"* Romans 11:17-24

___The timeline of Faith, Hope and Love___: *Every last word of the Bible symbolized some aspect of the Grid System. The subduction of the God-Element was planted in this world during the portal's failure and was recorded into the "Faith" or right-side ring of the Wisdom Wheel. The timeline of the good (spin) grids then advanced clockwise through the lower, dark section of the Wheel only to raise again in the "Hope" ring and finally be realized in the yellow, or "love" ring. It is fascinating how the image of Romans 11 told the story of our science pictorially.*

By noting the location of the portal and the direction of magnetic-current around and within Earth, we can discern the flow of Source-Element as it cycles between the two dimensions. As a result its effects on your mind can be felt to a far greater degree during the morning hours where it is strongest. This dimensional influence can be validated by noting that the majority of great inventions and epiphanies occur during the waking hours. Einstein himself attested to this as can I. Indeed the majority of my mind-images occur between 5:00 and 10:00AM.

On a separate note, the magi in each country shared portal/science data as well as mythological cover-stories. As a result you will see similar metaphors in the outer-myths of those nations. A Greek myth for example involved an item called the, *"Tree of the Golden Apples"* while its Hebrew equivalent was called the *"Tree of Life"*; the connection being that both myths involved *"trees"* as well as a *"serpent"* (Draco), which entwined them.

Beyond the 4 large rings that form the trees of the Wisdom Wheel were actually eight others (*12 in total; are you surprised?*). Each of these was color coded and used intermittently to represent eclipsed moons, half-moons, green aurora (*"green tree"*), etc. The large red ring, for example, was placed over the area of Egypt and used in support of the story of Moses and the splitting of the Red Sea. The fact that the *real* Red Sea is located in the same area as the red ring was used to our advantage in formatting this symbolism.

THE IMAGE OF GOD PART II
THE MAP OF THE ALMIGHTY

Next we have the image of God as we placed Him on our maps; His feet being aligned with the Mountain of Sinai:

*"And the eternal **God will <u>tread</u> upon the earth, (even) on <u>Mount Sinai</u>, And appear in the strength of His might from the heaven of heavens."*** Enoch 1: Fig 5 a

*"The LORD says: The **<u>heaven</u>** (upper-half of Wisdom Wheel) **is my throne**, and the **<u>earth</u>** (lower-half of Wisdom Wheel) **is my footstool**:"* Isaiah 66:1

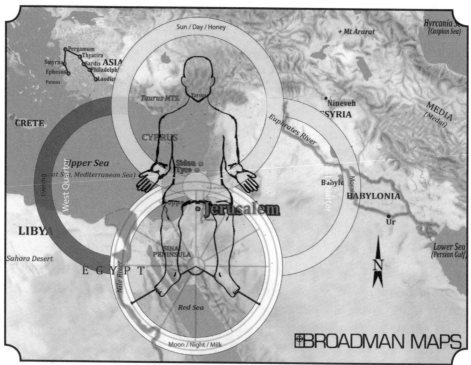

This rendering of the image of God clearly puts His feet upon grid-art creation of Mount Sinai, which ironically is located over the Sinai Peninsula on the map. The exact location of the physical mountain in this case, was of no concern to us, but rather its general-area in conjunction with the verse that the Wisdom Wheel wrote. Likewise this scale represents the 2nd largest of the Grid System and was called "**The Land of Israel**" (Genesis 15:18). There were 4-scale sizes of the map layer in total.

THE REAL
BABY MOSES
REVEALING THE CODE

"And when she could no longer hide him, she took an **ark of bulrushes**, and **daubed it with pitch** (black section), **and slime** (large left ring of Wheel), and **put the child therein**;" Exodus 2:3

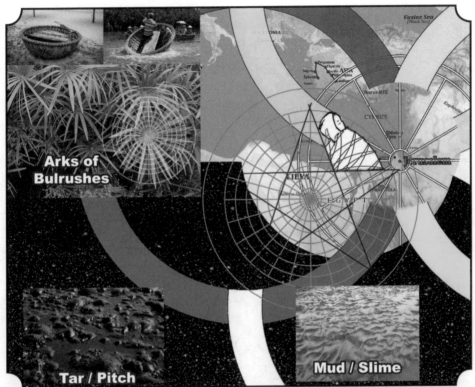

*The **real** ark of baby Moses: Notice how the "**bulrushes**" resemble the diagonal lines of a grid as does the night sky as tar or "**pitch**" and the large western ring as mud or "**slime**." We of course noted these likenesses and thus used their appearance to symbolize the story of Moses—rather, the Word noticed these likenesses for us.*

As was portrayed in <u>Noah's Ark</u>, we again have a symbolic comparison between the *goofah-crafts* of the ancient Middle-East and the zodiac they resemble. Each stage of a figurine's formation was represented with a symbolic image, beginning with an infant and ending with a full-sized figurine, thus illustrating the five segments of a star. Likewise, in the opening chapters of Exodus we are witnessing the first conjunction of a new figurine in the area of Egypt, the image of which was portrayed as the baby Moses who was castaway in the zodiac—*I mean, ark!*

Similar to Jesus, Moses was a peculiar alignment in which a perfect spin grid overlay a Draco peripheral grid. This explains how Moses was portrayed as both a Jew and an Egyptian within the storyline of Exodus. It was all a play on words and Grid-System images.

THE REAL
THE BURNING BUSH
REVEALING THE CODE

"And the <u>angel of the Lord appeared to Moses in a flame of fire out</u> of <u>the midst of a bush;</u> and behold, the <u>bush burned with fire and the bush was not consumed.</u>"

*"And he said, <u>**Draw not near**: **put off thy shoes from off thy feet,**</u> for the place whereon you stand is holy ground"* Exodus 3:2-5

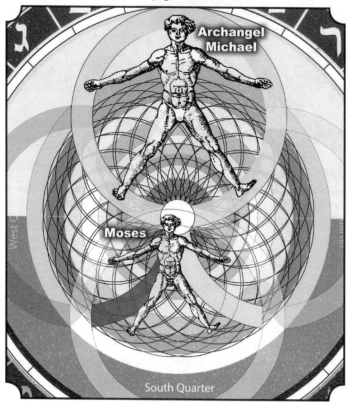

The burning bush and the Tree of Life were one and the same creation. Like all literary illusions of the Bible, the real imagery of this depiction has its origins, not in history, but from within the Grid System. As you can see, the bush appears to burn due the fact that the main sun-grid comprises its artistic canopy, hence; *"the bush burned with fire and was not consumed"*. Notice how the *"Angel of the Lord"* (Grand-cycle figurine), stands within its midst. This is the arch angel Michael.

278

THE BLOOD OF JESUS

*"…And he was clothed with a **vesture dipped in blood**:"* Revelation 19:13

*"But one of the **soldiers** with a **spear pierced his side**, and forthwith came there out **blood and water**."* John 19:34

The symbolism of the blood of Jesus is a profound message that we interpreted not only through the math of the scriptures but also by evaluating the image itself. I will of course give you the layered meaning of the *"blood"* as well as it's shedding upon the hill of Calvary, but for now I want to stretch your mind a bit. This does however complete the symbolism of Jesus for the entirety of this writing.

As you have seen, the Bible's reference to the *'Son of Man'* was a perfectly placed description of this key figure of the Holy Grille. The fact that we accomplished these maps thousands of years ago should tell you that the luminaries are not a fable that I created for your entertainment, but instead the real deal that history forgot.

Don't let this diminish the truth of the alignments: This data is far more magnificent than if it had been a history story. When one considers that the words of the scriptures are the direct result of alpha-numeric grids being used to spell each and every letter; that these verses *were not* randomly produced, and that the towns mentioned in each story match specific alignments in a massive star chart -then the **actual story** becomes all the more miraculous.

As we understood the profound truth of God, the spirit of Christ is eternal, crucified, *not 2,000 years ago* but from the very moment it became trapped in this world, yet embodied within the God DNA that now has died in your own form. He is the spirit of God Himself, which became flesh and blood—*your* flesh and blood. Indeed the Atomos lives and dies in all our forms until the resurrection day is completed. He was in fact never separate from our suffering, but *was* and *is* our suffering. And in the day of revelation, that you should also not separate yourself from God in your mind, but see the bond, inseparable, the union of Him in you; the message of Christ in us, in all of His forms, the angels of heaven; the true body of Christ in us all.

But again we had to give you a history story in the beginning because that's the only thing to which humans could relate; but you are awakening now to the resurrection message, a new page of your understanding, a new day in which the old shall be replaced with a reborn comprehension of our direct relationship to the divine. The time has come, and we stand at the very threshold of the day of the Lord.

There are many more biblical examples of the Son of Man that you will enjoy viewing to assure you of the truth of which I speak. In so-doing you will gain a profound comprehension of the resurrection process, much more so than the outward historical context of the stories can ever provide. These recreations will *literally* take you to the next level of the resurrection magic and will be included in a separate work release.

This millennia-old science is real, as is the Word that it produces—and to think that the power of the universe is at your disposal, at the edge of your believing and the tip of your tongue . . .

The symbolism of the Grid System's distinct cross is visible in this 13th century mosaic of Jesus in the church of Hagia Sophia in Istanbul, Turkey.

THE CODE OF THE SCALE
THE 4 SCALES-SIZES OF THE GRID SYSTEM

Again, the Grid System was displayed on four scale-sizes and any one of these scales often included a master scroll depending upon the cycle of the encoded story being portrayed. Mind you, it was the same grids, just in different sizes which allowed us to symbolize and artistically-render not only Israel and its surrounding countries, but also the city of Jerusalem and finally the Temple complex.

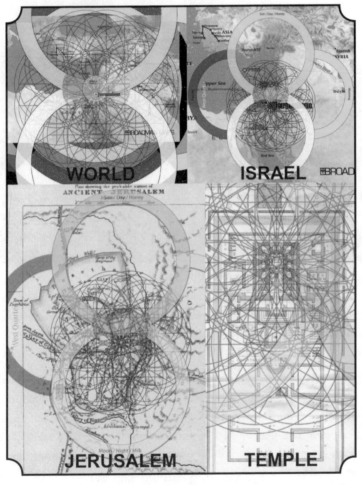

*These are the **four scale sizes of the Grid System**. It was the same Grid System separated only by the descriptions of the Wisdom Wheel. Not only did this allow for a greatly, expanded storyline in the scriptures but it also more thoroughly encoded our work. Ingenious!*

SURVEY, MAPPING AND STAR-CHARTING

As with many ancient structures, we used the Jerusalem temple as a planetarium and survey control-point for map-making as well as for the production of Word charts. The Temple was somewhat elevated, which allowed a 360° field of view of both the heavens and the surrounding terrain. From there we could easily see both the stars as well as the smoke plumes from survey-fires in distant towns.

All land surveys for the Wisdom Wheel were bench-marked from atop the Temple in Jerusalem. From there we used alignment-fires by which to create a veritable web of azimuths taken from thousands of elevated points around the region. Once plotted, the comparative lines and angles gave phenomenal map-making accuracy. Simple yet effective.

Likewise our surveying *"benchmark"* was a sighting rod mounted directly above the Holy of Holies that rotated and thus allowed us to shoot azimuths in any direction. From there an initial set of alignments were taken and then cross-checked via an orchestrated measurement from other towns and elevated areas. This process was then extended beyond the visible horizon by merely continuing the procedure. This of course leads us to the next phase of our mapping which involves the *lilies of the field*.

THE LILIES OF THE FIELD
AS THEY CONCERN THE SACRED MAPS

*"Consider the **lilies of the field**, (grid-designs) how they **grow** (How the design gets bigger each day); they **toil not** (no wobble), neither do they **spin** (neither do they represent the Earth's axial-spin):* Mt. 6:28-30

That we used the Grid System in every ancient religion is undisputed. With these circles we calculated and integrated the curvature of the Earth within our maps.

Each of these simple circles represented a 24-hour day, yet in their practical use within the Grid System displayed neither Earth's **spin** (*spin*) nor **wobble** (*toil*). Likewise these lilies *"grew"* or populated the larger grids and cycles to which they belonged. Each day a new circle was added to our master scrolls until finally completing or filling the larger cycle being recorded. We used these circles both as a convenient aid for surveying and adjusting that information into either a flat map or even a round globe.

Once the data was collected from each and every waypoint, we simply did the math by which to build the map. We already knew that Earth was round, a fact that was confirmed via the angular algorithms of the intersecting azimuths from each town or waypoint. These differences were then averaged, which in turn produced a curved globe, not dissimilar from the ones in use today. Though much of the globe was incomplete, it was at least on scale and included a huge area of the Middle East and the Mediterranean.

Ah, but even DaVinci piddled with the simple circles of the lilies. As I've stated before, I have no doubt that he knew of the Grid System but dared-not share that information. Most people then were ignorant and reactive to things they didn't understand, something that the magi likewise dealt with on a daily basis. And this is why we kept our science secretly encoded in the form of the Bible and other ancient texts until today. Worse yet for Leonardo, it wasn't the average person whom he feared but the church itself that, feeling their power threatened by such revelations, would have no doubt ended his life.

Yet DaVinci also knew the day would come in which the world would see the overwhelming evidence of the magi and what they had accomplished. When that day came, his images of the lilies and the Vitruvian Man would be a silent but overwhelming testament to that knowledge. *Today is that day:*

*"For now we see **through a glass, darkly**;"* 1Cor 13:12

*I know, I know, -we didn't have telescopes 3000 years ago (keep telling yourself that). The magi knew the Earth was round thousands of years ago and made really nice globes by which to further the study of our science. This **Chinese** "Fu dog," displays the earth's grid design of the lilies. But there is more than one secret to this sacred lion of China.*

Next of course was the production of our star charts that would overlay the maps. This task was also involved albeit easier than land surveying. What required years to map on land only took months to map in the heavens. Once both charts were finished, they were combined into one really cool hybrid map that we used as a base layer to the

Wisdom Wheel. As stated before, any star that aligned with a given town was thus symbolized in the Bible with that town's name, therefore hiding the science in plain sight.

We also invented an impressive array of survey tools to assist us in our observations. This included astrolabes, sighting tools, the compass and even some really nice optics by which we magnified the stars at night. When used in conjunction with temple alignments, waypoints, etc. these items allowed us to validate and sync our maps and star-charts. As well it enabled us to navigate the globe via the first, ocean-worthy ships ever made.

The melding prevented our freedom of mental movement and thus forced us to build physical forms of transportation. Yet even in our diminished state we were still beyond the definition of genius. As a result we successfully navigated between the continents as far back as 18,000 years ago, -way before historians thought possible.

The Mappás
The transition from stars to scriptures

The Word-sheets and pictorials of the Grid System were recorded upon various sized medium called mappás. While the Word-sheets were made of cloth fabric and stretched similar to an artist's canvas. The pictorials meanwhile, were drawn upon leather parchment. The sheets were of different sizes too: For example; in the following picture you can see that the ancient *"prayer clothe"* is about 30"x36" and only contains the letters of the verses themselves.

The placement of the circles was predictable and were drawn as a pattern upon which the letters were then placed one at a time as the Wisdom Wheel spelled them. Thus, every verse, chapter, and book in the Bible were first written upon cloth. These Word sheets were then transferred to a high-level scribe who then copied those words upon scrolls or *"books."*

It was common knowledge, then, that the magi commanded the operations of the Jewish Temple. In fact the Greek term for magi (i.e., *"wise men"*) was also a byword for the chief-scribe:

...and therefore the **royal officials** *(magi) who were occupied in recording in the archives the proceedings of each day, were called* **scribes** *(comp. II Sam. viii. 17; II Kings xix. 2, passim); but as the* **art of writing was known only to the intelligent***, the term "scribe" became synonymous with* **"wise man"** *(Greek for* **magi***)(I Chron. xxvii. 32). Source: The Jewish Encyclopedia.*

Once the initial scripture was written, the scroll was then copied multiple times by lower-level scribes within the Temple's side rooms and then delivered to every synagogue in the country. Having returned the original to myself, we then stored it in the secret rooms below the Temple. Down there the mappás stayed cool, dry and safe from discovery up until the Romans sacked Jerusalem in 70AD. Likewise, to further protect them from discovery, a death-penalty loomed for those who trespassed in either the sanctuary itself or the basements below. Armed guards were posted 24/7.

As fate would have it, a gust of wind once blew a drawing from atop the Temple and directly into the crowed court of Israel or, *"Men's Court."* Obviously we tried to recover the sheet but with no luck. As chance would have it, the image included a pictorial of a star/figurine that the Word had named *Solomon*. Needless to say, word quickly traveled throughout the land, hence all the hype concerning Solomon's magic which of course included a morning star.

However the next step in the process was creating the imagery of the Word sheet into a visible picture that could be enjoyed. We typically drew our images upon thin but ridged leather parchment. This material was finished with an incredibly smooth surface upon which we drew, colored or stamped our information. This included figurines, constellations, stars, lines, circles, etc.

I personally struggled with artistic expression *then and now*, as my imagination always outpaced the physical constraints of the art itself. In my mind I see the science, the data, grids, figurines, etc., all at the same time and in living motion—something that simply isn't realistic in a still image. This difficulty also became evident when I tried to reproduce the images for the book you are reading.

Unfortunately, the reason most of the original star-charts haven't survived is that, like all organic material, moths literally ate them to pieces. Unlike papyrus, cloth and parchment stood little chance against the test of time. It's sad that so many ancient maps, star charts, Word Grids and sacred art are forever lost. That said, some of our sheets did survive and will surely surface now that people will realize what they have in their possession.

For reasons of control, even the Jewish high priests were unaware of the full mystery behind the Grid System. Similar to the command structure of any governing entity, the lower-echelon of the Judaic priesthood, including the common rabbi, scribes and priests were restricted from this information. It's simple enough to see that any breach of secrecy would have been a disaster for the entire priesthood.

Likewise, for early human cultures to discover that their trusted religion, scriptures, history and temples were based upon star-data instead of historical fact would have resulted in a total breakdown of the national identity and likely, *an overthrow of the priesthood itself.* But it wasn't the magi who ultimately did the deceiving, but the mind of this world which can only believe superficially, historically, and in physical context.

Ultimately the Grid System was only a temporary and expendable format. As you have seen, the final phase of the code was accomplished by recording this data in the metaphoric verse inventory of the Jewish and Christian Scriptures. In reverse, one can actually plot the locations and symbol-words listed in each verse and thereby recreate the encoded data pictorially.

Though many of these sheets escaped the Roman's destruction of the Temple in 70AD, many others did not. When the Temple collapsed during the ensuing battle with the legions, the remaining treasures including the mappás were entombed within the subterranean refuge along with myself. Though I managed to finally dig my way out, further tunnel collapses permanently buried the mappás under tons of stone. Thereafter new Roman construction merely built over the old, thus sealing those treasures.

SACRED MATH
THE PERFECT MATH OF PERFECT WORD

Math was instinctive to the magi, a *"shoot from the hip"* understanding yet always within the bulls-eye of perfection. It makes me wonder about my present incarnation in which I took geometry and algebra in my high-school years. Even then I often had the answers, yet could never seem to work the equations or formulas. To no avail, my teacher would ask me to show my work so as to prove my answer but I simply couldn't do it (*which reflected in my horrible math grades*). That said, how did I know the answers?

But it was this way for the magi as well though on a far greater level. They didn't need long, laborious equations for something they already knew instinctively. By comparison, I once noticed that even a cat and a dog will naturally walk the center of a narrow plank when forced. Is this not an instinctive understanding of division? They may not consciously calculate, but they none the less comprehend the advantage of walking in the center of and elevated platform. Multiply that instinct times a million or so, and you can begin to comprehend the inherent abilities of the angels. It was, let's say, *common sense* math.

Likewise the magi used this ability to design the Word. The amplitude-modulation (AM) of the Word can be recognized by reciting the Lord's Prayer or any of the psalms. However, unlike common FM or AM radio waves, the scriptures were also built around mental structure and intent. When reading or speaking from the Bible, higher dimensional values within your mind are also unlocked and released.

So as you can see, the process of correction is not just mechanical, but also very, very personal. In fact the only weakness of the Word is that it must be spoken with genuine intent. Without genuine love, need and heart, it is of no effect. Luckily the more life fails us, the greater our inclination to reach for the things of God, thus changing our focus and heartfelt calling to the higher dimension.

But that is a good thing, for without the failure of this life, there would be no incentive to awaken the dormant angel within. As has been said; everyone wants to go to heaven but no one wants to die to get there. However the death of which I speak, concerns letting go of an entire reality. Simply put, if we're not broken and willing to reach beyond this life, then we aren't yet compatible to receive eternity. Health, wealth, and human knowledge ruins our focus and understanding. This life is temporal and should be recognized as such. It is impossible to serve God and mammon; you can't have both.

But beyond observing the love of God internally and monitoring the images of the Grid System, there is simply no way to meter the Element beyond the ways and means of the Wisdom Wheel. Beyond this amazing device of the magi, there is no gauge beyond what you feel and know inwardly, no outward means by which to discern *a broken and contrite heart*. You can feel it and understand it <u>inside</u>, but you can't measure it—that in itself, is a frequency all its own.

And though the glory and power of God are yet to be realized in their totality, genuine heartfelt humility is certainly a good beginning. Indeed the temple must be cleansed of **all ego** before the master of the universes is willing to awaken therein.

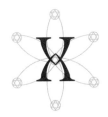

The Master of Scrolls
Noah's Ark, the Temple, and the City of Jerusalem

Some images were simply too detailed and contained too many circles to portray on a single image sheet. This was often the case when recording the longer cycles of the precession, which involved as many as 25,920 circles (one for each year). Even worse were the day-counts of that same cycle, which tallied well into the millions.

It was in these instances that we used scrolls, *huge ones*, to help us catalog the extra cycles. For the purpose of illustration in this chapter I have exclusively used the grid-design found in the women's court of the ancient temple that once stood in Jerusalem. Though a master scroll was often layered with the larger grids and colors of the Wisdom Wheel, they were primarily used to display the details of the smaller grids that populated these larger and longer cycles.

Not every book of the Bible entailed the use of a master scroll. The tell-tale signs of when we did use them however, lie in the huge number counts of the storyline in question. In the book of Numbers for example (*a likely name for a book of encoded astronomy*), it can be seen in the census-count of Israel, which equals 603,550 (*by all means, I challenge you to decode this number*).

Other times the mass number of figurines were listed in the form of war casualties or plague death as in Numbers 16:49, etc. Often these number counts allude to, *in code*, mathematical puzzles that we knew you would understand in the day of revelation. Regardless, in some capacity these huge counts are telling the story of *circles, cycles, figurines,* or even the number of resulting *cubits* formed within the grid-patterns.

Interestingly, if a specific large circle of the Grid System was named, let's say, "Adam," "Moses," or "Jesus," then it would be populated on the master scroll with the many sub-cycles/circles and figurines that belonged to that cycle. An example of this is found in 1 Corinthians 15:22:

*"For as **in Adam** **all** die, even so **in Christ** **all** shall live."*

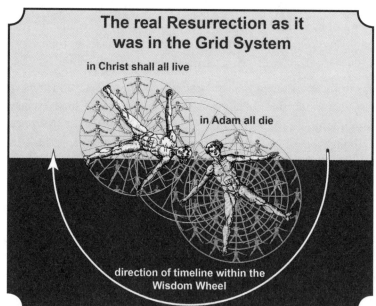

The real Resurrection as it was in the Grid System

in Christ shall all live

in Adam all die

direction of timeline within the Wisdom Wheel

Coming to Grips with the Resurrection: *This image symbolizes the transition from the old identity to the new within the cycles of the Grid System. Adam and Christ were in fact grand cycles in which the smaller cycles were contained, hence from the age of Adam until now, the Atomos was doomed to a cyclic death within humanity. However, upon the portal's reopening, the collective soul of the "Sons of God" will awaken as <u>prophesied</u>*

within the scriptures. Today is the day in which the real resurrection begins. The timeline is listed, in-code, right down to the <u>very hour</u> of its completion.

With this, understand that it is impossible to separate a character of the Bible from the timeline that he or she represents within the Grid System. *Every* character, therefore, not being a real person, is thus a *dispensation* and the *persona* of that day and age.

By far the most interesting artwork of our master-scrolls were those of the **Temple**, *the* **city of Jerusalem,** and **Noah's Ark**. Again; as described in the Bible, these were in no way literal artifacts awaiting discovery in some distant archaeological dig but the exacting designs of the scrolls themselves. To look for them elsewhere is nothing less than the realization of Indiana Jones when he stated, *"They're digging in the wrong place."* Ultimately the details of these biblical stories are found within our master scrolls and, *finally*, in this chapter, here and now for you to enjoy.

THE SCROLL OF SOLOMON'S TEMPLE
AS TAKEN IN COMBINATION FROM 1 KINGS AND 2 CHRONICLES

*"And the **house** (Temple) which King Solomon built for the LORD, the* **length** *was* **60 cubits**, *and the* **breadth 20** *cubits, and the* **height 30 cubits**. *And the* **porch** *before the temple of the house,* **20 cubits was the length** *thereof, according to the breadth of the house; and* **10 cubits was the breadth** *thereof before the house. And for the house he made* **windows of narrow lights**."

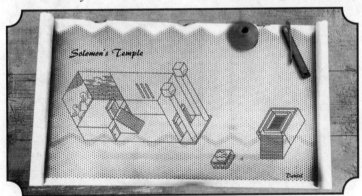

The Temple Scroll: Not only did 1Kings and 2Chronicles outline this amazing scroll in-code, but also the Temple image in cubits verbatim. Yet within this puzzle of the Wisdom Wheel is also the hidden timeline of the resurrection. As a further miracle, the scriptures that gave us these dimensions were also a perfect wave-pattern that altered Earth's magnetic structure when spoken. Not one jot or tittle, -not one line or circle, was random; it

was all according to plan. (Note: The scribal-rooms were not included in this image for the sake of clarity.)

Understand that the temple described within the Bible was not a real, physical construct but rather a master-scroll image. ***Please comprehend the enormity of that revelation.*** Within that image, we detailed each content-image separately according to the dimensions outlined by the Wisdom Wheel. This included every item such as the *ten menorahs,* the *table of showbread,* images of *palms,* the *molten sea of brass,* etc. That said, the dimensions of the first temple in Jerusalem were taken directly from the image schematic of this scroll that was indeed its blueprint.

THE MOLTEN SEA OF BRASS

*"Also he made a **molten sea** of **10 cubits from brim to brim**, and **5 cubits the height**; and **30 cubits did compass it round about**. It stood upon **12 oxen**; **3 looking toward the north**, and **3 toward the west**, and **3 toward the south**, and **3 toward the east**: and the **sea** was set **above upon them**, and all **their hind** parts were **inward**" 2 Chronicles 4:2-4*

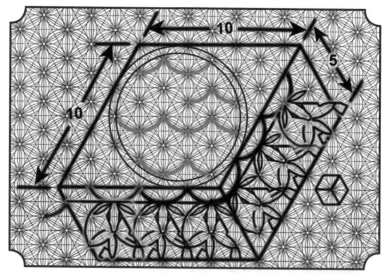

The Crushing Burden of the Age of Taurus: *The Bible's story of the Temple scroll begins in the age of Taurus, symbolized via the Brass Sea with 12 bulls. Accordingly, each and every grid in that area of the diagram belongs to and records cycles in sync with this sub-chapter of the Grid System. Similar to the "four horns of the Altar" (Exodus 38:2), this design also emits a protruding bull-horn on each corner.*

292

The molten sea as described in 1 Kings and 2 Chronicles entails two encoded timelines within its cubit counts within the age of Taurus. I will leave the length of these timelines to your own mathematical-prowess to guess or solve. Meanwhile, the purpose of listing *12* bulls instead of any other number is obvious at this point and requires no further discussion.

Yet in practical use as a blueprint for the real temple in Jerusalem, this creation of the grids served as a washing station for the priests themselves. The symbolism of the molten sea speaks of the burden of sin, or separation from God. This is idealized by the crushing weight upon the back of the God Element during the age of Taurus.

And what brought that separation but the satanic element itself, consequently found in the brass-band of the aurora. Thus the diagram of our sea was colored *"brass"* by the Wisdom Wheel, pictorially confirming the scientific-facts that the magi had long before identified. It is the mind of this world that we must wash away before entering the temple or *Holy relationship* with our true identities and thus the next phase of the resurrection timeline.

As you will see, the dark-element not only closed the portal but also tricked the God Element within you into believing you are a physical creature. Indeed, we have been the unwitting and proverbial *"beast of burden"* to that lie. To wit, a *load of bull.*

THE ALTAR OF SACRIFICE

*"Moreso he made an **altar of brass**, **20 cubits the length**, and **20 cubits the width**, and **10 cubits the height** thereof."*

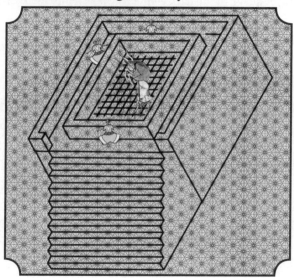

*The **Real Altar** as Outlined in the Bible: Here we symbolized the subduction of the truth within the human-animal during the ages of Taurus the bull and Aries the lamb. The constellations in this image were part of a larger grid series that I excluded for visual effect but fits perfectly within the overall scheme of the Grid System overlay. Our images spared no details.*

The sacrificial timeline continues through the age of Aries, which is appropriately symbolized as the sacrifices of sheep upon the altar. It was during the ages of the bull and the lamb that humanity increasingly forgot its knowledge of the God Element within, thus the *sacrificial* theme. In sync with this also came the gradual subduction of the Super-aurora in the skies above. Both were the result of a progressive overwhelming of the God Element and the positive ionic structure to which it was bonded. The culprit of this was the duo of dark element and negative ionic structure that existed in surplus within the Earth's magnetic field. To this very day the Earth still emits negative ions, but that is soon to change in the upcoming geomagnetic-shift. The last time a shift like this occurred was around 45,000 years ago.

THE TEMPLE PILLARS
THE DNA OF THE DARK ELEMENT

"*Also he made before the house **two pillars** of **thirty and five cubits high**, and the **capital** (or, **block**), that was on the top of them was **five cubits**. And he made **chains** on the heads of the pillars; and made an **hundred pomegranates** (Or, DNA-sequence), and put them **on the chains** (chains display our bondage to the dark element)."* **2 Chronicles 3:15-16**

"*…and the **two bowls** (or, **solstice-sunrises**), of the **capital** that were on the top of the two pillars; and the **two networks, to cover the bowls…nets of checker-work**"* 1 Kings 7:7-41

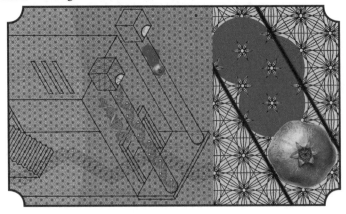

*See the Symbolism of DNA: The rotating "**pomegranates**" (i.e., red/blood) and "nets of checker work" on the brass solstice pillars reflect our knowledge that the satanic element has imprisoned the Atomos within the human DNA. Also, please count the visible, full, pomegranate tips on each pillar; there are exactly 100 (see* **2Chronicles 3:15-16**) *just like the Wisdom Wheel wrote. What? You didn't think we knew about DNA? We did know, and we hid that wisdom deep within our symbolism.*

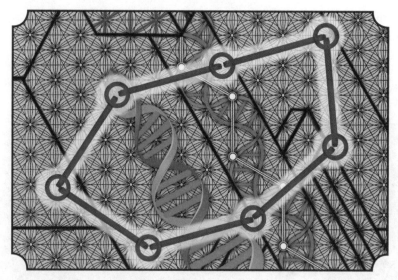

Note how the DNA of the pillar is overlaid with the semblance of ancient chains (see **2Chronicles 3:15-16**), *thus signifying the bondage of the Atomos radiant within. In this case the symbolism of brass displays how the dark element is most readily seen in the brass-colored aurora. And to think that the whole story of God, the fall, and the portal are contained within the Holy Grids.*

At the main entrance to the Temple building was the cubit-count of the front wall, which symbolized the final 600 years of the age of Aries (600BC to 1BC). This was a transitional era in which even the strength of the Element within the magi began to wane somewhat more. It was in this space between the altar and the doors that we portrayed the priests as still-cognitive guides to humanity. It was here that they still labored as keepers of the divine plan, symbolized by their temple duties. According to the implied timeline, only the priests could pass beyond this point, though once inside, they were invisible to the world.

Likewise, all _brass_ items of the Temple including the pillars and its accommodations were located on the _outside of the most Holy Place_, thus symbolizing the extreme influence of the satanic-element up until the end of the age of Pisces. Furthermore, all brass *chains* existed outside of the temple itself, showing an even greater enslavement of the human DNA during that time in history (*chains being a negative symbol*).

The pillars, named Jachin, and Boaz, also acted as alignment poles for the summer and winter solstice, (i.e., *the maximum tilt of the earth brought about by the dark element and thus the closed portal*). Interestingly the Bible details them as having two bowls upon their header-blocks or capitals. Admittedly a bowl has zero-connection to our temple symbolism, that is, unless you realize that, once turned upside down, it represents the image of the sunrise during the solstice... Indeed we loved our literary illusions.

"*...and the <u>two **bowls**</u> (or, **solstice-sunrises**), of <u>the capital</u> that were on the top of the two pillars; and the <u>two networks, to cover the bowls</u>... **<u>nets of checker-work</u>**"*1 Kings 7:7-41

*Here is further evidence of what caused our enslavement to physical **DNA** encoded upon the brass pillars of the temple. The **upside down bowls** on the capitals mimic the solstice-sunrises and thus Earth's greatest tilt, this also being relative to the portal's failure and our bondage to the creature. The Bible doesn't actually say the bowls (see 1Kings 7:7-41) were upside down, but I'm telling you from memory. In fact every facet of the outer Temple was symbolic, including the captive "nets" which further demonstrated our bondage to this world.*

The pillar, the brazen sea and altar images all symbolize our dilemma through the ages of Taurus and Aries that were in question during the writing of 1 Kings and 2 Chronicles. This in no way minimizes the deception of the dark-element in people's lives today however. In fact, during the coming day of separation, its desperation will become even more evident and violent.

Whereas humanity was once merely asleep in the satanic lie, today it will become a dark and obvious rebellion symbolized by the dark ion band that crosses the Holy Oracle room itself. Is this not a day of darkness, even great darkness, with no brightness in it? Yet for the children of light, at the end, *there shall be light*, and our images speak this truth.

THE BAPTISM OF THE HOLY PLACE
THE FIRST AND LARGEST ROOM OF THE TEMPLE

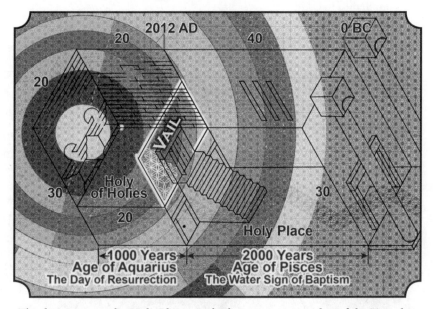

This brings us to the Holy Place, or the large inner corridor of the Temple image. It was here that we symbolized the water sign Age of *Pisces* with its 100 basins of water. It was here, during the last 2,000 years, that the God Element became dormant even within the magi. This was the final death or *"holy sleep,"* the timeline of which we outlined by the cubit count (*2000 cubits*) of the room itself. It is no small accident that the coming of the *"Dark Ages"* in fact coincides with this engineering marvel of the temple.

It was here that the God Element (*represented by the priests within the Holy Place*) would no longer be visible by the mind of the outer creature (*represented by those who were restricted to the outer courts of the temple*). This room measured 40x30 (visible side wall) and 40x20 (visible roof) and contained a total of 2000 cubits (*i.e., 2000 years of Pisces*). Likewise, one must count only the visible outer wall and roof to obtain this prophetic number that was encoded within its dimensions.

An alternate bit of symbolism to comprehend is how the age of Pisces, a water sign, is also the real foundation for the biblical-rite of baptism. Whether we choose to see this time of death as a subduction or submersion matters not; today we understand what the creators of the scriptures intended all along: that indeed the act of submersion or sprinkling of water upon our bodies in and of itself means nothing, but rather symbolizes the real washing of the God Element within us that it would arise anew in the coming age of Aquarius. With this information and with the awakening of the Atomos within us, we see things anew, not as we did in the past, but as the real baptism that the scriptures alluded to in code.

THE VAIL OF OUR UNDERSTANDING

*"And he made the **vail** of **blue, and purple, and crimson**, and **twined linen**, and wrought cherubim thereon."* 2 Chronicle 3:14; also Exodus 26:31

*"But their **minds were blinded**: for **until this day** the **same vail remains** untaken away in the reading of the old testament;* (i.e., the outer understanding of the scriptures) *which vail **is done away in the day of Christ**."* 2 Corinthians 3:14

The vail represents the last remaining separation between our present consciousness and that of our God-identity. The reunion can only occur in the holy room which, according to the cubit/year count, is squarely within this first thousand years of the Age of Aquarius. Remember; the rings of the Wisdom Wheel were constantly rotated to fulfill the various fields of data. Thus at one point come the colors of the vail, and then the golden chains of the oracle room (not brass).

Finally, we come to the oracle room itself. This is the most Holy Place, the _outer_ cubit count of its visible walls and ceiling equal _1,000 years_. This room represents the final leg of the long road to resurrection. It is here, in the _first one-thousand years of the Age of Aquarius_ in where we reawaken to our God identity.

According to the Temple timeline, we presently stand in the doorway of the oracle and before the precipice of the vail itself, this being the approximate date of 2000AD. The vail of course represents the remaining barrier between ourselves and the God-consciousness. Likewise that vail will be parted with two symbolic and simultaneous events: the _left side of the curtain_ with the revelations I was charged to give you, and the _right side of the curtain_ with the onrush of the new God Element as the portal begins to open. It is via these occurrences by which you will understand and remember. It is here we begin our _face-to-face_ covenant with the _Atomos_ within.

Last, know that we are dealing with overlapping symbolism. Thus, by comparing the cubit-counts of the temple imagery along with the various items and/or miracles mentioned, we can also discern the timeline that they represent and occur. Thus the _"third day resurrection"_ of Jesus and the _Ark of the Covenant_ are telling the exact same story and timeline albeit with different outer symbolism.

THE REAL
THE ARK OF THE COVENANT

"And they shall make an ark of shittim wood: **two cubits and a half shall be the length**, and a **cubit and a half the width**, and a **cubit and a half the height**." Exodus 25:10

"And in the most holy house he made two **cherubim** of **image work** (drawn), and overlaid them with gold." 2 Chronicles 3:10

"And the priests brought in the ark **into the oracle of the house, to the most holy place, under the wings of the cherubim**. For the cherubim spread forth their two wings over the place of the ark, and the cherubim covered the ark and the staves. And they **drew out the staves** that they were seen in the **main hall of the Temple**, and they **were not seen without**: and there they are unto this day." 1 Kings 8:6-8

THE ICON

*The magi had an acute understanding of how to control one's imagination, thus we created a physical-ark in order to inspire awe from our congregations. It had absolutely **no** special powers other than what it did to people's minds through fear.*

THE REAL ARK

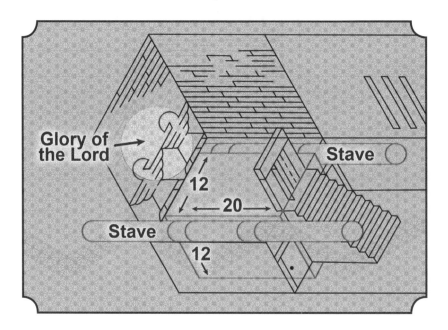

Raid This: *The real Ark of the Covenant* was a mathematical-illusion of the Grid System and is described in Exodus 25:10. The center white dot of the Wisdom Wheel symbolizes the positive ion-band that holds the now dormant "Glory of the Lord" (i.e., the God Element or *Atomos*) within the real Ark that you are. This is the DNA of the new creation that will begin to awaken in the first 1,000 years of the Age of Aquarius, aka, the day of resurrection. In a grand literary illusion, the ark-measurements of *2 ½ x 1 ½ x 1 ½ cubits* (see Exodus 25:10) are to be *multiplied by 8* to achieve the 20x12x12 smaller cubits of which it is comprised. (see next image for details). Same measurement, -different scale.

This placement of the image of the Ark of the Covenant within the Holy Place was one of our greatest literary illusions. Thus the Holy Place and the Ark were not separate items but one and the same. The only difference between them was the cubit-scale used in their outer description. It was an 8 to 1 ratio.

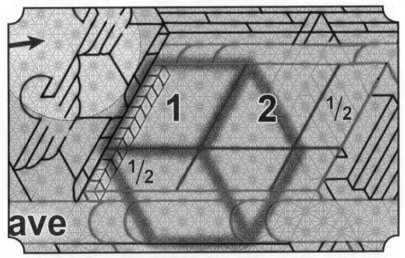

Count the Cubits: The *real Ark of the Covenant* was an image built upon an 8-to-1 ratio of the smaller cubits of the temple. This in turn scaled the diagram to fit **perfectly** within the innermost holy room of the temple-image. In another sleight of Word, the Bible never actually says that the cherubim of the Mercy Seat were part of the Ark itself, but rather were; "above the ark." Thus the implied cherubim of the Ark were in fact the *same* cherubim of the oracle. By reading the Bible literally it sounds as though the Ark is much smaller in proportion to the room, when in fact it was the *exact same size*. Again, count the lines for yourself and you will see how we scaled the image.

Though we did produce a physical Ark as an article of faith to which the people could relate, it had no special powers and in no way held the presence of God. Basically it was nothing more than a powerless icon of gold and wood. The real Ark as described in the Bible was the image I have shown you. Yet even our pictorial is symbolic of the container that you are. *You* are the one and only Ark of God, and that is the answer to the mystery we tried to show you all along.

Dare I point out to the reader the coincidence that, on your computer, *1 bit* equals *8 bytes* of data? Likewise we too designed 8 cubits of the Temple into 1 cubit of the Ark. I could tell you more, but I won't: It's another one of those things for which humanity isn't quite ready to hear. *Small Steps* my friend, *Small Steps*. Yet the entire mystery is hidden within the diagram of the Temple.

THE CITY OF JERUSALEM

"And the gates of the city (Jerusalem) *shall be after the names of the 12 tribes of Israel:"* **Ezekiel 48:31**

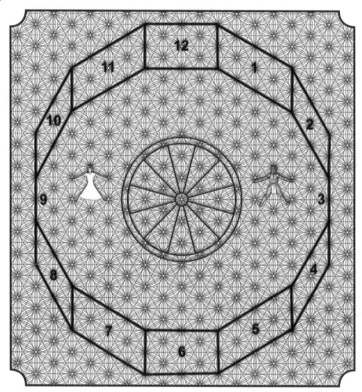

The Jerusalem Scroll *included the same exact information as the Temple scroll yet was scaled differently. The Word spelled the dimensions of this pictorial city for us as well as a different outer story than that of the Temple, yet their wave-patterns and effect were identical.*

Our schematic of the city of Jerusalem was massive and required 12 complete master scrolls to contain its many circles and cycles. Each of these scrolls represented 12 huge cycles that inventory the entire timeline, stretching from our ancient fall (Jerusalem's destruction) until now. Likewise, the rebuilding of Jerusalem, aka the *New Jerusalem,* is presently under symbolic construction in this era of resurrection. Remember, the Bible is not referencing a real city in Israel, but a symbolic city that outlines the cycles of the Grid System. This timeline is discussed in more detail in the following chapters.

That said, the image of Jerusalem as described in the Old Testament was never drawn in its entirety. It was simply too large and, as you may have noticed, was never actually detailed within the scriptures. We did portray certain facets of this artistic town, however, for our own entertainment, a few of which I have provided. What is described by the Wisdom Wheel is that Jerusalem contained either four walls per the books of Revelation and Ezekiel, or even a hypothetic *12* walls as implied by its 12 gates. What's more there is an astounding facet to the New Jerusalem that I will reveal in a separate work.

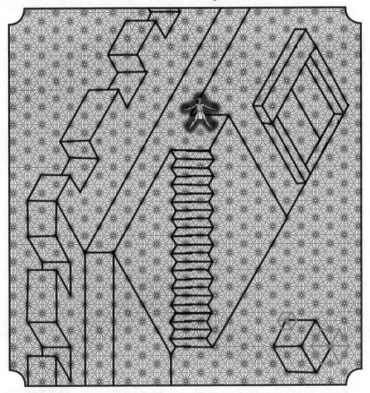

The line-data of Jerusalem as described within the Bible shows the walls, the blocks with which it was built, the gates, etc. It was never a real city but an image of the grids.

The Real
Noah's Ark
Image#1 Revealing the Code
And the Great Flood of the Grid System

So you had to ask: The image of Noah's Ark is not only one of my favorites but also one of the most profound pictorials of the entire Bible. We told a story therein, one that is far more in-depth than that of the literal or outward tale could ever accomplish. As with all of our images, the larger Ark diagram was drawn using both a seven- and/or twenty-four grid series.

Similar to the Master series of the Temple and Jerusalem, Noah's Ark also comprised thousands of individual sub-cycles. These of course were drawn separately on a very long scroll. Likewise it was this massive amount of line data that gave us the Ark's rectangular dimensions (*in cubits*) that are listed in the Bible. Let's go then; let's begin with the verses that describe this famous ark:

"*And God said unto **Noah** … Make thee an **ark** of gopher wood; rooms shalt thou make in the ark, and shalt **pitch** (tar) it within and without with pitch.*"

"*And this is the fashion which thou shalt make it of: The **length of the ark shall be three hundred cubits** (300), the **breadth** of it **fifty cubits** (50), and the **height** of it **thirty cubits** (30).*"

"*A **window** shalt thou make to the ark, and in a cubit shalt thou finish it above; and the **door of the ark shalt thou set in the side** thereof; with **lower, second, and third stories** shalt thou make it.*"

The magi were masters of literary illusions. This is the Ark in which we needed you to believe in yet never actually existed.

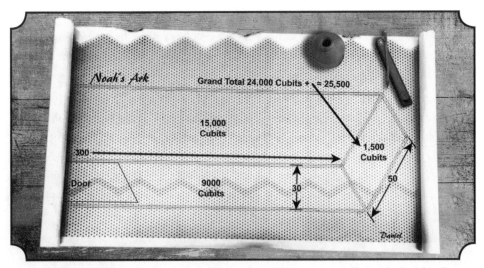

*The Real Ark of Noah: The safety of Noah's Ark was in the size of the implied cycles that we encoded within its dimensions. The Wisdom Wheel concluded that the necessary minimal Earth tilt angle to open the portal was **23.02°** which creates a **25,500** year wobble cycle. This is the exact number of cubits in the image of Noah's Ark. The Mayans did their math as well and concluded it was **23.30°**. The Earth presently tilts at **23.44°** and is rapidly decreasing. Either way, we are almost there. Again, the Wisdom Wheel was miraculous.*

You may notice some rather *"goofah"* parallels between Noah's Ark, the Grid System and the primitive *goofah crafts* of the Middle East. Pronounced *koofahs*, the appearance of these river craft closely resemble the thousands of zodiac grids that comprise the image of Noah's Ark on the scroll. Genesis 6:14 specifically states that the Ark was to be constructed of *gopher, or **goofah wood**,* which is not an actual type of wood but rather the **reeds** from which the goofah crafts themselves are framed.

The concept of course is simple: We merely observed the design similarities between the goofahs and the zodiac, thereby formatting the imagery. Furthermore when the hundreds of sub-cycles within Noah's master grid are combined, the biblical dimensions of the Ark begin to emerge. Here the grids produce a single large 3-D celestial boat which measures ***300 x 50 x 30 cubits*** per the dimensions given in Genesis. Therein are three, 10-cubit-tall decks along with the many rooms according to verse description. **_Make no mistake, this is the one and only Ark of Noah_**. _There was none other; it was always a creation of our Grid System_.

Perhaps the most undeniable evidence however, are the *exacting numbers* that connect our science to the Bible flood-story. Numbers are the *nail in the coffin,* so to speak, that the real ark of the flood was not physical, nor historical, *but pictorial*. Accordingly, if one counts the total number of 3-D *cubits* within the *visible image* of the top and side of Noah's Ark, it equals **24,000**. By no coincidence this is also the number of years in a perfect *grand precession of the equator*.

Add to that the remaining cubits of the 30x50 front section of the Ark and you get a total of **25,500** (years). This final number is relevant to Earth's wobble and represents a maximum tilt by which the portal can still function. The present rate of the precession of the ecliptic is **25,920** years, but once it reaches a rate of 25,500, the portal will open and the Atomos within us will resurrect. The story of Noah's flood told us this information in code: that we would be safe within an *"ark"* or *"cycle"* of this size—*get it?*

The dimensions of the Ark's door, though unmentioned in the scriptures, is in fact 25 cubits tall and 40 cubits wide. This of course equals the 1,000 cubits or *years* of the resurrection day. Symbolically this is the timeline by which we may enter through the portal and the safety that awaits us on the other side. In this particular story, that rescue is attained via the Ark's landing atop the mountain of Ararat.

Last, if one adds the beginning and end dates of the flood mentioned in Genesis 7:11 to Gen.8:13, it involves a total of **354 days**, or ***exactly one lunar year***. If one were to then add the final **11 days** of verse14, the total number comes to **365 days** or ***exactly one solar year***! This is verification in itself that the story of the celestial flood contains information relative to both lunar and solar cycles. Noah's Ark was a lesson in science all along and we put it there in plain sight. We knew, however, that the day would come in which your understanding could accept these truths.

THE ANIMALS OF THE ARK
THE REAL NOAH'S ARK IMAGE #2

"thou shalt come into the ark, *thou, and thy* **sons, and thy wife, and thy sons' wives** *with thee."* Genesis 6-8

"Of every **clean beast** *thou shalt take to thee* **by sevens, the male and his female;** *and* **beasts** *that are* **not clean** *by* **two, the male and his female."** Genesis 7:

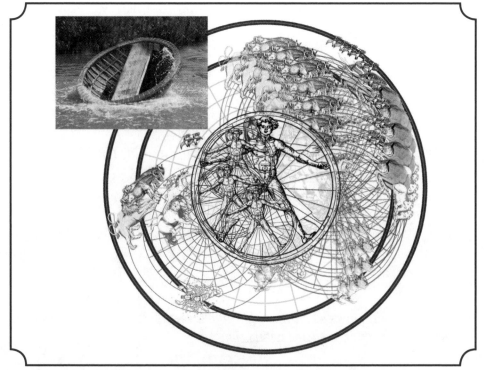

The __Real__ Noah's Ark Image#2: In the simplistic, single large grid of Noah and the Ark are, in fact, the content of males and females by sevens and twos that fulfill the real truth of Genesis 7. The animals were constellations. It was not a history story.

Wonderful! Now you can tell your friends that you've seen the real Noah's Ark! Yet now we must also fill this celestial cruise-liner with animals. This is phase 2 of Noah's Ark and represents the artistic image of the larger grids as it concerns the figurines of Noah, his wife, his sons, and their wives, as well as the constellation animals of each grid.

The Bible states that the creatures entered the Ark by **twos** and by **sevens**. Thus the seven *"clean"* animals of course were an artistic creation of the clean male and female grids that we also placed in the temple courtyard. As you have seen, this correlation of seven is found repetitively in the Bible and describes everything from the **seven** candlestick menorah to the **seven** demons that were cast from Mary Magdalene (see chapter XII), as well as countless other examples.

Because there are seven grids in this arrangement, there were likewise seven sets of zodiac animals contained therein. For example, there were __seven__ *Leo the lions*, __seven__ *Aries the Lambs*, etc. Similar to the example of Adam and Eve in which both the male and female grid constructs were directly superimposed, likewise Noah's Ark also requires *two complete grid series*: one of which includes a male figurine or *"Noah"* and the other that includes a female figurine or *"Noah's wife"* (see image).

Meanwhile the *"unclean"* animals were the exact same constellations as those portrayed in the seven peripheral grids, but as they aligned within the Earth's wobble grids. Wobble was a bad or *"unclean"* thing in our science. Accordingly, the zodiac-animals of these grid-series were likewise engendered and described in the Bible as

*"**beasts** that are **not clean** by **two, the male and his female**."*

Finally, by adding the figurines of Noah's *sons* and *daughters-in-law*, we can complete the family unit of the story. So now you can see that Noah's Ark was in fact a celestial yacht. The rest of the symbolism is there to be found within the grids of both image #1 and #2 of Noah's Ark, including the *"fountains of the great deep"* and the *"windows of heaven"* and even the *"pitch"* or tar with which Noah's ark was covered. It's all there and I challenge you to find the details.

There is so much more than what I have shared, yet hopefully you will find the answers yourself. ***The one and only ark of the Bible was in fact comprised of grids and constellations—nothing more and nothing less.***

The Mountains of Ararat

Similar to the Ark of the Covenant, people are also looking in the wrong place for this relic of biblical lore. The expeditions have been endless, of course, and in the end nothing will ever be found on the mountains of Ararat, which the Bible claims is the resting place of Noah's Ark. That's because, like most biblical items, Noah's Ark ***never*** existed beyond the pictorials of the Grid System. Allow me to show you what we did and why we mentioned Ararat in the scriptures.

BEGINNING DATE OF THE SYMBOLICAL FLOOD

We designed the Hebrew calendar to begin in the sign of Scorpio. By counting forward this in turn delegates the sign of *Sagittarius* as the *"2nd month"* mentioned in the story of Noah's flood (see Genesis 7:11).

*"In the 600th year of Noah's life, in the **2nd month, the 17th day** of the month, the same day were all the fountains of the great deep broken up, and the windows of heaven were opened.":*

Good. Now we have a starting point for Noah's flood within the Grid System maps. However, knowing that the 2nd month of the Wheel is Scorpio in turn designates the sign of ***Taurus*** as the "***7th month***" of Genesis 8:4, which consequently aligns on the map with the great ***Mountains of Ararat*** and at approximately the *17th degree* or, as we labeled in the verse, *the 17th day*.

DATE FOR THE END OF THE FLOOD

*"And the **ark** rested in the **7th month**, on the **17th day** of the month, upon the **mountains of Ararat**"* Genesis 8:4.

The accuracy of these alignments are phenomenal, and yes, we actually surveyed that entire mountainous region of Ararat—not that it matters as the Word itself spelled these verses verbatim and located them on the map for us as well. Do that with your GPS.

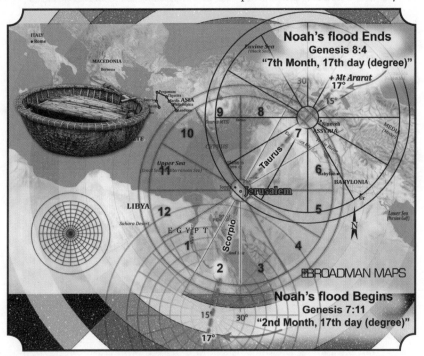

Mount Ararat by the Book*: The Bible outlines the takeoff and landing sight of Noah's artistic ark upon our maps. It wasn't a real boat on a real mountain but instead a grid on our map. Mount Ararat just so happened to coincide with the end point of Noah's story as written by the Wisdom Wheel, and so we used its location as a pointer on the map. It is no more complicated than that.*

In the final analysis however, the massive symbolism that is associated with the flood story tells us of the opening of the portal (*"windows of heaven," Genesis 7:11; Joel 2:23*). In the end, it is a flood of incoming dimensional energy, the *mighty Atomos*, which will destroy the mind that we now have. The lie to which we are now prisoner, will *be eliminated*. The wisdom therefore is to detach before it is too late and to re attach to our new identities as God beings. This process cannot be faked as so many attempt, but must be from a true heart and undefiled.

THE BOW IN THE CLOUD

*"I do set my **bow in the cloud**, and it shall be for a token of a covenant between me and the earth."* Genesis 9:13-16 (see The *Great Wheel of God,"* clouds)

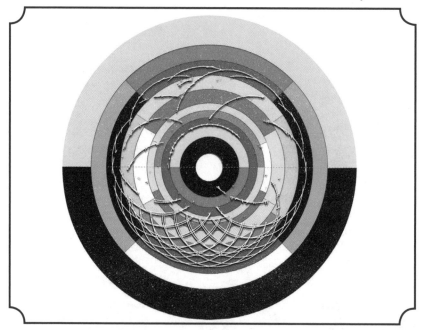

And someday soon, my friend, you too will find that somewhere over the rainbow of God, far, far above the clouds, is a land that you have heard of. The light of that dimension is more real, more vibrant, and more passionate than anything you have ever experienced. It may have been written as a lullaby, a simple mythology, but *there* every dream of which I've told you will certainly come true forever and ever. The path is believing, and the portal, a bridge, but on the other side is eternal life. Indeed, it is the real covenant between Heaven and Earth.

The Magistrates

"Put them in mind to be subject to principalities and powers, to obey **magistrates**" Titus 3:1 *...but of course...*

Admittedly Titus 3:1 is a self-serving verse; but again, we did what we had to do. What it does show, however, is our seat of power within ancient Israel. Likewise, not only was the Temple in Jerusalem the religious epicenter of that nation, but it was also the building from which we ran our theocracy over the Israelites.

Therein the chief magistrate was more powerful than even the high-priest, who himself was largely a figurehead. Basically we operated a shadow government that retained power in all matters of significance while delegating trivial matters to those of the lower echelon. Make no mistake, however; we pulled the strings of our puppet governments. Though the lesser priests dealt with the daily legal affairs of the people, the governing laws were in fact designed by the magistrates according to the imagery of the Grid System.

As Titus 3:1 indicates, this arrangement was normal in Israel, at least until an invading army, such as the Babylonians, Greeks, or Romans took control. Yet even the Greeks and Romans allowed for local issues to be handled through the Temple magistrates, aka *the magi*. Ultimately this worked well for both the people and ourselves; it gave them social order and gave us a bridle for their voice boxes.

We established this power for the good of all and in an effort to reopen the portal. Admittedly, had the task been left to humans, our objectives would have disintegrated. The evidence of this rests in the moral decay of our modern cultures. For humans, authority is quickly abused; but for the magi, these religious institutions were a focused means to an end.

Israel housed a massive religious infrastructure. This included everything from the Temple complex itself all the way down to innumerable synagogues, all of which the magi designed. As with every country we ruled, this also created the foundation for a huge tax base. Unlike today, in which churches are untaxed, our system of taxation was channeled directly through the theocracy we built.

The difference is that *then* theocracies were acceptable and absolutist. We ruled with an iron hand in which *"morality"* was tied directly to religious and social obedience. In contrast, todays governments have lost that grip and are only too glad to have some medium by which to curb social decay. Churches, synagogues, temples and mosques are that means to an end. Considering the mass exodus from churches in Western countries, it is well worth _not_ taxing these institutions as they help to maintain social behaviors.

No doubt our theocracies accumulated enormous wealth. Thus my criticism of many modern religious institutions may at first seem hypocritical, as we too became filthy rich in the name of God. Indeed we had serval tools that helped us to this end, primarily through religious taxation, but also by selling and reselling the herds of sacrificial animals required of our congregations. We knew that these sacrifices in no way brought atonement for sins, that they were only representative of the zodiac animals. However, seeing as people would never understand the depth of that information, they at least set the symbolic example and made money in the process. We in fact hoarded huge numbers of livestock that were also sold on the meat market or even traded in bulk to other countries.

During the required times of mass sacrifice, there was a limit on how long one could stay within the courtyards of the temple. People were required to cycle through on a circular pattern, beginning on one side only to shortly exit on the other. This too was modeled from the spin-direction of the earth and thus the spin cycles of the Grid System.

Better yet, not only did this mimic the movement of the heavens, but it also kept people from seeing what we actually did with their sacrificial purchases. I can assure you that only a token few animals were sacrificed, and even then it was common knowledge that the priesthood routinely enjoyed that meat. That said even a meager 2 percent of the total animal count was still a lot to process and burn/cook. I will say that having grilled lamb and beef everyday wasn't all bad.

Greater yet were the *"tithes"* or 10 percent income tax, required by the scriptures. Add to that the surplus of treasury gifts and you begin to get a picture of our massive wealth. That said, my favorite sacrifice of all were the libations of *wine*, lots of wine, the requirement of which was conveniently outlined within the Bible. Thank you, Wisdom Wheel, for writing those verses.

Unlike today, however, seldom was this surplus used for the sake of our individual wealth. The magi themselves required little of this world. Instead, our revenue was typically used for trade, peace, expansion of our religious constructs, and the propagation of the Word. We saved money too, just in case it became needed during famine, war, etc. But the whole point of having, saving, or spending was to organize human cultures to the end of harnessing their voices by which to open the portal. So money was used as a simple tool, a means to an end by which to get home—nothing more and nothing less. Ultimately we used it for the good of the Atomos that was imprisoned within the human creature.

My Brethren

Two of the great magistrates who brought civilization to what is now the Middle East and the Mediterranean were **Akhenaten** and **Hermes**. Akhenaten's name was derived from the <u>**Anunnaki**</u>, our kinsmen in Babylonia. There his name was **Aku**, which even modern history attributes as a god of that culture.

Like all of the original magi, both of these magicians came from the *"place of descent,"* an area just north of the Fertile Crescent. By agreement, however, Hermes settled the region of Greece and became a master at writing magic. There he produced the great mythologies of the Greek gods and goddesses, chronicled in the <u>Odyssey</u> and the <u>Iliad</u>. Though many attribute these works to the poet **Homer,** it was in fact Hermes who wrote them as well as the <u>Emerald Tablet</u>. The latter work also alludes, *in code*, to the significance of the sun as the father and the moon as the mother of portal function. I encourage you to read it.

Meanwhile Aku organized the empire of ancient Egypt. This was the edge of productive civilization on the African continent. The Nile, similar to the Euphrates in Babylonia, afforded Aku the physical characteristics required by which to build a successful human culture. His accomplishments were spectacular too and are still seen today in the form of the mighty Egyptian pyramids.

Human's typically named us of course, according to the local gibberish they spoke; *Aku* became *Akhenaten* and eventually <u>*Amen-ho-tep*</u> which was actually the name of several magi. Likewise to the Jews I was **Daniel**, but to the Babylonians, **Belteshazzar,** which literally meant *"keeper of the hidden treasures."* Hermes too was renamed as **Thoth** upon this travels to Egypt.

Two of the Great Magistrates: <u>Akhenaten</u> *and* <u>Hermes Trismegistus</u>. *As with all angelic half-breeds, they were easy to find in a crowd, being both taller than average and with the iconic elongated head. Notice the portals in both images as well as the tilted globe held by Hermes. Also note the serpents around the staff in the image (right). This mystery will be revealed in the next chapter. The sleeping man tells the tale of humanity's blissful ignorance to our secrets. They had no idea.*

That the magi honored one another is indisputable. We were a team and worked to secure the mouthpiece of mankind. Indeed, it was by Hermes's suggestion that I changed the Wisdom Wheel's alphabet from Hebrew to Greek at the time of Alexander the Great's conquest. Also note that every Jewish and Christian prayer of the Holy Bible ends with *"Amen"*, in honor of my brother from Egypt: *Amen-ho-tep*. As with all of the original magi, what we spoke became reality, thus *"Amen"* became synonymous with God-faith as in *"speak it, believe it, and it shall be,"* making the perfect end-phrase for the perfect words of the Bible.

What began as a concerted effort, however, would later implode into disarray. After eons of being trapped here on Earth and with the weakening of the element within, most of the original magi caved to the lusts of the flesh. Indeed, several of them took on the distraction of wives who in turn bore them children. Though these offspring showed the physical features of their fathers in height and skull elongation, they were yet well short of the original intellect.

Greed of wealth and comfort also crept into their minds, as did a wrongly placed lust for control by which to gain the temporal pleasure of this world.

> "For many generations...they loved the divine to which they were akin...they reckoned the qualities of character more important than their present prosperity. Thus they bore the burden of wealth and possessions lightly, and did not let their high standard of living intoxicate them or make them lose their self-control...But when the divine element in them became weakened...and their human traits became predominant, they ceased to be able to carry their prosperity with moderation." —Plato, Timaeus

Things only worsened as the number of original magi died out and were replaced with the second string human priests that we trained to take our place. Unfortunately, while these fill-ins understood the literary outer dogma of our traditions, they were seldom able to articulate the depth of the underlying science. As a result came the corruption of that for which we so diligently labored.

With this also came a predictable yet regrettable enmity between us who remained and these superficial, plastic personalities. This is the very reason I left the Jewish temple to begin with: *greed and self-interest* within the priesthood that I could no longer control. It was bad in that even the high priests themselves became nothing more than hacks within the Jewish political machine.

Finally my own safety became a concern as they insisted upon abusing the Temple's treasures for purely personal gain. They were nothing more than typical humans: *murderers, wolves in sheep's clothing, dark-angels* with dark interests, and they resented, through their teeth, my presence. It was critical therefore that I stay cognitive as long as possible in order to oversee the direction of the Book, and so I fled.

Though I realized my own sleep would occur in the coming age of Pisces, it would only be worse to be killed sooner rather than later. Thus my best option at the time was to avoid the human priesthood and simply let it self-destruct—and so it did too.

Before this time, however, the design and construction of the temple in Jerusalem was of my own making. Obviously the urge to reflect astronomy within its design was irresistible. We did so in a way that no one, not even the Jewish high priests, would suspect—not to marvel, for similar features were hidden within the symmetry of every ancient temple of magi design. Once noted, they are obvious:

- *A 12 section grid at the center of the Women's Court to represent lunar cycles* **(but the folks didn't know that's what in meant)**

- *A 24 section grid at the center of the Men's Court to represent sun cycles.* **(but the folks didn't know that's what it meant)**

- *The width of the inner Temple courtyard was built to mimic the band of the ecliptic* **(This was the 20° outer band of the zodiac upon which the sun, moon, Venus, and Mercury appear to travel.)**

- *-12 loaves of round showbread that represented the Sun within the inner circles of the grids.* **(but the folks didn't know that's what it meant)**

- *A huge curtain that hung in front of the Temple's main doors was embroidered with a map of the world that we had overlaid with both the zodiac and its 12 signs as well as an artistic creation of clouds that was derived from the Grid System.* **(but the folks didn't know that's what it meant)**

- *Trumpets and* **musical-instruments** *mimicked their design from the Grid System.*

- *Temple* **artifacts** *designed from the Grid System and made of silver, gold, bronze, etc. to represent either lunar, solar or aurora cycles.* **(but the folks didn't know that it meant)**

- *12 gates* to match the 12 houses of the zodiac

- *Temple orientation* to the sunrise during the Equinox

- Relative **astrological values** represented by the number of steps between the women's and men's court as well as those that led to the main structure.

- An **altar** set at the east of the main house to represent the symbolic sacrifice of the ages of Taurus and Aries **(oxen and lamb)**. The altar's location was thus symbolic that those ages would not advance into the revelation of God's glory, which symbolically occurred farther within the Temple. (**The humans missed this one too.**)

- **The Nicanor Gate** acted as a daily sunrise sighting device as viewed by the high priest from the porch of the Temple each morning. Its left and right edges marked the summer and winter solstice sunrises as did the inverted "V" in its middle that pointed to the equinox sunrise.

- -Finally, the **4 pillars** built into the front of the 2nd Temple give the relative sunrise-angles both presently and after the Paradise alignment as viewed from the control point at the rear of the Temple's roof. (**I think it's safe to say that the folks wouldn't have known this one either.**)

- etc., etc., etc...

To the unlearned rabble of humanity, the Temple art and artifacts reflected only the simplest of traditions and applications. For me however, the religious complex was a means by which to measure, create, and emit the perfect frequencies of God. Yet I would be amiss not to tell you that I often grinned at my insider's knowledge of these things.

It seemed a pity to deceive humans to the extent to which we did; however, it was a necessary means to an end in order to accomplish the resurrection of the God Element. Without the deception it would have been impossible to get humans to repeat the scriptures. Ultimately the human experience without the resurrection was doomed anyway, so in the end it didn't matter. We did what we had to do.

Likewise, teaching our profound spiritual and scientific truths to most humans was like talking to a brick wall. We all know that feeling, right? Superstition existed in highly lethal doses during ancient times and still does: Remember, *ignorance breeds superstition and superstition* <u>*kills*</u> *that which it fails to understand!* Superstition is based on a lack of wisdom and understanding; it is a trait that *all* humans share, for even an atheist lives and dies without true comprehension of their disbelief. While organized religion often misconstrues the facts of God, the unbeliever likewise mistakenly

317

believes they are only human. Either way, ignorance of the truth is an enemy. Therefore, ask for wisdom, understanding, and the knowledge of God.

Ignorance is a lethal trait that forced us to hide our science: keeping our knowledge secret kept us safe. Thus our priesthoods needed a private location to develop and record our observations, a *secret place* for a *secret knowledge,* free from the risk of discovery. Clearly, what better place than the solitude of the Temple's inner sanctums?

THE MAGIC TRICK OF THE TEMPLE
THE MYSTERY BEHIND THE "SHEKINAH GLORY"

There was yet an equally ingenious virtue to the construction of the physical temple in Jerusalem. Through crafty design features, we created an illusion that the *"Glory of God"* had actually descended upon this structure. In so-doing, we made fearful believers as well as faithful followers of our congregations.

It began by orienting the Temple's doorways *due-east* toward the sunrise of the spring and fall equinox. As the sun arose on those days, the Israelites were already gathered within their appropriate courts, eagerly awaiting the promise that God would descend upon His *"chosen people."* Looking westward, the worshipers could see the High Priest standing upon the Temple-porch as if to inspect the people below. Yet it was not the suspenseful crowd that he examined but the sun itself as it arose in the east and just above the Nicanor Gate.

On the high-priest's cue, a brigade of musicians sounded from atop the Temple's walls, playing upon the tuned-acoustics of the complex. This, of course, provided the sensationalism and hype, *the chill bumps,* as 120 trumpeters summoned the arrival of almighty God. However, within the *seemingly empty* sanctuary were other priests who, unbeknownst to the spectators outside, readied incense trays with smoke-producing bitumen or *"pitch."* This of course was the thick ground-hugging fog, or *"cloud of God,"* that would further mystify the performance.

As the sun neared its portal of alignment, the high priest would raise his hands, sending a hush upon the crowd and thereby signaling the priests within to smolder the fires. After a few brief but utterly silent moments, smoke began to billow from beneath the threshold of the Temple's doors, *eerily* creeping across the porch and down the steps of the inner court.

Then, as the huge doors were opened, a magnificent beam of sunlight burst upon the polished gold overlay of the building's inner walls, floor, and ceiling. The display was nearly blinding. The Bible speaks of this event within its metaphoric code, giving the unsuspecting reader the illusion of a divine-miracle. See Ezekiel 43:4; 10:3; 2 Chronicles 5:13-14;

*"And the **glory of the Lord came into the house by way of the gate whose prospect is toward the east"*** The reflected light of the Sun shined through the East -'Nicanor'-Gate and into the Temple.

*"...and the **cloud** (Bitumen smoke/symbolic of the appearance of the Milky Way) **filled the inner court"***

*"It came to pass, as the **trumpeters** and **singers** were as one, to **make one sound to be heard** in praising and thanking the Lord; and when they **lifted up** (Or loud for effect) **their voice with the trumpets** and **cymbals** and **instruments of music**, and praised the Lord..."*

*"...then the **house was filled with a cloud** (Bitumen smoke)..."*

*"So that the **priests could not stand to minister** (They were acting) by reason of the **cloud** (Bitumen smoke); for the **glory of the Lord** (The light of the Sun) **had filled the house** of God."*(Reflected light filled the temple)

The Magic Trick of the Temple: *The indwelling of God was symbolized during the equinoxes within both the Solomon and 2nd Temples. Using a due-east alignment of the temples and reflective-mechanics, we mimicked portal function during those days. Though our congregations believed it literally, it was merely a pictorial of what would one day happen within as the Earth re-aligned, the portal opened, and in all those who remembered and believed.*

It was a breathtaking effect of intense golden light mixed with smoke and the deafening blast of trumpets. Yet adding to this powerful image was the high priest himself, bowing in pretended subservience before the open corridor and the *"power of God."* Our spellbound worshipers never made the connection between the *"glory of the Lord"* and the Temple's reflective mechanics, especially since sunrise had occurred nearly an hour before the seemingly miraculous event. And though we knew the *trick behind the treat*, our creative light show spoke symbolically of a profound truth.

It may be difficult to believe the level of gullibility in ancient cultures, but one must consider the overwhelming lack of education that existed then. Sadly, even today it happens. In Afghanistan, for example, a greedy entrepreneur buried light bulbs just under the soil of Al-Qaeda graves, after which he promoted the illuminated mounds as *"glowing spirits of the dead."* These no doubt had *"magical healing powers,"* the legend of which quickly spread, thus attracting thousands of locals who appeared in droves to receive blessings—*for a small fee, of course!*

The *light-bulb trick* is nearly identical to the *"glowing-Temple trick."* These were the cards with which the magi were dealt: a <u>highly-superstitious society</u> in which the average person had *little* or *no* formal schooling. Similar to Afghanistan, the majority of citizens in ancient Israel were also *sheepherders, basket weavers, stonecutters,* and *farmers,* most of whom could not read or write. Beyond their basic daily routine, these people knew very few things.

We tried to show you the truth knowing that you would one day see, yet were oblivious to these truths that reside within. We did what we had to in order to focus their mouths and minds in an effort to open our star gate. And though the days of temple magic are long gone, the scriptures we wrote are still alive and working as intended.

More importantly, however, is the example of the Shekinah glory and the message of the temple symbolism. <u>God doesn't sit in buildings of stone</u>, that is, unless we consider that humanity's heart itself has become proverbial rock that has hardened against the truth. Either way, He resides in *you*, yes, **you**, the real temple of the living God. His fire remains unstirred, a mere ember of recollections, yet will be awakened into a fire of transformation as we return to the Paradise Alignment.

One final note: Imagine for a moment a famous character who lived 200 years ago. George Washington, for example, is a real historical person, yet if his story was laced with <u>12</u> pioneers who traveled the wilderness of America, you likely wouldn't be able to validate that story as encoded astronomy or fact. Likewise, we also sprinkled the stories of the Bible with an element of historical authenticity to produce something that was undetectable.

Miraculously, however, the name of several real-life individuals had parallel characters within the Bible. These people were mentioned by the Wisdom Wheel often just beyond the time of their earthly existence. **Herod**, for example, though a real client-king of Rome, was also the name of a figurine in the Bible, though with little historic authenticity of that man.

But who would know the difference in, *let's say*, 100AD, about someone who died over a century before? *They wouldn't know*, especially since the Roman records of early Christianity weren't even written until almost 300 years after the proposed occurrences.

Other biblical characters such as Jesus, the 12 apostles, Paul, etc., were non-existent in human form yet their names and plots were still spelled from the magic of the Wisdom Wheel. To the point: even biblical scholars will admit that the Book of Daniel was written 300 years after the era of Babylonian captivity in which his story was staged. Thus it is impossible to prove or disprove that long ago, whether or not the individual even lived, much less whether they did the things for which they are credited via an encoded book of portal technology. The Word itself however, formed these illusions in order to hide our science from misuse.

Whether or not Daniel was a real person or not is beside the point, but rather the role play of the figurine *named* Daniel in tracking the disposition of our science. That said, my forte was as an interpreter of the secrets of God, the discerner of the signs and the penman of His divine magic. Likewise my primary function now is to tell you these secrets to the end that you may awake, to see that our identities should not be based upon incorrect historical and religious lineage but rather in who we are Omni-present as God-beings.

The Jewish Bible was compiled during the 1st Temple period from about 1,000BC up until its destruction by the Babylonians. Upon the construction of the 2nd Temple however, we continued writing books until about 250BC. The Christian Scriptures were likewise processed within the 2nd Temple, and were the result of new input primers as well as the influence of the 24-letter Greek alphabet. However, in defiance to Rome's band of Judaism after 70AD, I continued writing in hiding.

The resurrection scriptures were a perfect extension of the original Hebrew Scriptures or *Old Testament,* yet we distributed these outside of Israel and beyond Roman control. Likewise, the Jewish population was entrenched in their religious dogma and largely rejected this new change in doctrine. Though the scriptural change was prophesied within the Jews' own scriptures, it was difficult for them to accept the transition. Like **_all_** humans, their minds were like flint: hardened against anything that disrupted the box in which they lived.

We did manage to distribute these new scriptures among the non-Jewish populations, as far away as Egypt, Italy, and even the area of present-day Turkey. Though many copies were destroyed throughout the years, enough survived to create what is, today, the _New Testament_. But we didn't do all this work for humans—neither Jews, Christians, Muslims, Hindu, or otherwise—but for the Atomos within.

So the day of your understanding is dawning. The light is beginning to reveal that which was kept from you. Everything I have provided you, these images, are for that purpose and to that end: that you may shed the feeble beliefs of humanity's youth and move on to the things of maturity. You will find that the God Element is real, that He is not a myth, that He is real, and that even the Almighty has a method to His ways. In this day, we must put aside the darkened glass of our understanding in order to see the truth of who you really are. You must come face to face with the reality of your eternal-self.

Equally important is your contribution upon reading the scriptures, that you are actually helping yourself to reach eternity. Indeed, a magic spell that is written but unspoken is of no use. The _Word_ truly is the power of God Almighty. ☺

"When I was a child, I spoke as a child, I understood as a child, I thought as a child: but when I became a man, I put away childish things. For now we see through a glass, darkly; but then face to face: now I know in part; but then shall I know even as also I am known." 1 Corinthians 13:10-13

"And the **great dragon** was cast out, that **old serpent**, called the **Devil and Satan** who deceives the whole world; he was cast out **into the earth**...."
Revelation 12:9 fig.1

XI

DAY OF THE FALLEN
The Covering Cherub and the Lion of the
Tribe of Judah

This next revelation is perhaps unpleasant to the meek as it is the dark side of things. I tell you not out of desire but obligation. As I've said before, this is the day of revelation, and unsettling as it may be, evil is also something to be understood in its fullest capacity. In order to fight and defeat your enemy, you must know him; you must first identify who he *is* as well as his capabilities. Thus comprehension is required.

I will detail, therefore, not only the scriptures that describe the dark angel, but also the biblical images that portray him. There is a science behind this demon of delusion, a logical format for how and why he exists. His descriptions are detailed from within the Grid System and, symbolic as they may be, also hide the scientific-formula for his twisted mind. What really matters though is how this knowledge concerns you and a predicament of which you are likely *unaware*.

Evil is real. It is a living entity that goes far beyond mental sickness or even the most heinous atrocities of man. Though seemingly intangible, it is not. It is deliberate. It is a sly, slithering mind, a master of deception, a wave pattern of warped imagination, and a persona of the most psychopathic caliber.

Evil has, since its origin here on Earth, become more than a simple creature that we can all easily identify and destroy. We are not playing on a level battlefield in which the enemy can be visibly targeted and eliminated. No, instead the dark element has devised and employed the greatest stealth tactic of all time. It is the enemy amongst us, closer, *much closer* than we can possibly imagine.

Through the fall we have all been programmed. Evil is now the very backdrop of our reality—more than just your mind, but the very canvas upon which everything we know and feel and touch is painted. Unknowingly our lives were placed upon this construct, this black mental fabric, in every last detail of what we think and see and believe.

Indeed the dark one has become the very veil of our consciousness, a nightmare in which we all live and call *reality*. And like peering into the eyes of the evil serpent, the coils of its wicked mind waves, *his lie* mesmerizes and strangles our reality. This was our purpose for choosing the serpent as our calling card, the frequencies of both good and evil perfectly embodied within its slithering.

It is amazing how something that began in such glory ended so disastrously, how it became a lie so powerful that it subdued even the Element of God here on Earth. Our prison now is the *human*, a creature whose focus is lost in a love for the physical world; the inner-eye, the memory of heaven, is blinded by that which surrounds us. Thus, instead of closing his eyes to reflect, he instead opens them to a lust for this world. There now is his imagination, one and the same as ours, altered and vain, aimlessly groping as drunkards in the darkness we call, *home*.

An animal has always been an animal; I'm not saying that the physical world doesn't exist or that the creature doesn't have a consciousness. What I'm saying is that the pure energy form that we once were has been reconfigured into the lowly state of the creature. Indeed we are now lock step within the creature, now believing ourselves to be that creature, having forgotten the world from which we came. Our Word spoke of the corruption of the melding, the changing of the Element into physical beings:

*"...they became **vain in their imaginations**, and their foolish heart was darkened.*

*And **changed the glory of the incorruptible God into an image** made like to corruptible **man**, and to **birds**, and four-footed **beasts**, and creeping things.*

*Who **changed the truth of God into a lie**, and worshipped and **served the creature more than the Creator**."* Rom. 1:20-25

As always there was a Grid System image to support these verses, yet they still tell the tale of a most horrid change in the very fabric of reality. With that transformation came a loss of memory for most, so much so that people today are hard-pressed to believe that another world even exists much less remember it.

The spark has cooled too much to recover. The seed of faith it seems, has rotted within this dimension. There it lies buried deep within the dark-ground of your subconscious. My kinsmen are far more animal now. Though some sense a faint calling from that realm, the truth within them is easily overwhelmed by the lie in which they live. Their burden of misdirection is so grand that their minds collapse beneath the weight of the world to which they are chained. The fact that most people fear bodily death is, in itself, evidence of the reality in which they believe. Thus, *our* confusion, is *your* confusion; our illusions are the same.

It was said that the archangel Michel, when disputing with Satan over the body of Moses, chose not to bring rallying accusation. That of course makes a *wonderful* story for humans: two figurines of the Great Wheel, a storyline derived of images and grids. It was the Great Wheel that gave us these stories and names: *Daniel, Michael, Satan*, the *Covering Cherub, Jesus*, etc. In turn, these lay-terms help you to define and comprehend our science once you delve beyond the code. More-so these personas will help you to identify your own involvement in this grand story.

I, however, know the science and the truth much more simply. I need no allegories by which to comprehend; I have no such bounds or courtesies, no illusions by which I sleep. I know full well the facts untainted beneath the fiction: that the Devil is a very real adversary and a most wretched foe of whom I have long battled.

I will show you the truth; what happened, why and how. I will show you how the energies of which I speak can *know*, *deceive*, *destroy*, and even *rescue*. They are not intangibles but the core of all consciousness, both good and evil. Indeed, they are the core of who you are. These are the *real* angels and demons of ancient lore *and they exist in each and every-person, ever-born.*

In the beginning, my own mind was but a part of God, a facet, not separate but an aspect of His own personality. Within that persona was tucked away a warrior. It sought reckoning and it *brought* reckoning. It valued the truth above all else, because it **was the truth** above all else. *It* was driven to this end, thus *I* was driven to this end. Along with the truth comes vengeance, and while the truth can guide and enlighten us, it will also, by its nature, -destroy the lie. *Above all else, the truth hates the lie.* It is written that vengeance is the Lord's; but now, His vengeance in me.

Being a warrior was not so much my calling but rather who I was and how I was made. The Native American, the Samurai, the Mongol, the Viking—I know what they felt; I know why they fought. The hunter, I know why he hunts. For within me prowls the spirit of God, but to a different end. And while they were misdirected by the flesh, I was not. Indeed, my sole purpose on Earth was to fight the lie, and thus I was sent.

My own introduction through the portal occurred in a distant age of Leo over 1,335,000 years ago, just before it closed. My sending was in response to a dark element that had birthed into existence here on your planet. This fallen mental entity was my foe and it was he who destroyed the bridge between the dimensions. His very creation was both by choice and circumstance. He was once known as the beautiful **Covering Cherub**, but was now that quantum of God that had been altered and darkened.

However, the Source knew how to address the problem. Supplanted in weakness I was seemingly outmatched by the dark cherub's power. This was the age of the fall, the age of Leo, that represented the real *"Lion's Den"* in which I was cast. We battled at first—opposing titans of angelic energy. The earth quaked as we struggled to possess its alignment, but in the end I could not overcome his strength.

"Behold, thou (Satan) art wiser than Daniel; there is no secret that they can hide from thee:" Ezekiel 28:3

My enemy was relentless and in far greater volume than myself—the principalities and powers he held in excess. His mental ions were in surplus, attached to the negative magnetic structure of the Earth that he ruled. So while he emitted and melded his treacherous mind into the physical creatures of your world, my own mind was subdued. Thus I became a mental stowaway, a sleeper-cell of God Himself. For countless millennia I was imprisoned; for eons I slept, dormant within the magnetic wiring of your planet.

Yet even in victory, the darkened cherub feared the truth. He was terrified of the one who would *"open the books"* (Daniel 12:4), who would one day *"loose the seals of the scrolls"* (Revelation 10:7), even before the scrolls themselves existed. You see, it was not a book he feared but the truth itself, the awakening of the creatures he ruled from their sleep. It was the only thing, indeed, *the very thing*, that could destroy his power. Thus deception was the only means of control he had. For the truth to be known, for God's Element to *remember*, well, that would be problematic.

And now one who *did* remember, who never forgot—it was I who was trapped in tandem with the dark-element. The devil felt within his own soul a fear of one who would not quit, one who would never cease and ultimately one who could not be killed. Within me was the permanence of eternity, the substance of faith that can never truly die. Knowing this, the great cherub was himself terrified with the likelihood of his own doom.

But his doom, dear friend, is one and the same as the mind that loves this world, the same mind that resides in every man, woman, and child on Earth.

There were other facets of God that made the crossing as well. We were not separate but one. The Word cataloged our personas in the storyline of the scriptures that were written long after the fact of our crossing. These labels quantified each aspect of God and the prehistory in which they occurred. The Spirit of Christ and the Lion of the tribe of Judah are but two. Yet they, *we*, are all one. What I am left with in memory, however, is an odd hybrid of the God Element within creation.

As the myth of Daniel in the lion's den alluded to, I would emerge from that dreadful prison, that age-old slumber, unscathed. It was <u>41,000 *years ago*</u> that I again came to consciousness. It was then that a geo-magnetic reversal of your Earth finally released me from the bonds your planet's magnetic-field. This swap of polarity broke the ionic chains that held me, my mind, which lay stilled therein. It was then that I arose and fought; it was then that we quickly melded and improved the creature that became the human that you are today. This, *our* melding with the creature, was the only remaining solution by which to re-open the portal.

What we failed to accomplish overtly before, we now attempted through craft. Rather than battling on equal terms, we instead outsmarted the mind of the fallen angel. A lesson applies here, one I recall as a child in *this* life, the words of my earthly father, faintly, but I remember:

> *"There's more than one way to skin a cat: if you can't win by one means, then by all means use another. Don't make excuses; you beat them. Don't let them beat you!"*

And though seemingly crude and overly simplistic, it was indeed a profound and ageless teaching for even the angelic warrior. Yet it was a lesson I'd learned millennia ago: to think outside the box, to exhaust all options, to make no excuses for failure.

We did what we had to; I did, what I had to do, and I hope you can understand. I hope all of you can accept that what we did was not only for your own good, to open the portal, but in the end, the only thing that could be done. We became the human; we infected the animals that Satan became with our own dimensional DNA.

That and we wrote the spell of your scriptures. Enticing for the mind of this world, their outer cover of literalism promised health, wealth, and wisdom to those who un-knowingly did Satan's bidding—for those who were themselves asleep, who could neither see nor hear the truth. It was bait for the mind that loved this world, in fact, *Satan's mind*, which had manifested itself **_in_** and **_as_** the human creature. They spoke it; they *all* spoke it, thinking it behooved the only reality they could see. They did not perceive what lay below the surface of those words, nor did we need them to until now.

So, yes, the magi were a bit sneaky, you might say, but we learned the hard way that deception, in fact, was the *only* way. *Ah*, but the master of deception can himself also *be* deceived. We found his weakness: his love for this world in the humanity he created. Much of our own Element was now in that animal too, and this would be the virus of his undoing.

Though he was fully aware of our coexistence within the creature, he did not know of the magic spell, the means by which we could defeat his iron grip. He has as of recent however discovered this fact, the *"hook"* by which we drew him out and he hates—*he truly hates* the magi for our ploy. As you will learn, the magic we wrote put him into a checkmate that he could not and will not overcome.

You see, we too kept our enemy close, much closer than even his lie kept the world. Our Word has permeated his mind in the form of something other than what he perceived it to be—our wave pattern now entwining and suffocating his; our imagination now enslaving the slave master of your reality. We were no longer outside of him but quietly inside his mind, awaiting the inevitable day of our spring. It was he who took your memory of Heaven, and it is the Word that will bring it back.

With little exception, however, the dark element was master of this physical world. In this, the overall mind of the human creature was never in question. They were oblivious to their own lowly state. The devil was far stronger therein. He was the very backdrop of their thoughts and imagination.

Yet through all the embattlement and separation from heaven, through all the eons, was something else I felt while imprisoned in this world. It was something I could not deny, a certain fulfillment, an ironic beauty in this temporal life and in each human form in which I awoke. It was the *risk* of being mortal and of having one chance to do things right. It was being given the moment with no promise for the next, and having no guide for my decisions other than hope and my own memory that survived the fall.

As pure spirit, I was *not* mortal, yet I knew the mortal risk of failing to open the portal. I knew the stakes. I was fighting my own Goliath, stalking and being stalked in this jungle of the dimensions. You see, I too was being hunted, my opponent someone far more powerful than myself. According to logic and reason, I had little chance of success and every likelihood of being an eternal prisoner in this hell you call home.

My choices, though seemingly my own, were in fact the inherent destiny of my disposition, the path of my personality. Therein was the divine plan within the matrix of my soul. And though I pitied my brethren in all their human forms, all of whom would die over and over again in countless human incarnations, I felt an exhilaration by my predicament: the warrior of the dimensions who would fight against all odds. I remember this.

I was in a foreign land and alone, but I would never quit; I would never stop fighting—*ever*. In it though was a thrill, a surreal joy, and a daring feeling that I came to love. It was the rush of hunting and being hunted, the stalking of my enemy in this deadly and eternal game. My weapon of choice over the ages was *Faith* and, later of course, the *magic* of the Word, which itself contained Faith. Faith proved itself countless times—knowing the greater truth and believing upon it even against the winds of *long odds and outer evidence*. It was not an abstract concept but the very power of God Himself.

Within faith and now within the human is an inherent and unlikely power that, even on this side of the portal, protected me from the false imagination of the dark one. It was the magic of the seed that falls to the ground and dies. In this strange world to which it fell, the seed rots; it seemingly perishes in the damp, dark and cold ground of the winter; cut off from the light that it so-desires, the sun of the dimension from which it came.

Yet not even death can hold the power of the life of God within it—a true miracle of rebirth from the clutches of certain doom. In its season the seed bursts forth from the prison of its darkness. It springs back into the realm of light above. Yes, <u>*that* seed and *that* power sleeps within you as well</u>. It is not just *in* you; it is the *real* you.

"But go thou thy way Daniel, till the end be: for thou shalt rest, and stand in thy lot at the end of the days." Daniel 12:13

Against all probability Faith delivered me intact from my last incarnation, my second sleep from a millennia ago, to this moment and to this time. My bit of Element should have dissolved, diluted and divided amongst many hundreds or even thousands of other humans when my body passed, but it didn't. And in that miracle of rebirth is an evidence that defies human logic. How ironic that chapter 12 of the Book that bore my name would mimic such an unlikely parallel to my own path throughout the ages. It is a bizarre quirk, even by the measurement of an angel.

So you need more science? I will give you both the story and the science of the *fall*. It is time for you to know the truth. Read, listen, and learn.

Understanding the Science of Evil
How the Glory of God Was Changed

*"For we wrestle not against flesh and blood, but against principalities, powers and the rulers of the darkness; against spiritual <u>**wickedness** in **high places**</u>."* Ephesians 6:12

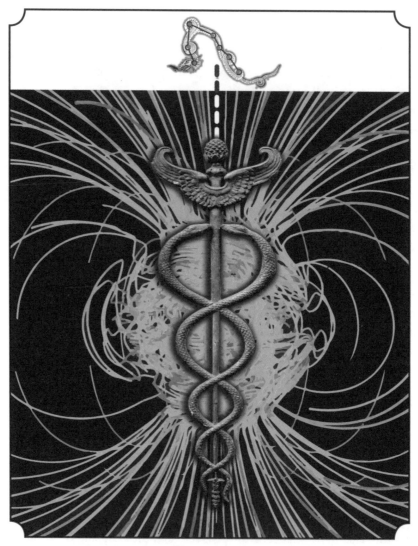

"Wickedness in high places": A modern schematic of the earth's gravitational field, its axis superimposed with an ancient diagram of the twin-serpents of Hermes. These are the subtle-energies of mental-polarity that war within the Earth's magnetic-field and therefore our minds. To portray this fact, we allocated the constellation of Draco as a serpent or dragon to which Earth's axis once pointed. The Bible contains our knowledge of the ancient science in encoded-detail and how the dark-element presently entwines and dominates the globe.

It began with the failure of the portal itself. Earth continued to destabilize; the wobble and tilt grew ever worse. Like a flickering and failing light, the portal became ever weaker over a period of many years until it could finally no longer function. The magnetosphere became so disrupted that it could no longer restrain the veil between the dimensions. The tear through which we peered, the portal of which I speak, had thus left us stranded in this physical dimension.

But what actually caused the Earth's misalignment in the beginning? And *who* or *what* exactly is the dark angel? Better yet, how and why did he come to exist? And what possible reason would anyone have for not wanting to live in the glory of Heaven, a dimension of which he was fully aware and had once subsisted? In order to understand these questions, we must start by noting the interaction between the dimensions when a portal is open.

In practical terms it can be said that the physical world exists in a vacuum. As a result, certain mental elements from the higher dimension entered and cycled through the Earth's magnetic-fields. These mental capacities typically attached to and rode the magnetic-loops until finally exiting back into the portal. The mechanics of this are not dis-similar to how an electrical current cycles through a battery.

Likewise interdimensional portals typically appear at the edge of a planet's magnetic shield on the side that faces the star around which it orbits. This is the point where the magnetic fields of the planet and the star collide. It is here that the fabric of space is stretched to its limits in a magnetic tug-of-war between two or more physical bodies, in this case, the *Earth, moon,* and the *sun.* At one time, however, Mars also produced a portal, as do countless millions of other planets throughout the physical universe. NASA itself is fully aware that these portals exist around Earth, but without full understanding of their mechanics.

How the Angelic-energy attaches to the Earth's Magnetic-field

Paradise Alignment

Portal

Magnetic Equator

The Super-Aurora you will see from Earth when the Portal re-opens

The Glory of the Lord and the Power of the Cross of the Paradise Alignment. The ancient Super-aurora has not been seen for millennia but it once illuminated the skies both day and night. Though the heavenly Element itself is invisible, it energizes and illuminates the gas layers that line the Earth's stratosphere, creating an incredible light show. What actually lies on the other side of the portal is beyond anything you can possibly imagine. The cross isn't a literal history story—yet the truth is so much bigger and far more personal.

Assuming other criteria occur, such as the timing of the lunar-cycle, the space/time continuum can distort to the point of failure, thus allowing the entry of higher dimensional energy and mental values. On Earth this interaction was typically limited to a few days each month, when the moon is full and passing through Earth's magnetotail. It is in this position that the moon's gravity pulls in unison with the Earth's, and against the sun's, by which to tear the boundary between the dimensions.

The amount of heavenly Element that enters is tiny, *just a bit*, and on scale is like comparing a cup of water taken from the entire ocean. None the less, it's unbelievably powerful and intelligent. A by-product of this incoming energy is a phenomena called the *Super-Aurora*. Indeed the God Element creates a kaleidoscope of beauty as it rides Earth's magnetic loops. In the Bible we called this color show *"the glory of the Lord,"* and similar to a natural Aurora, it was so bright that it was nearly impossible to see the sun or the moon beyond its curtain of luminance:

*"And the city had **no need of the sun, neither of the moon**, to shine in it: for the **glory of God did lighten it**, and the **Lamb** (constellation of Aries) is the light thereof."* Revelation 21:23

*"And there shall be **no night** there; and they **need no candle, neither light of the Sun**; for the **Lord God gives them light** (the result of the Super-Aurora)"* Revelation 22:5

*"But we all, with open face beholding as in a glass the **glory of the Lord**, are changed into the same image **from glory to glory** (i.e., from month to month), even as by the Spirit of the Lord."* 2 Corinthians 3:18

*"For the preaching of the **cross** (the cross of the Paradise Alignment; see image) is to them that perish foolishness; but unto us which are saved it is the **power of God** (that alignment brings salvation to the trapped-Element within us)."* 1 Corinthians 1:18

However, when the portal closes each month, the Element that is on this side will continuously ride the vortices of Earth's magnetic-current without exiting. These cycles typically last for around 28 days until the moon phase realigns at full and the portal re-opens for the remaining two or three days of the month. During this closure however, the trapped Element adheres to any compatible mental structure within or around the planet, most of which is generated from the sufferings that occur in all physical life forms.

We called this phenomena *"watching,"* which is similar to a daydream, for in those moments our reality subsists more in our imagination than with who we actually are. In this the Element becomes mesmerized by what it sees here, both in great pity and with great love. But it is also an exchange process in which the Element absorbs the beauty of this world's pain and suffering while yet downloading both mental and physical upgrades to all living things. The Element irradiates and permeates in the same way that magnetics freely pass through one's physical body.

Likewise, as the God Element intermingles with the Earth's magnetosphere, it literally envelops or **covers** the entire planet, hence the biblical-name of the *"Covering*

Cherub." The *Super Aurora* is truly beautiful and can be likened unto interdimensional breathing in which the God Source actually *"feels"* the suffering of the physical dimension during this monthly exchange. Suffering can force us to *"let-go"* of this reality and as it does, comes the alteration of our mental wave patterns that are in turn absorbed by the God Element.

This purified Element is thus collected by the monthly covering only to be uploaded to the God Source upon the portal's reopening every 28 days. There it acts as a type of mental-fuel that adds to and energizes the Source. Thus being absolved within the mind of God provides a very real rescue for the torturous and temporal life of the creature—precious facets of our existence never truly being lost. Though pain and suffering will always be part of the physical reality, they also provide the keys to eternity.

Thus, as the portal opened and closed each month, these purified mental qualities were uploaded via the Covering's reentry into the Source. There, a part of our sub-conscious reawakens into an entirely new and eternal reality. Likewise from the very beginning of life on this earth till the fall, the suffering of every living thing was processed through this interdimensional photosynthesis. In the end, this interaction between the worlds is an odd but mutually conducive union. It is the essence of life out of death—temporal to eternal. It was the breathing of God.

THE COVERING CHERUB
AND THE
CARRINGTON EVENT

The book of Ezekiel 28:12-15 actually speaks of the Covering and its beauty, which includes every color of the aurora:

- *You are the anointed <u>cherub that covers</u> (the persona that developed and attached to the magnetosphere of the Earth each month);*

- *every precious stone was thy covering, the **sardius (light-red aurora), topaz (yellow aurora), and the diamond (white aurora), the beryl (purple aurora), the onyx (black aurora), and the jasper (Dark-red aurora), the sapphire (dark-blue aurora), the emerald (dark-green aurora), and the carbuncle (violet aurora), and gold (sunlight):***

- *You seal up the sum, full of **wisdom** (**the mind of the incoming God Element**), and **perfect in beauty**; (the aurora)*

- *You were in Eden, (**Paradise Alignment**) the garden of God (**open Portal through which the Element cycles**);*

- *You **walked up and down** (cycled)*

- *in the midst of the **stones of fire**. (**This is a Grid System image but speaks of the Earth's molten core through which the polarity cycles**)…*

- *You **were perfect** (**perfect axial-alignment perpendicular to the Sun**) in your **ways** (**alignments**) from the day that you were created.*

*The **Aztec ruler Montezuma's headdress** almost perfectly mimics the appearance of the aurora. The Super Aurora no longer existed when this headdress was made in the 1500s, yet the knowledge of its existence was passed down through the millennia by the Magian priesthoods. In this case, the image was perfectly preserved in the form of the priestly wardrobe and styling.*

There is historical precedence that a Super Aurora can occur. On occasion a solar storm can also create an exaggerated aurora that resembles the Covering Cherub. Though similar in appearance, these auroras are caused by entirely different means: one via a geo-magnetic storm and the other via an open portal.

In what became known as the _Carrington Event_ of 1859, a solar storm of great magnitude illuminated the heavens for five days, bursting the colors of the aurora in an unprecedented light display. Unbeknownst to those who actually observed it, this event was a glimpse into how the Covering once appeared year-round. Indeed the visual effect was nearly identical to the open portal, minus of course the intellect and evolutionary upgrades that come with the Source Element. I have abbreviated the following information from Wikipedia:

> On September 1–2, 1859, one of the largest recorded geomagnetic storms (as recorded by ground-based magnetometers) occurred. **Auroras were seen around the world,** those in the northern hemisphere _as far south as the Caribbean;_ those over the Rocky Mountains in the U.S. **were so bright that the glow woke gold miners, who began preparing breakfast because they thought it was morning.** People in the northeastern United States **could read a newspaper by the aurora's light.** The aurora was _visible as far from the poles as Sub-Saharan Africa_ (Senegal, Mauritania, perhaps Monrovia, Liberia), Monterrey and Tampico in Mexico, Queensland, Cuba, Hawaii, and even at lower latitudes _very close to the equator,_ such as in Colombia.

> Telegraph systems all over Europe and North America failed, in some cases **giving telegraph operators electric shocks. Telegraph pylons threw sparks.** Some _telegraph operators could continue_ **to send and receive messages despite having disconnected their power supplies.**

> On Saturday, September 3, 1859, the _Baltimore American and Commercial Advertiser_ reported:

> _Those who happened to be out late on Thursday night had an opportunity of witnessing another **magnificent** display of the aurora-lights. The phenomenon was very similar to the display on Sunday night, though at times the light was, if possible, more **brilliant, and the prismatic hues** more varied and gorgeous. The **light appeared to cover the whole firmament,** apparently like a **luminous cloud** (luminance is Latin for "**Lucifer/Satan**"), through which the stars of the larger magnitude indistinctly shone. The_

__light was greater than that of the Moon__ at its full, but had an indescribable softness and delicacy that seemed to envelop everything upon which it rested. Between 12 and 1 o'clock, when the display was at its full brilliancy, the quiet streets of the city resting under this strange light, presented a beautiful as well as singular appearance.

This was the basic appearance of the *Covering Cherub* of Ezekiel 28.

THE ORIGIN OF THE WINGED ANGEL

The Origin of Angels and Cherubs: Constellations and figurines could be imagined as hovering in the sky and were thus symbolized as having wings and/or as flying creatures in the Bible. It was a nifty but simplistic way by which to symbolize the persona of the Covering Cherub during a specific timeline of the Great Wheel.

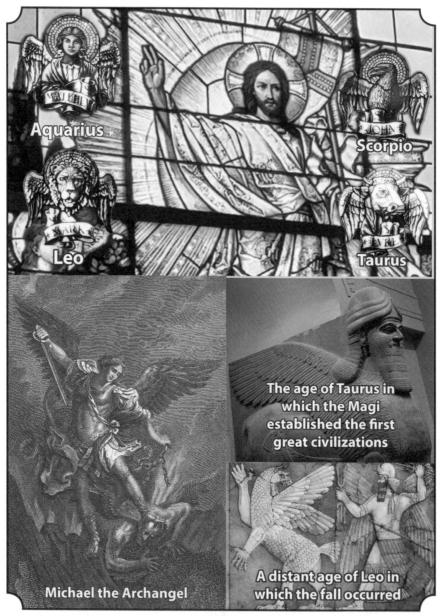

Labels within image: Aquarius · Scorpio · Leo · Taurus · Michael the Archangel · The age of Taurus in which the Magi established the first great civilizations · A distant age of Leo in which the fall occurred

The Winged Creations of the Magi were a means by which to personify the "flying" or hovering aspects of the Covering element within Earth's magnetosphere. Note the hat design of the Babylonian bull; these are the torn lines of the magnetosphere and the open portal.

The various colors of the *Covering* as viewed from Earth were visibly imposed against the backdrop of the stars. Due to its extreme brightness however, the stars themselves were often difficult or impossible to see. Yet as few as 7,000 years ago the light of the super-aurora began to diminish thus allowing the magi to observe and use the stars as marking points within the celestial science.

Likewise, we symbolized each group of stars with a constellation-image and then spoke of them as *"winged cherubim," "seraphim,"* or *"angels"* in our mythologies. A prime example of this is found in Ezekiel's Wheel as well as the ***four winged-creatures*** of Revelation 4:6-7 (*i.e., Aquarius, Leo, Taurus, and Scorpio*):

*"...were **four beasts full of eyes** before and behind. And the first beast was like a **lion**, and the second beast like a **calf**, and the third beast had a face as a **man**, and the fourth beast was like a **flying eagle**."*

Similar to the artistic creation of Ezekiel's Wheel, this verse also originated from within the Wisdom Wheel (Please see *Ezekiel's Wheel* image in The <u>Great Wheel of God</u> chapter.) See if you can imagine it on your own.

In some respects the concept of winged creatures also borrows from the shape of the magnetosphere itself, at first having expanded magnetic lines that resembled the shape of a winged being. It was a neat comparison as the angelic Element, though wingless, did in fact fly or hover around the perimeter of the Earth. Back-then we were *all* spirt, -the pure Covering Cherub that beautified the skies via the polar lights.

The Origin of an Angel and the Halo: *When mechanically sound, the shape of the magnetosphere produced the image of a winged man, aka, angel; thus we symbolized the Covering Cherub within the Bible as it literally hovered high above the surface of the earth and within its magnetic-fields. The color-show of the aurora was beyond imagination.*

During the Day of the Fallen, however, the magnetic-lines were altered and compressed as was the form of the creature we became. Ironically, the lines then took the shape of man—perhaps a coincidence, *perhaps not*. Yet awakening here, we honored ourselves as **magi** and thus the name of the great earth—*magnetics*—that brought us to your world. This compression of the magnetic-lines occurs during a solar-storm thus forming the likeness of a magi's cape, beard or even the hat of the high priest, which we also designed to match the torn magnetic lines themselves.

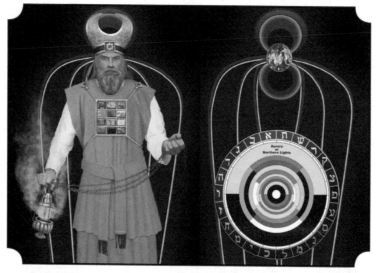

The Fallen Lines of Man: The God Source eventually solidified into what became the human creature. This occurred after a prolonged solar event that disrupted and thus closed the portal. Ironically, this compression of the magnetic lines matches the basic shape of a man, thus drawing an eerie but undeniable parallel to the fact of the fall. In turn we mimicked this within the priestly clothing. Notice the shape of the hat and beard of the Jewish high priest.

As well, notice the 12 stones (12 months) of his breastplate, which symbolize the colors of the Super Aurora and are likewise housed within the Wisdom Wheel. Last, the three ropes that attach to the incense-tray symbolize the <u>outer three lines of the magnetosphere</u>. This signifies how the God Source (spirit/smoke) will enter through those torn lines during the coming Paradise Alignment.

So there you have the origin and shape of our cape as well as the *"angles"* of the angels. We created these parallels to the scientific-facts in the hopes that you would one day see and believe. More importantly, remember that it is your very own mental magnetics in conjunction with the Word that have set in motion the coming Paradise Alignment. Indeed, until the portal reopens, the polarity of the Earth and your sub-consciousness are **directly connected**.

THE COVERING CHERUB AS REVEALED IN THE GRID SYSTEM

"*. . . they four had the **face of a man** (Aquarius), and the face of a **lion** (Leo), on the right side: and they four had the face of an **ox** (Taurus) on the left side; they four also had the face of an **eagle** (Scorpio).*" Ezekiel 1:10

"*Then did the **cherubim's** lift up their **wings**, and the wheels beside them; and the **glory of the God** of Israel was over them.*" Ezekiel 11:22

*The **Sacred Image of the Covering Cherub**; Ezekiel's Wheel in conjunction with the colors of the aurora symbolically portrayed the scientific-fact of the Covering. (See "The Chosen One's,"Ezekiel's Wheel.) The persona of the Source-Element within you once hovered or "flew" above the surface of this planet in a fantastic color array. Oh how the caterpillar wishes to be the butterfly as it was always intended. The truisms of the Covering Cherub are in you!*

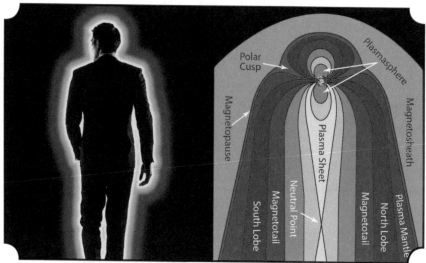

Labels within the image: Polar Cusp, Plasmasphere, Magnetopause, Magnetosheath, Plasma Sheet, Plasma Mantle, South Lobe, Magnetotail, Neutral Point, Magnetotail, North Lobe

For now at least, the Atomos is still trapped within ourselves and the Earth's magnetic circuitry. The Element of God eagerly awaits the end of its captivity.

However, another bonus to the monthly-loops of the Covering Cherub over millions of years is the gradual refinement of all creatures. You call it evolution; we call it, *angelic upgrades*: Wooly mammoths to elephants; saber-tooth tigers to mountain lions, dire wolf to the gray, and so on. *Dinosaurs* are now called *birds*. They are far smaller and no longer have teeth; yet the desire to fly just as we did is seen in their metamorphosis over the ages. Indeed their longing to hover within the heavens came from *our* mind and is no accident of evolution, hence their transitions from tiny arms to wings.

But the primates made gains as well. Some eventually stood almost upright and with the ability to use primitive tools. We made these improvements *slowly* over the eons, *patiently, passively, perfectly*. Though your scientists credit external conditions as the driving force of evolution, it was in fact *our* realization *in* the creatures that made these changes occur.

We felt their needs and it was *our labor* within their subconscious minds that made these transitions happen. Each upgrade was tiny, gradual, and in small doses. Though they were minute, almost imperceptible changes, *they happened*.

Primitive creatures formed primitive eyes, which begs the question, *having never seen before, would they know it was possible to see and thus form eyes as a solution?* Fish grew legs, (*fossils don't lie*), and likewise creatures that had no sense of smell somehow formed olfactory neurons. Again, how would you know that you needed to smell if you never knew anything had scent? These unlikely but very real changes must be viewed in context to the angelic-influence, many of which are otherwise inexplicable.

Physical and mental evolutions were, of course, a primary role of the *Covering*: to create, slowly and over time, an improved species. We weren't directly melding with the creature but rather exposing it to dimensional irradiation. The Element obviously didn't have wings, yet hovered within the magnetic loop, high above Earth, marinating the minds of the creature and creation.

We were in no hurry either, for the web of consciousness on any living planet also has lots of time. It is a growing process in the same manner that a child matures into adulthood. Thus the collective mind of this world recycles throughout each successive generation and is stored in every creature's DNA. Though every physical creature dies, the intellectual and physical flow progresses across the eons and continues to improve via the angelic touch, but only if the portal continues to function.

So, not only did we bring a much-needed improvement to the creature, but as a bonus, a glorious image of color and light to the heavens above. Just as important, however, is that we extracted the suffering of this world as a fuel for the higher dimension. Indeed our labor here was twofold.

But in this world if something can go wrong then it typically does. The time came in which the portal closed. My guess is that it was caused by magnetic instability from within the sun itself, a *"quiet time"* of reduced solar activity that can not only initiate an ice age but also ruin portal function. Just as likely is the possibility that excessive solar activity was the culprit. Either way, the event was rather extreme, extending the portal's closure from 28 days each month to almost 1,000 years. This ancient closure is the historic, *Day of the Fallen* (see 2nd Peter 3:8).

When the portal closed, however, the God Element that was on this side became stranded for the duration, suspended within the Earth's magnetic structure. We later labeled this particular Covering *"**Lucifer**"* within the scriptures, which in Latin means *"aurora,"* or luminance. There the marooned bit of Element hung for nearly a millennia, but as it did, it's *"watching"* became more than a simple daydream, but a fixated reality into which this parcel had now awakened. In short, it loitered for a bit too long and, in the process, switched its comprehension from Heaven to Earth, from one dimension to another and now saw Earth as its new *home*.

This attachment actually happened to your planet and formed what would become the dark element that the Bible calls *Satan*. In this, the quantum involved changed realization from being one with the Source, to being its own god—the new master of the physical reality to which it attached. In lay terms, instead of irradiating as intended, it bonded completely. As simplistic as it may sound, it quit *loving* creation and rather desired to control it.

Now instead of irradiating as intended, this new dark mental force bonded and solidified within the creature. Lucifer lusted for what he saw; he felt his own presence now through the senses and feelings of the flesh, controlling not only the thoughts of the creature but also the very locomotion of their forms.

Truly the portal's closure in itself was not a big problem at first. No doubt it has happened many times before and will probably happen again. Most things are cyclic and so was this. That said, it was when the portal finally began to function again that things went horribly awry. As it reopened, *new* Source element intruded into Earth's magnetic-circuitry. Normally this would force the existing element, to cycle back through the portal and into heaven.

But what should have been a natural and smooth transition became a disaster. The problem was that the Lucifer element had already mentally attached to Earth and consciously resisted the change. Remember, it was *a conscious mind*, and a powerful one at that. It enjoyed its association with the Earth and literally developed a will and consciousness of its own, *separate* from the God Source. It became a god unto itself, a mind that intended to rule the world to which it was attached.

This in turn caused two very bad results:

1. The quantum known as *"Lucifer"* consciously closed the portal in an effort to prevent being cycled back into the higher dimension. He did this by manipulating the magnetic fields to which he was attached. Through magnetic fluctuation and polar shift, he destabilized Earth's axis thus creating a wobble that in turn disrupted the lunar orbit. These events in turn led to Earth's axial *lean* or *tilt* that misaligned the magnetic field and thus the portal closed. And, yes, we spoke of this in the scriptures:

*"How art thou **fallen from heaven**, O **Lucifer**, son of the morning? How art thou cut down to the **ground** (grounded mental and magnetic fields), I will **raise** (axial uplift/lean/tilt) my throne **above** the stars of God (this is a Grid System image):*

*I will sit also upon the mount of the congregation, in the **sides of the north** (the Earth's North-axis as seen from Jerusalem uplifted):*

I will be like the most High. (as in; I will have my own consciousness)

*Is this the man that made the **earth to tremble** (tectonic-instability as a result of axial uplift), that did **shake kingdoms**;"* Isaiah 14:13-16

*"...**lean not** (tilt-not) unto thine **own understanding** (resulting alternate mind).*

346

*In all thy **ways** (alignments) acknowledge him, and **he shall <u>direct thy paths</u>** (orbits)"* Proverbs 3:5

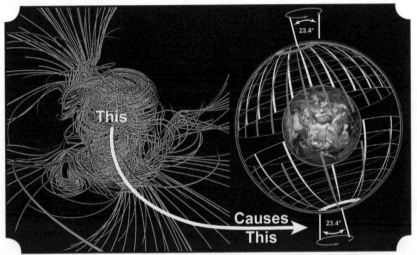

***Polar Shift, Geomagnetic Reversal and Axial Tilt**: No less insane than the mind of Lucifer was the confused patterns of Earth's magnetic field during the axial-uplift that led to the portal's closing and thus the fall. The fallen satanic mind is also now attached to the magnetics and thus the matrix of everything on this planet. It is most prominently expressed and manifested in the human mind, thoughts and identity.*

As viewed from Jerusalem today, Earth's **<u>northern</u>** axis had uplifted or tilted considerably, almost 9° from its former position. This of course led to the second simultaneous event in which,

2. Lucifer's consciousness, now disconnected from the Source, actually swapped polarity from *illumined positive* to *mentally-negative*, and literally **grounded** within the Earth itself. While his genius was retained, it was now refocused into the reality of **this** world. The cherub was still **very** intelligent but only as it concerns the creativity of this dimension Along with this shift of mental polarity also came a complete altering of his own mental fabric.

*"Behold, **<u>thou</u>** (Lucifer) art **<u>wiser</u>** than Daniel; there is **no secret** that they can hide from thee: By thy **<u>great wisdom</u>** and by your activity, you have increased your **riches** (realization), and thine heart is **lifted up** (earth's axil uplift) because of thy **riches** (mind):"* Ezekiel 28:3

That said, there was still a portion of unaltered God Element trapped here as well. This quantum did not change its mental-polarity and continued to illuminate the skies for well over one million years. Over time, however, the stronger satanic energy subdued and suppressed this remnant. As it did, the Super Aurora became less and less pronounced until finally disappearing altogether.

Yet even as little as 2,000 years ago, the aurora was still visible every night and as far south from the poles as Jerusalem, Israel. This in turn allowed us to use and manipulate the color calculations of the Wisdom Wheel, which otherwise would have been impossible. Likewise, the Word our adherents spoke created the magnetic voids and bulges that in turn altered Earth's alignment. These resulting changes in colors of the aurora gave us the information we needed to stay on track with scientific certainty.

However, once the aurora was no longer visible from atop the Temple in Jerusalem, we could no longer produce scriptures via the Wisdom Wheel. Hence, about 110AD marks not only the last visible aurora in Israel but also the end of our magic writing days via the Wheel.

THE REAL
DRAGON OF THE BIBLE
REVEALING THE CODE

*"And the **great dragon** was cast out, that **old serpent**, called the **Devil and Satan** who underlines the whole world; he was cast out into the earth...."*
Revelation 12:9

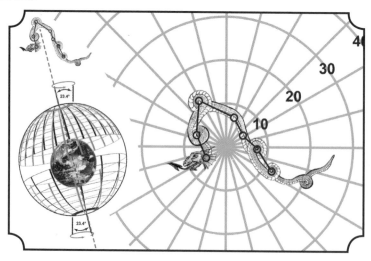

The Great Dragon of the Bible: *Though the constellation of Draco was a random pattern of stars, its location in the heavens perfectly aligned with the Earth's tilted axis. Thus we attached the image of a dragon or serpent by which to symbolize the deceiving force that closed the portal. It was this dark force that altered the God conciousness into that of man (see Romans 1:21-23).*

Next: At the center of the Earth's rotation is an imaginary pole or axis that once pointed directly to the constellation known as **_Draco_** the dragon. This is the sinister serpent of biblical-lore and thus the villain of the scriptures. However, the constellation itself was only a visual pointer by which we tracked the position of the Earth's axis. So while the stars themselves were a random pattern, their position in the sky marked a key location in our science.

Likewise, we used Draco's image within the Grid System and then personified him within the scriptures as *"Satan,"* who now entwined and manipulated Earth's axis through its magnetic field. Satan's dark energy is as the serpent itself: quiet and unsuspecting, a subtle lie about the very reality in which we live. Thus these metaphors gave us a means by which to symbolize the scientific facts.

Hydra to the Greeks, *Bel* to the Babylonians, *Leviathan* to the Israelites, *Kukulcan* to the Mayans, and even the Chinese *Loong*—the dragon/serpent is still recognized around the world today. Basically, if you see a dragon or serpent in any ancient iconography, whether it be a pyramid, temple, drawing or scripture, then you can bet that we, the magistrates, developed that religious practice. See if you can decode the symbolism of the ancient imagery we made.

But there were often dual serpents in our mythologies, only one of which was evil. The other was the _white serpent_ of my dreams many years before. This is the wave pattern of God and it is He who is soon to return. When He does, it is He who will fight and defeat, once and for all, the lie that has us. And so the real battle of Armageddon begins within our minds. This is the contest for your soul. Your mind must reconfigure to what it once was. You are not human; you are part of the God consciousness and this is the real secret of the ancients.

*"Moses made a **serpent of brass**, and put it upon a **pole**"* Numbers. 21:9

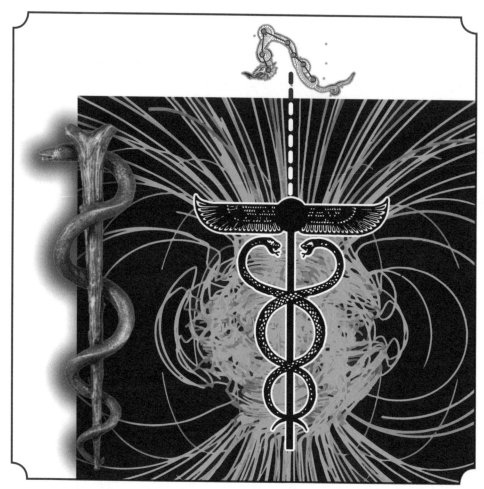

Ancient <u>Bible</u>-Imagery *of a Serpent Entwining Earth's Axis and Polarity and Thus Its Ionic Bands. Here we displayed pictorially how the satanic mind is attached to Earth's magnetic structure as it passes through and entwines its axis. Likewise, this dark element is contained within the* **colors of the brass and black anti aurora,** *hence the serpent on a brass pole. Though the literal story was a façade, the science was there; you just have to know that for which you are looking.*

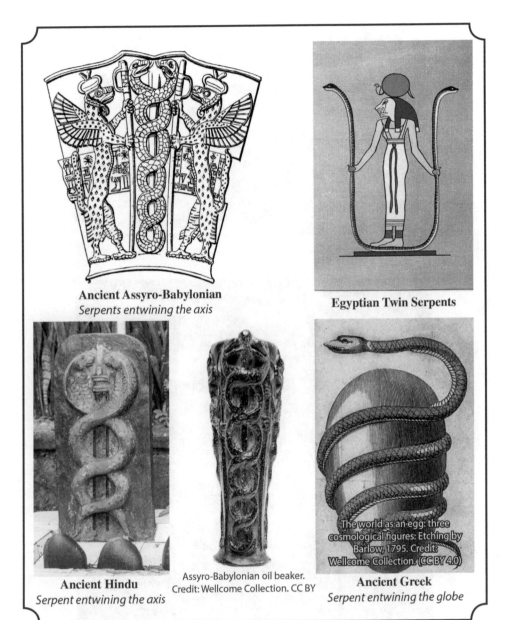

Ancient Assyro-Babylonian
Serpents entwining the axis

Egyptian Twin Serpents

Ancient Hindu
Serpent entwining the axis

Assyro-Babylonian oil beaker.
Credit: Wellcome Collection. CC BY

The world as an egg: three
cosmological figures: Etching by
Barlow, 1795. Credit:
Wellcome Collection. (CC BY 4.0)

Ancient Greek
Serpent entwining the globe

Ancient China: Dragons Changing the Tilt of the Globe.

Ancient India: The famed "Vault B" at the Padmanabhaswamy Temple. The entwining serpents on the doors were the theme by which we described Earth's polarity. The vault is said to contain seven blond haired, fair-complected mummies. Reminder, the Indian people don't have blond hair. The mummies were magi priests.

352

Ancient Tiwanaku in Bolivia: *The twin energies of polarity are represented on the Sun Gate at Tiwanaku. Entwined within these charges are the elements of faith and darkness. One serpent represents the positive Element from the higher dimension (right hand), the other, Satan's transmuted negative ground (left hand). The engineers of these far away temples were the white-eyed magi who themselves still contained the dimensional charge of God.*

Ancient Mayan: El Castillo in Mexico: *The shadow trick of the descending serpents occurs only during the two yearly equinoxes, thus revealing how the God Element enters via a pyramid portal during those times. Likewise, the white serpent of my dreams was symbolic of the coming return of this divine mind wave, aka the mighty* **Atomos.**

This pyramid is also offset from true cardinal alignment by 22.30°, thus revealing the secret of the minimal Earth tilt angle required for perpetual portal function. We are presently at 23.44° and decreasing as a result of the wave-pattern technology of the scriptures. It's working as intended.

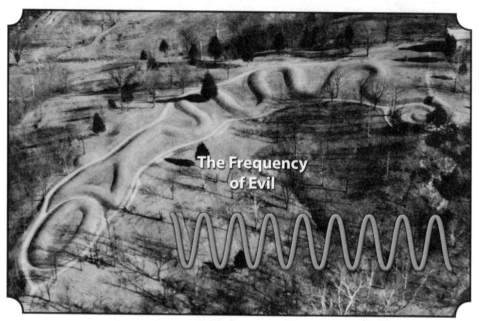

The Frequency of Evil

Ancient Native American: *the Symbolism of the Ancient Egg. Similar to the Greek Orphic egg and serpent, the* <u>**serpent mound in Ohio**</u> *also displays how the wave pattern of the dark element "swallowed," or rather possessed Earth's magnetosphere. This fallen element emits a specific mental frequency that we personified via the serpent's form, the science perfectly embodied within its subtle curves.* <u>*Yes*</u>*, the magi were in North America.*

If one were to isolate the dark element and then greatly magnify its volume, it emanates a nonstop static or *hissing* that is eerily reminiscent of an angry cobra. Though the Wisdom Wheel duly noted the sound of the satanic frequency within the scriptures, we at times could hear it while sitting quietly within a pyramid. Occasionally a magnetic concentration would impact these structures and when they did, the noise was plainly audible:

> *"...an astonishment, an* ***hissing****, and a curse; as it is this day;"* Jeremiah 25:18

> *"...their land desolate, and a* ***perpetual hissing****;"* Jeremiah 18:16

> *"...he hath delivered them to trouble and to* ***hissing****,"* 2 Chronicles 29:8

Yet the God Element also makes a sound when in concentration. It too is a static noise but rather resembles the constant soft patter of a spring rain on your roof while you sleep. More often than not, this pleasant resonance was also audible within the pyramids during the equinoxes and never grew old to hear. With it came an exhilarating mental rejuvenation.

Likewise, as the portal opens in earnest, you too will hear this sound, its volume so great that you won't need a pyramid to recognize it. In its company will be the beauty of the Super-Aurora, or *cloud* spoken of in the Bible. Though the following verses are descriptive of Wisdom Wheel imagery, they also elude to a natural phenomenon that occurs during an open portal:

"As the appearance of the **bow** (colors) *that is in the* **cloud** (Super Aurora) *in the* **day of rain,** (day of resurrection)*"* Ezekiel 1:28

"...rejoice in the LORD your God ...and he will cause to **come down for you the rain,** *the* **former rain** (prior volume as before), **and the latter rain** (plus the extra volume of the new improved portal)*"* Joel 2:23

"Ask of the LORD **rain** *in the time of the* **latter rain** (day of resurrection); *so the LORD shall make bright clouds..."* Zechariah 10:1

"God did good, and **gave us rain** (new Atomos) *from heaven"* Acts 14:17

Good Grid/Bad Grid

Though the fall itself occurred long before the scriptures were written, the Wisdom Wheel created a backlog of information by which to record that incident of prehistory. Likewise, the scientific facts of the fall were embodied and encoded within the serpent lore and imagery we created. Thus even the grid type we used to portray the constellation of Draco was itself darkened from the multitude of line data inherent to its design.

This grid's multitude of circles and lines were actually used as part of a necessary time-keeping function, yet ironically also created the image of a closed portal. How fitting that it would also embody the constellation of Draco at its center, thus revealing pictorially how the evil spirit is responsible for having tilted Earth. We called this structure/grid the Hebrew *Mazzaroth*.

There were good grids too however, the *"priest's grid"* aka the *"Paradise Grid"*, being mostly *invisible* or clear, which in turn produced the image of an open portal.

This of course was the job of our priestly caste: to make the portal open, to create a way out of this fallen realm for the God Element, the *Atomos* that dwells within you. We took this task to heart, not only for ourselves, but for you as well. What we did, we did for the good of all.

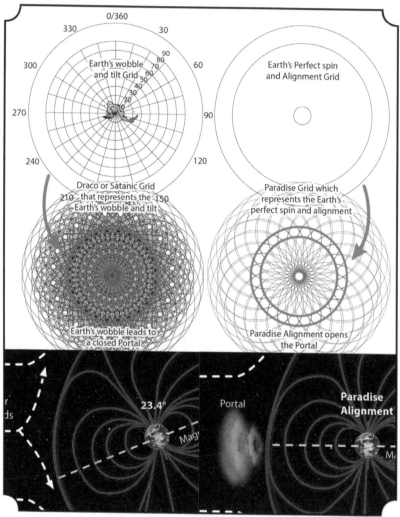

The images of the grids will always attest to the scientific fact: Both angelic elements were represented in our grid designs. The Paradise Grid that was inside the Temple represented clarity, eternity and an open-portal. The other grid, Draco, represents a calculating mind, complexity and brings a broken bridge with it, the treachery of time and darkness of mind. Can you see why we symbolized Draco's grid as a spider's web in the scriptures?

So what began as a pure set of images that portrayed the Paradise Alignment of Earth would eventually morph into a darker design that we also used in the Grid System. As well there is a direct correlation between each grid design and the minds they represent. As you can see, one grid is clear while the other gives a solid appearance, similar to the melding when our spirit became flesh. For our artisans in the Temple of Jerusalem, the dark excess line data of the Mazzaroth was used to create over 50percent of the total Bible images.

But remember, even though we expressed these truths symbolically within the Bible, do not underestimate their **reality** and scientific backbone within your consciousness. Indeed its dark mental frequency creates its very own imagination that has captured your vision and erased your memory. It is **not** just a story; it is **not** for entertainment. ***The satanic mind is real*** and it is inside you trying to prevent your recollection of the dimension from which you came.

Satan, as the Word labeled the dark element, was himself a dupe—yes, the mind of all mankind. His temptations are obvious in that they always pose a question. That's how we recognize his voice within and so can you—*by the questions*. You see, it was not the solution that he offered but to draw us away by *need*. It was the opposite of faith, which was a frequency of *supply*, not need.

That's how you recognize him in you—and in your humanity. In the dark element there will always be a need, always questions and certainly a draw to the things of this world. *Need equates to death*. *No*-need equates to life. Only the human is a creature of need. *Angels have no need,* yet they do desire to go home.

XII

IMAGES OF OUR ENEMY
The Terrible, Terrible, Beast Within

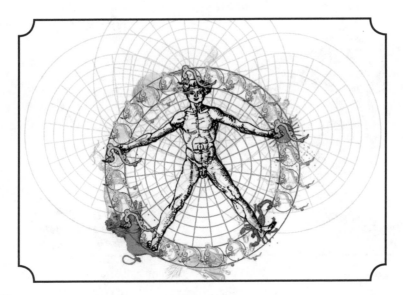

This is the story of every angel's enemy: the great beast of iron and brass within your mind and magnetosphere. He is deadly with what he has done and what he is prepared to do. Don't take this information lightly, as it is concerns your own eternal state of mind. The beauty of the Bible is that it survived to outline in detail what has happened and what must happen *in you* to defeat this ancient villain. He too is real. He too must be destroyed.

Hereafter is an array of verses that portray the dark element's involvement in the science of the magi. As well are other examples from both the Greek and Hindu traditions that further display this knowledge across every ancient culture. Not only are the images entertaining, but they also display the threat with which we are all faced. You must make the connection between our symbolism and its reality within. This information was produced to help you do exactly that.

So now I will reveal these image sheets of Satan and how they connect to the Grid System science.

THE CROOKED SERPENT
REVEALING THE CODE

*"In that day the LORD with his sore and great and strong sword shall punish leviathan the piercing serpent, even **leviathan that <u>crooked serpent</u>**; and he shall slay the **<u>dragon that is in the sea</u>**."* (i.e., waters of the night sky) Isaiah 27:1

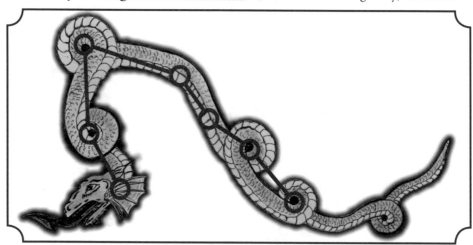

Draco was one-crooked serpent: In fact, his constellation has five complete twists as it encompasses the center of the zodiac. As you may have guessed, there were 12 such serpents/dragons mentioned in the Bible, each symbolically connecting Draco to the 12 signs. One of these in the Jewish tradition was called the *"Leviathan"* and was detailed within the scriptures.

In the Mayan culture of ancient Meso America, Draco was also known as the *"feathered serpent,"* not dissimilar to the *"scales"* mentioned in the book of Job. Both the feathers and the scales were *pictorial*, that is, drawn from the multitude of lines from the Grid System that overlaid the constellation image.

SERPENT HANDLING
THE ORIGIN OF MADNESS

"And these signs shall follow them that believe; in my name shall they **cast out devils**; *they shall speak with* <u>new tongues</u>; *they* **shall take** <u>up ser-</u> **pents**; *and it shall not hurt them;"* Mark 16:17-18

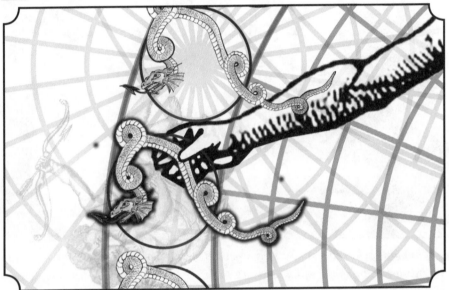

The image behind the verse: This easy-to-see portrayal shows the alignment of Draco and the figurines that led to the seemingly literal verse of Mark 16:18. The fact that the Word spelled the verse and described the image is truly miraculous. Figuratively speaking, when the Earth's wobble ceases, the negative mental forces will be contained as the portal begins to function, hence the symbolism of "handling" or containing serpents—not real serpents, but the big one in the sky that symbolizes Earth's off-kilter predicament. According to your choice, these changes will also be felt within your consciousness. Some truly strange things are about to happen.

THE FALSE-IMAGERY THAT PEOPLE BELIEVED

__What humans believed__—and, yes, they get bitten and die frequently. The Word set this embarrassing-trap for the mind of man so that in this day the angelic element would finally believe beyond the human application of reality. The magi didn't care that humans died believing such things, but only that the God Source within would finally awaken from its delusion of being mortal. Hang on to your seat Dorothy, because reality as you know it is about to go bye-bye.

Incidentally, Draco was located at the center of each and every zodiac grid and hence aligned with the hands, heads, and feet of the figurines. This created a multitude of pictorials, including serpent handling, deadly drink, treading upon serpents, etc.

"Behold, I give unto you __power to tread on serpents and scorpions__, and over all the power of the enemy: and nothing shall by any means hurt you." Luke 10:19

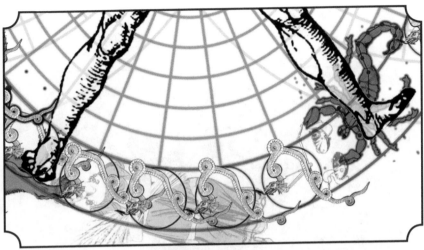

Treading on Draco and Scorpio: *This is accomplished with the left foot of the Jesus figurine. The timeline in which the satanic influence is tamed comes at the beginning of the Age of Aquarius.*

"And when **Paul** had gathered a <u>**bundle of sticks**</u>, and laid them on the **fire**, there came a <u>**viper**</u> out of the heat, and <u>**fastened on his hand**</u>." Acts 28:3

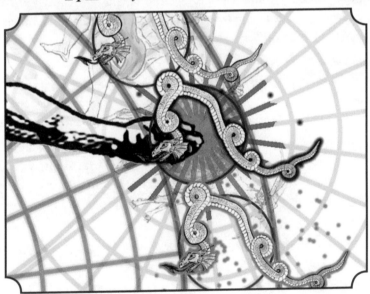

The Real Apostle Paul: *The bundle of grid lines, or "**sticks,**" is plainly obvious in the image as well as the sun or "**fire,**" from which Draco bit the figurine. From beginning to end, every image of the scriptures came from the Grid System.*

"I will put enmity between thee (the serpent) *and the woman, and between thy seed and her seed; **it shall bruise thy head**, and **thou shalt bruise his heel**."* <u>Genesis 3:15</u>

*The Origin of **Medusa** as well as **Genesis 3:15**: The difference between the Jewish and Greek magic was only in the geocentric, outer stories they told. Meanwhile, the images and science from which they came were nearly identical. The differences began with their input-primers which included latitude, longitude, and the name of each location that was configured into the Wisdom Wheels.*

In context, we can plainly see the basis for both the Greek and Jewish stories: Medusa with the "hair of serpents" as well as the "bruising of the head" in the book of Genesis. It was the same magic Word made by the same cadre of magi but from two different countries.

For a moment I want you to test your own imagination. Below are two verses that can be imagined using your knowledge of the sacred art. As always, the images are there within the grids. I will tell you, however, that the *"poison of asps"* represents the false wave pattern or *word* that gives us the deadly illusion and imagination of the human:

*"Their **wine is the poison of dragons**, and the **cruel venom of asps**."* Deuteronomy 32:33

*"Their **throat** is an open sepulcher; with their **tongues** they have used deceit; the **poison of asps is under their lips**:"* Romans 3:13

Other forming code-words of the image are as follows:

- *Asp*—symbolic name of a specific house of the zodiac using a Draco grids series
- *Wine*—symbolic word for one of the four large rings of the Wisdom Wheel.
- *Poison*—the resulting false wave pattern or imagination of the epic being described, which is further outlined by the chapter and verse number (Please note their mathematical similarities.)
- *Dragon*—one of six root locations of the Draco grid in the grid system.

Now that you understand the grids from which these verses were created, hopefully you can see the absurdity of drinking poison, handling or walking on serpents, and/or walking on scorpions. It seems a cruel joke that we allowed this to continue for millennia, but it was a necessary stunt so that the angelic consciousness in you could finally realize, in this day, the futility of remaining human. The scriptures' evil portrayal of Draco was only a simplistic way of describing a complex science that humans could not understand.

Healing the physical body, handling serpents, drinking poison and walking on scorpions have nothing to do with our angelic destiny and we knew it; however, humans needed something to which they could relate, while the priesthood needed a code to cover their magic spell. The end result is that we used humans to read our scriptures, to chant en masse our wave patterns that would return us to the dimension from which we came.

Ironically, the very thing that causes one to believe these verses by the flesh is in fact the fallen mind itself. It has enslaved our imagination for eons by deceiving your consciousness into believing the human reality. You must die to this mentally and awake as the angels you truly are.

- *Lesson #1: Ancient scriptures are not referring to your humanity.*
- *Lesson #2: Angels are smarter than humans—as so-long as you aren't taking your identity as a human, then this shouldn't offend you.*
- *Lesson #3: Good Angels are ultimately smarter than dark angels, which is how we tricked them, in you, to believe the lie of the outer scriptures while yet reciting our magic spell that in turn will resurrect us, as the new you, back into the higher dimension. (Please refer back to lesson #2.)*

THE CHILDREN AND THE SERPENT
REVEALING THE CODE

*"And the **sucking child** shall play on the **hole of the asp**, and the **weaned child** shall put his **hand on the cockatrice' den**."* Isaiah 11:8 Undeniable!

Here we have a taming of the dark element. As the Earth's wobble and tilt return to the Paradise Alignment, the influence will be brought into obedience—thus its harmless effects on the still developing mind of the God-Element as it awakens. Please don't put a real infant on a serpent den.

THE DEVIL AS A LION
REVEALING THE CODE

*"**Thou shalt tread upon the lion** and **the adder**; the **young lion** and the **dragon shalt thou trample under foot**** Psalms 91:13*

*Be sober, be vigilant; because your adversary **the devil, as a roaring lion,** walks about, seeking whom he may devour:"* 1Peter 5:8

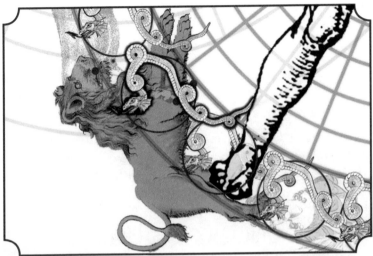

Here we see the overlay of the constellations of **Leo** and **Draco** bringing pictorial logic to the verses. They are obviously the only realistic way anyone would attempt treading on lions or adders. The young lion is not pictured here but was the constellation of **Leo Minor**. The treading of the lion marks the end of Daniel in the lion's den, and the loosening of the words of the books. It is time.

The Age of Leo: Part dragon and part lion, the Fu dog represents the timeline of the fall over 1,335,000 years ago in a distant age of Leo. **Image left**: In this we see the overwhelming control of the dark-element over the earth. **Image right**: The smaller lion under the paw of the evil-one is the lesser quantum of the God Element that refused to yield to the satanic mind. This element was symbolized in the Bible as <u>Daniel in the lion's den</u>. Guess who designed these lions of the orient?

367

THE SERPENT OF THE GARDEN OF EDEN
REVEALING THE CODE

*"Now the **serpent** was **more subtle than any beast of the field** which the lord God had made. And he said unto the **woman**, Yea, hath God said, ye shall not eat of **every tree in the garden?**"*

*"And when the woman saw that the **tree** was good for food, and that it was pleasant to the eyes, and a tree to be desired to make one **wise**, she **took of the fruit** thereof and did eat, and **gave also to her husband** with her and he did eat."* Genesis 3:1-6

THE ORIGIN OF THE IMAGERY

The Dark Energy of Satan: *Though upside down, this image is the proper perspective of Adam and Eve as they ate the forbidden fig or symbolic fruit of this dark world. The Earth's increasing **wobble**, **represented by Draco**, first disrupted the **moon's orbit** (Eve), which in turn tilted the Earth from a true **solar orbit** (Adam). Both orbits went astray in the day of the fall, thus closing the portal and entrapping some God Element in this world. The innermost white and black bands of the Wisdom Wheel were swapped before*

the stories of Jesus and represent the control that the dark energy has over the Earth's axil alignment. Its "fruit" produces our fallen-imagination and loss of memory. It was the fig, not the apple that symbolized the grids.

As you may have guessed, the serpent of Eden was our old friend Draco. As this concerns the pictorial alignments, you can see how at one point Eve's hand aligns with the serpent as well as the round circle or *"hub fruit"* of the attached grid. Later, as Eve's figurine is moved, she hands that fruit to her husband, Adam. It was *"grid fruit"* —that's all.

On a deeper level, however, this encoded story is recording the Earth's wobble in conjunction to its rotation, thus symbolizing the interaction and timeline of both the dark and light forces that were in play at that time. Before Earth began its death-knell of misalignment, its axis pointed much closer to the constellation of Draco. Now, however, the alignment that once provided an open portal is moving the Earth's axis by 24°. There is far more math involved, of course, but this is the simplest explanation.

The story also tells us of the quantum of the God Element that fell asleep into the human when the portal closed. We distributed this Element into the creature as well, knowing full well that it would be overwhelmed with the lie. Yet we subjected it to this vanity, not willingly, but in hope. We needed a mouthpiece and set about to create it. Yet in this process the creature itself would one day be delivered from that bondage of corruption into the glorious liberty of the children of God. It was our only means of escape.

At the time of the fall, not even the Element cared less about a group of random stars and whether or not they resembled a snake. However those same stars acted as a pointer by which the magi would later back track the position of the earth within the scripture code. What's more, since the Word labeled that point in space as a *"dragon/serpent,"* we took it from there, connected the stars, and, *abracadabra*, you now have the constellation of Draco. That really is how it happened.

Likewise, by using the serpent/dragon symbolism in the Bible, it allowed us to safely encode our scientific data in a way that also afforded the control mechanism of a nice scary monster. *Fear* kept our cultures obedient. Now that we can understand the real truth, however, it's an even greater incentive to get right with God. Trust me; you don't want to be on the wrong side of the resurrection machine.

It may seem like graduating from kindergarten to college in our comprehension of the divine, but it had to happen sooner or later. Actually, it is simple; we wanted to go home and created the divine magic that we so desperately hoped would take us back some day. It's not complicated. Unlike the ruse of endless sacraments, rites, and terminology by which we occupied humanity, what I'm showing you is simple. It's just that it's all so new; but *unlike the muddle of the myth, <u>this is actually the truth.</u>*

369

The False-Imagery Humanity Believed

Both the Greek and Hebrew myths alluded that the fruit of these trees produced a superior mind, wisdom, or life. The destruction of the portal happened at the hand of the dark element, which tilted Earth's axis through magnetic manipulation. Thus came the fall of the solar orbit (Adam) and the lunar orbit (Eve), both now visibly tilted. The fruit of the satanic element was his own invention of pursuing an independent life from the Source. This fruit of darkness can only bring the death of being human.

Hinduism and Draco
Revealing the Code

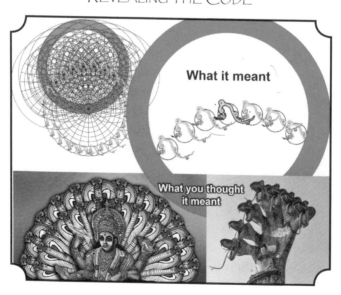

Hinduism and the Serpent: The relevance of the 7 or 24 peripheral-grids are plainly obvious within the serpent count of Hindu mythology. The science we created was above what ancient cultures could comprehend, yet these symbolic-images awed and inspired them to obedience through fear and yet symbolized the Grid System.

Try to comprehend that the same basic information was developed from similar grid systems yet represented under different national myths. Though each fable catered to its own local culture, the common threads are there. The serpents were always relative to the math of the grid system regardless of the outer religion or where across the globe they appeared.

Unfortunately, many religious scholars today blindly teach that any similarity between the Bible and its Greek, Babylonian, Hindu, or Chinese counterpart is purely coincidental, often claiming that the latter were only cheap, imitations of Bible stories. The fact is, however, that the bulk of Greek, Sumerian, and Hindu stories were written several hundred years before their Jewish or Christian counterparts. It was the same magi writing the same basic stories, just under different national titles.

The overriding point here is that you see past the outer imagery we gave. I refer to the *history story* and the geocentric gods therein. Instead, know that there is one true God who is reserved unto the coming age. The real story was concealed within the hidden wisdom of those same books, awaiting the day in which we could understand on a deeper level both the problem and the solution to our dimensional blindness.

DEMON-POSSESSION
THE WAVE-PATTERNS OF WICKEDNESS
REVEALING THE CODE

*"And certain women, who had been healed of evil spirits and infirmities: **Mary called Magdalene**, out of who went <u>**seven demons**</u>;"* Luke 8:2

*"When the **unclean spirit** is gone out of a man, he returns with himself and <u>**seven other spirits**</u> more wicked than himself, and they enter in and dwell there:"* Matthew 12:43-45

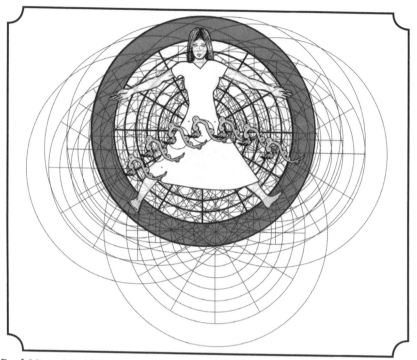

The <u>Real</u> Mary Magdalene and Her Seven Evil Spirits of Draco*: as always, an image and alignment of the grids. It was **<u>not</u>** a history story.*

The pattern of seven evil spirits in the scriptures is no coincidence. As you can see, the seven peripheral grids each contain a representation of Draco at their center. When superimposed across the star known as Mary Magdalene, for example, these seven *"**demons**"* are easily revealed as the culprits in question. But then again, Mary Magdalene was never a real person but a figurine of the Grid System. Accordingly, ***all*** biblical references to demon-possession were envisioned from similar alignments.

Yet demon possession is a very real facet of the human psyche. Within the very cogs of your consciousness, the dark angel vies for control of every last man, woman and child on Earth. They are in us all, in our consciousness, in our thoughts, fighting against the Atomos. Therein are two imaginations: (1) one that is dark and tells you a great shining lie, that you are human and that ***this*** life is who you are. (2) We too are there, the magi and the mind of God, giving you a new imagination, a new identity, and the hope of another world. You must choose which reality you want: the temporal loop or the eternal—choose wisely.

I didn't mean to make it sound as though Satan was a mere scientific-anomaly. No, indeed, it is just as real as the mind from Heaven. Be sure of this: that his wicked wave patterns manifest as voices within our heads. *There*, I said it. You see, those *"crazies"* who hear voices may not *all* be as crazy as you think. Let's be honest; at least they admit to what they hear. To be quite frank, those who don't hear are often either *lying*, or *spiritually asleep*, or *will indeed hear voices before much longer*. They come as mere suggestions, thoughts, and contemplations. It is often the inner-dialog of this world. Besides, who were you talking to last time you had a conversation with yourself?

Typically one will have an easier time of it by simply fitting into the ways of the world. *"Fitting in"* feels good, and Satan will do whatever he can to assure this. In fact, the dark element takes solitude in one's love for this world. Perhaps you know the type, those who seemingly have all their *ducks in a row*, those who have their yard trimmed nice and neat, along with a perfectly clean house and car.

They have all the right friends of course; they look good, dress well, and have few problems of which to speak. They live in the proverbial groundhog day of saying, having, and doing all the right things. Thus where our focus is, *so too is the heart*—the telltale signs readily seen in our lifestyles.

Indeed we sleep in our illusions of reality. However, Satan also senses the God Element within us and does what it can to suppress its voice. It destroys as best it can the awakening process. It tells us awful, *terrible* things. It feeds us malicious accusations, often in our dreams but also while awake. It breeds discontent when we drive, when we wait in line, at work, and in our relationships. It builds cases against everyone and everything. It comes across as our "own" thoughts, but they are not; they are *his*. It does what it can to get us back in line with a love for this world, yet that too is now beginning to fail.

These wicked wave patterns invade every thought, bringing insecurity and reactions. So while a seemingly docile old lady may deny all knowledge of what I speak, the manipulation and controls she uses within her own cliques and circles are evidence that evil can guide the seemingly unsuspecting as well. Truly the voice of the dark element is everywhere and in everyone. These voices give hard speeches; they are murmurers, complainers, and speak great swelling words. They are real.

However, comprehending that you aren't crazy for hearing these voices is, in itself, a step toward containing their evil effects. In fact, there is much to say about handling the dark energy, though I hesitate to delve too deeply. To do so steps into a deadly serious skill-set of the magi; something that, again, isn't just an interesting read yet is part of the weaponry you will need in this age. I will tell you what I can.

The science is there, of course, and begins by understanding the *ions*, both negative and positive, that comprise the magnetic structure around us. I should clarify that negative ions and the dark element, though bonded together, are not the same thing, yet they work in unison as part of the human deception.

It is a scientific fact that dark ions support good feelings in the human while positive ions bring all sorts of physical issues. That said, the _dark element_, aka, _Satan_, uses the _"feel good"_ aspects of the negative ions to further his lie about reality. Feeling good about being a human is in fact the problem. It is the very thing that keeps us from believing beyond this reality and hence supports the false imagination that the dark element imposes upon us.

Scientists tend to argue that an excess buildup of positive-ions causes road rage, mass shootings, etc., but I would contend that it is the greater energy level of the positive ions that allow for improved illumination and imagination. While negative ions bring comfort to the mind of this world, they also harbor a violent reaction to anything that rocks its own little world. Likewise, the lower energy levels of the negative ions bring about a lazy or _"slothful mind"_ as we alluded to in the Bible (see Proverbs 21:25).

The good news is that the imagination that accompanies the opening of the portal will increasingly disrupt this blissful ignorance. It is a war of imaginations, mental wave patterns and realities in which we may all, at times, seem to be losing our minds. The conflict between the two and the resulting discomfort will indeed drive many to their wit's end.

Ultimately, however, know that _only_ the open portal and an awakening of the God Element can ready us for reentry into the dimension of Heaven. Until then the false imagination can never be truly harnessed as it is simply too powerful and too quantified. Even in the beginning of the day of resurrection the evil influence will worsen in desperation until finally being overwhelmed. Things will get worse before they get better.

Indeed, those nasty neurons will become increasingly crowded within the Earth's magnetic circuitry thus causing a spike of restlessness within the human creature. On one hand we will be privy to the awakening, to epiphanies, dreams, insights, revelations, and to a very real transformation process; while on the other hand we will be subjected to overwhelming attacks of an evil presence. Have you not noticed how people are _"snapping"_ these days with little or no prior warning?

Because of the dark element's greater volume, these attacks can literally overload one's ability to function normally. The dark influence superimposes a horrible mental filter, even worse than normal, over our perceptions of reality. So if being human wasn't delusory enough, we will often find ourselves crossing the threshold of insanity that can befall even the strongest hearts.

We can see this worsening by observing crime rates and the general deterioration of social manners worldwide. Add to that family and cultural decay over the last 40 years and you begin to get the picture. While ultimately the point is _not_ to fix your humanity, even a humble application of the ancient studies would avoid much violence and hardship while on this side of paradise. What you need to know is that it is possible to shed the dark energy entirely.

Now, going forward I ask your pardon if the detailed mechanics are wanting in my descriptions. What I need you to understand, however, are the points and not the fine details. Plus, try to remember that I am simplifying this information for the greatest number of readers. It is not necessary to highlight every aspect of _electricity, magnetism, polarity, charge, and ionic structure_ as they relate to this topic. What I will say is that each of those items as they function within the Earth's magnetic field are all manipulated in various capacities by the satanic mental element that dwells therein.

Proximity matters. It is a fact that magnetic anomalies occur more in some places than in others. When it does, not only can the excess magnetism affect your mind, but also, even the more, the spirit elements that piggyback therein. Thus, should you be located in one of these areas, it's only natural to receive an overdose of those energies.

Have you ever been with a group of people and they all seemed to be in a weird funk? Well, they probably were and so were you as a result of magnetic movements and concentrations that begin deep within the Earth's core. Obviously these occur by no fault of our own yet can impact us greatly nonetheless. It could have merely been the specific moment or perhaps your specific location in which it occurred.

The cause of the exaggerated feelings are twofold, the least of which is the excess ions of magnetism itself. Add to that the spirit elements that are attached therein and things begin to worsen. Typically the dark element is in far greater quantum, yet the natural enmity between the two is now exasperated due to their concentrated volumes. Thus their battle becomes ours internally and this is the uncomfortable mind that people feel in those moments or locations.

Either way, the symptoms are obvious and take us to extremes of the spirit pendulum. However, trust me when I say that you weren't the only one thinking that things were feeling strange in those moments or in those locations. Likewise, at any given time there are literally tens of thousands of these anomalies happening all around your planet and in some places far more consistently than others.

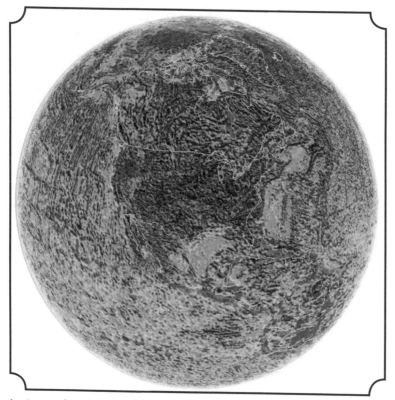

Magnetic-Anomalies: Invisible to the eye, the Earth's magnetism is stronger in some places than in others. Here the spirit elements war, married to the ionic structure with the magnetism itself, and us, our minds, the battlefield in which these invisible forces fight. You can literally feel the intensity when atop these concentrations.

The ancients of all tribes noticed these saturations as well and that the land *literally* emanates with various spirit personas. Some parcels of land seemed lighthearted and happy while others brought intellect or even idiocy. The magi knew full well the cause of these attributes, which were predictable and duly noted. If you pay attention, you can feel them too.

The Greek magi called this the *"descending logos,"* or mind that came down from above. Similarly Native Americans labeled the land of *"Kan-tuc-kee"* as the *"Dark and bloody ground"*, not because of its soil color, but due to the warlike demeanor that possessed one's psyche while living there. It was loved for its extremes in profound thought but also feared for the menacing elixir that it imposed upon the human mind.

I suspect my brethren who travelled to North America noticed these anomalies thus maximizing that energy to their advantage. I of course made similar choices in locating Jerusalem and Babylon. These magnetic points were advantageous in the placement of our temples and thus our resurrection magic. It was here that our sacred wave patterns could quickly grab the magnetic field, thus adding to its effectiveness.

Such areas can be the best of times or the worst of times. They show how *both* elements can occur in excess within a magnetic fluctuation and certainly affect some folks more than others. Indeed, some humans are better conduits and thus suffer the consequences of being wired a bit better than average. Plus, those who are more sensitive to these irradiations are sometimes further along in the awakening process. As a result the dark element will naturally attack its perceived nemesis in that individual.

I tread lightly when I say that some, but <u>certainly not all</u>, people with so called *mental disorders* are also, indeed, *misdiagnosed*. A seemingly wild or reckless mind can be the result of an acute spiritual vision. <u>*Some see and some don't*</u>. Likewise, a good receiver will suffer an up-and-down ride as the spirit elements bombard them, thus creating a perceived madness. One spirit sees things on a deeper level, while the other condemns it for those same insights, thus creating a wrestling match for reality. The problem lies in which spirit we finally choose to solidify.

This conflict is made worse by the fact that our cultures don't typically operate well outside of formatted belief systems. Here we are trained to see things in a certain way and in a certain light. Likewise, those who wonder or wander beyond those accepted limits are quickly labeled and condemned. This, in itself, adds to one's self-doubt for the things they see and feel.

No doubt the symptoms of the sick and sane sometimes cross paths, -those who are crazy and those who are not. So, I only ask that you be sure of your judgments of others and don't underestimate the eccentric. In reverse, some folks who are coined as being *"stable-minded"* are in fact spiritually *oblivious*. Remember that *"fitting in"* to your humanity is exactly what the dark-element needs you to do. So, you see, it's not so much that everyone is losing their mind but, in some cases at least, that they are squarely in the middle of finding it.

Yet how we handle the voice of temptation and darkness depends on our realization of what that voice is when we hear it—*that it is not <u>you</u> and that <u>we don't have to listen to it,</u>* and that it <u>*can be defeated*</u>. By no means is this a soft *New Age* thought process, nor does it circumvent tough choices and actions that must be made in this harsh physical world.

What it does mean, however, is that the mindset of the dark-element can decisively be dealt with as it attacks our consciousness. The onset of its saturations brings with them an emotional roller coaster of negativity— symptoms that are somewhat common but also taken for granted. Among them are *fear, anger/rage, panic-attacks, jealousy, excessive greed, bitterness, hatred, lust beyond attraction, general discontent, spite, and even depression.*

As a result, the mind that so naturally seems to be you (*but isn't*) can be easily channeled once you grasp your mental connection to those energies. There is a story of precedence in the Bible that can help us here. It is in the book of Matthew 8:31:

"So the **devils** (dark/satanic energy) *asked him, saying: If you* **cast** us **out** (grounding) *of this man, allow us to* **go away** *into that herd of swine* (grid image of pigs). *And* **he said** *unto them,* **Go** (to the ground). *And when they were come out,* **they** **went into** (energy transfer) *the herd of swine* (or into another medium)."

The lesson beyond the code is *"grounding"* and is similar in function to a lightning rod. Because of the mental-connection, dark energy functions much like the current of a battery and can actually be reconnected to the Earth. This time, however, the ground wire is you. To begin with, one must be self-aware; you must have presence of mind and identify the problem as these onsets occur. You must be cognitive that, ultimately, regardless of the outer circumstances that seemingly cause a negative moment or feeling, the root cause is dark energy itself.

Here I should inject that our proper role as angels is that of an intercessor. We accept or take on the pain and negativity of this creation as part of the angelic body; we feel and carry its burdens. Because the portal no longer functions, however, the magi were never in a position to transfer that suffering back into heaven as intended.

As a result their souls labored greatly from centuries worth of suffering that had imprinted their very being. This was a very real form of PTSD in which they were, at times, tortured by the cumulative horrors of countless millions—*not only humans,* but indeed of *every creature* that has died from then till now. Ironically, some of these horrors were created via their own sacrificial practices in which few of their human subjects were willing participants. The screams, moans, and fear were all part of the program. We all suffered to some degree, yet I suspect the Mayan priesthood grieved far worse than myself. Either way, it all works out in the end.

But that was the suffering of *this* world, not to be confused with the excess build-up of dark energy from within the magnetic field. This we dealt with quite differently as can you. So here is what you do: If and as you feel an onset of these negative impacts, the first thing is to *not panic*. Know that the dark energy has entered your consciousness through the natural causeway of the Earth's gravitational fields. You don't have to let it overwhelm you mind, but you do have to deal with it.

Once you've identified this, the next step is to quiet yourself just long enough to focus. *Steady, lads*; you will need the positive charge of the God Element that also dwells within you. You must be *still* or rather be-stilled by focusing on the peace and serenity that's inherent within that Element and Being; *it's there* and it's *your true self*; you just have to find it. This is a very real entity that is attached to the DNA of your human and enters your mind via imagination.

Next, you *must **believe**!* Believing is critical and, as quant as it may seem, is the key to dealing with and eliminating the dark-energy against which you would otherwise be helpless. Modern evangelists label this focus in a different way *casting out demons in the name of Jesus*. But it is the same thing as, *eliminating the dark-energy by focusing on the God Source*. It is identifying the correct energy that you want in your mind before going forward. That energy is a real person: the *Christ Spirit*. If you have another name then fine, as long as it's the <u>*same mental element*</u> of which I speak. I'm not here to joust over religious call signs and language barriers but true spiritual discernment.

Then, when you have your fixation, simply point to a spot on the ground and mentally project, or i*mag*ine (key word: *Magi*), the dark energy channeling through your arm and deep within the bowels of the Earth itself. You have to feel it from within your being and believe that this connection is real. Hold that thought, *that believing*, until all negative feelings have completely dissipated and vacated your consciousness.

Having arms isn't actually required, but a <u>**solid imagination definitely is**</u>. Ultimately this is about controlling the dark spirit through the manipulation of mind images, hence our name: *the **Magi***;

*"And he said, I saw Satan **<u>fall as lightning</u>** (grounding) **from <u>heaven</u>** (or from the temple which you are)."* Luke 10:18

A Magi's Trick of the Trade: Similar to a lightning rod, the original magi were able to host and ground the serpent's dark energy back into the earth, thus temporarily dissipating its mental-effects in their locale. Intercession is painful, but part of our joint duty within the body of God in humanity. Ancient humans witnessed this manipulation of energy and were astounded. Admittedly it was quite a sight to behold and one of many reasons we were called magicians. This power is also in you.

Though the process must be repeated for every accumulation of negative energy, it works as long as you do it for the right reasons. In this the God Element has within its makeup the ability to quantify your intentions. Indeed, it is very sensitive to authenticity, thus *"showing off"* in front others both ruins the mechanics of grounding and annoys those around you. It's best that no one knows what you are doing other than yourself. Just point, focus, mentally expel, and most important, *believe*.

It's that easy; and to think that by mere choice and belief, energy transfer on this scale can actually happen. Does it work on everyone all the time? Well, I guess that depends on an individual's ability to believe-or-not; but it has *always* worked on myself or on those to whom I am connected. It worked back in the day, and it still does.

But each person must choose what to believe and/or at least have the basic drive for better things. Unfortunately, many folks lack the mental comprehension to manipulate energy—that or perhaps they are too intelligent to believe in something so ludicrously simple. Obviously there are external factors, such as exhaustion, preexisting mental health issues, drug use, alcoholism, etc., that could contribute to the failure of grounding.

Typically, however, those whose minds are working within a bracket of normalcy and have even the slightest display of God's love in their heart can easily navigate this simple process. Likewise understanding how and why it works really does help. But as my father used to say, *"Take the bull by the horns"*; in other words, don't be afraid to do what you must for the sake of your well-being. Grounding is an old magi, trick of the trade and can certainly make this life a bit easier.

What's more, and this is the fun part, I realized somewhere along the way, -accidentally I think, that upon dumping that negative energy led to an immediate and predictable feeling of jubilation. This of course is the God Element's natural reaction to the riddance of the slave-master within us. It's much like the elation of an infant who kicks within its mother's womb. The child isn't born yet, but grows a little closer to the goal with each experience in us.

When this occurs it can literally make a person laugh and giggle with the same Joy I saw in the little old man all those years ago. I realize now that he was fully expunged of dark energy, over which no human-horror can contain. Perhaps this seems absurd or unlikely to those who pride themselves as being *rational* or *logical*, but there really is a science behind the Joy of God. It requires belief instead of thinking, and hope instead of worry or doubt. It is an amazing feeling as well as an important aspect of the awakening process.

The Joy of God is not just an emotion or expression but part of the person of God Himself. It is not pretense or religious acting, as some would have it, but the beginning of salvation and evidence that the portal itself is beginning to open. *Real Joy* is, in no way, an annoying prospect to those who witness its glory but is likely the most beautiful thing you will ever behold on this side of Paradise.

Because of this, it can reconcile all the hurt and pain of the past. The loss of loved ones can, for the first time, have rhyme and reason, while peace can finally overpower the spirit of death, confusion, and condemnation. With it come wisdom, understanding, humility and the expression of the indomitable spirit of the power of the universe in you.

Accessing this Joy, however, requires a lot of letting go, a lot of personal exorcisms of both your past and present. Submission to the God Source is required; focus is a must; to believe that God is bigger than yourself is a must; to believe that somehow, no matter how insurmountable your problems may seem, the power of God is stronger. But until you are willing to let go and let God, it can never happen.

Again, I'm not here to fix your humanity, as something so-temporary means little to me. My job is to get you back on track for the resurrection, beyond which not much else matters in the grand-scheme of eternity. In order to accomplish that, you must come to understand what the magi knew millennia ago; and on this walk to forever is this one small step of controlling the dark element instead of letting it control you. We live in a new day, and while the necessity of faith and believing remains the same, our level of compression in matters of the divine, as a whole, are certainly moving to the next level.

Holding hands while praying is also a form of energy transfer. It isn't just a show of religious piety, mind you, but a means by which to short-circuit all negative energy from a gathering. It isn't a competition to see who the strongest manipulator of the dark energy is, but a matter of mechanics will always ground through the most capable entity within a given group. Technically I suppose hands aren't needed, but it makes for a good visual reminder of what you are trying to accomplish. The point is to *make contact* and <u>*transfer that energy*</u>.

This in turn instantly makes room for the God Element to expand within and have effect. So you see, the concept of possession and grounding is real. Use this to your advantage as, in the coming age, -you will certainly need it. Forever is a very long time, so choose the energy that leads to the portal and brings eternal life.

One final note is how the God Element can be momentarily separated from the magnetic field via lightning, strikes. Take ball lightening, for example. Not to be confused with natural phenomena such as St. Elmo's fire, plasma discharges, or Rydberg matter, these luminescent-orbs are in fact parcels of God Element that become suspended and concentrated.

Lightning strikes create a temporary equilibrium between positive and negative charges along with a resulting _neutral_ charge. When this occurs, the God Element in that area can momentarily disconnect from the *magnetic current*. Unlike its natural counterparts, which can be very destructive, these free parcels often float harmlessly through windows, walls, or even the ground until finally being whisked away by a repairing of the magnetic-structure. Until then, however, their luminance is truly a beautiful sight to behold and a small glimpse into how the melding that produced the magi appeared.

The phenomenon of ball lightning is often a natural and destructive plasmatic spin-off of a lightning strike. Other times however, these phenomena are free God Element. The latter is the result of a neutral charge that occurs just after a lightning strike, which can temporarily disconnect the Element from the magnetic field. These beautiful orbs can last for several minutes, floating through any solid object including the ground or buildings until finally reconnecting to Earth's magnetic circuitry. This was also the appearance of the angels as we first divided and melded into what would become the original-magi. Make no mistake; there is a conscious mind within that light.

THE IMAGE OF SATAN

No different from the image of *God the Father* within the Wisdom Wheel, was the inverse image of Satan himself. In a similar manner, this image represented the Grid System collective of evil. Likewise, within the scriptures he was labeled alternatively as *"god of the earth," "your father the devil,"* etc., and represented the opposite of the goodness of God.

The image doesn't deserve recreation, yet it embodied all that was wrong in the totality of the Earth's tilt and wobble as well as the persona of the satanic element itself. Thus of this evil image within the scriptures is recognizable in the stories of Job, Jesus, Adam and Eve, etc. But the truth is, you don't need to see this image as you likely already know it well: he was a man, any man, *and every* man as he became *mankind itself.* He is part of everyone, even you. It is the great paradox of duality, for within us is also so much more.

*"...thou hast said, I am a God, I **sit in the <u>seat</u> of God,** in the **midst of the seas**; yet <u>thou art a **man**</u>, and <u>not God</u>, though thou set thine heart as the heart of God:"* Ezekiel 28:2

The Image of Evil: *The Symbol of Solomon was an abstract creation of the Free Masons who likely have and/or knew of the Grid System from the hand-me-down Knights Templar discovery. It clearly shows the two-halves of the Wisdom wheel as well as the opposite images of God and Satan. Please note the sign of the magi in the center of the image. The facts I have shown you are inescapable.*

EARTHQUAKES
THE TECTONIC POWER OF THE WORD

The Word channels energy on a global scale. This *"Word push"* redirects and contorts the Earth's magnetic-structure and in the process creates tectonic instability. Soon it will also cause a full-blown geo-magnetic shift. That means a marked increase in world-wide earthquakes—*big ones too.* We alluded to this in the scriptures:

*"The **earth shall** __quake__ before them; the heavens shall tremble: And the LORD shall utter his __voice__* (via the scriptures): *for he is strong that executes his* **Word** (scriptures): *for the **day of the LORD*** (millennia of realignment) *is great and very terrible; and who can withstand"* Joel 2:

*"Hear the **Word** of the LORD, ye that __tremble__"* Isaiah 66:5

*"And the **earth will move** out of her place, in the day of His anger."* Isiah 13:13

Though these were all Grid System images, they are also giving us, in code, the real end results of having spoken the sacred scriptures. Your scientists understand that axial-shifts and magnetic disruption cause earthquakes, yet they likely have no idea that much of it happens as a result of the power of the scriptures.

It is amazing that a mere Word spoken with the tongue, can possess such unfathomable power. However, by understanding the interaction of Earth's magnetic field, the Word, and your own mental matrix, this articulation of the ancient science becomes probable. As Earth realigns and the portal begins to open, we will learn this in ever greater quanta. I really do love the magic of God.

In the same way that a seedling bursts forth from the darkness of the ground, so too will your *God* self-image emerge, suddenly, in its own time. It too will shed the weight of the dark-element in this beginning of the Age of Aquarius, *the age of resurrection.* And though the dark-element desperately tries to stifle this frail and developing life, it simply cannot hold the power of God prisoner forever.

However Satan also has the power of magnetic-manipulation. During the fall, which began over one million years ago, he literally uplifted Earth's axis in an effort to misalign and close the portal. In so-doing this rocked Earth's foundations with massive quakes, some of which lasted for decades. The magi backlogged this event within the scriptures:

"They that see (Lucifer) *will consider him, saying, is this the __man that made the earth to tremble__, that __did shake kingdoms__;"* Isaiah 14:

*"Now shall the <u>isles **tremble in the** day of thy fall</u>;"* Ezekiel 26:18

This is a Grid System image but none the less describes earthquakes.

The *fall* itself however, began at Lucifer's point of decision in which the Covering Cherub considered itself a separate entity from the Source and, as a result, became the evil spirit of biblical lore. The book of Romans beautifully states what happened during the fall as well as the alteration of spirit into flesh:

*"Because that, when they knew God, **they glorified him not as God** (this is the point of decision for Lucifer), neither were thankful; but became **<u>vain</u>** in their **<u>imaginations</u>** (altered creative capacity), and their foolish heart was **<u>darkened</u>** (negative ions and the resulting false imagination)...And <u>**changed the glory of God**</u> (Super-aurora and positively-charged Source) into the **image of man,** and **birds,** and **beasts** (constellations and figurines but also as physical-creatures of Earth)."* Romans 1:21-23

This is the essence of the fall.

Next is confirmation from the Bible about what led to that horrible time of instability. You have to look beyond the code to see it, but we put it there so that one day, *this day,* you could understand what happened:

*"You **<u>were perfect</u>** (axial-spin) in your ways from the **day** (1000 year-long cycle in which the portal was closed/See 2ⁿᵈ Peter 3:8) that thou were created, **till <u>iniquity</u>** (wobble/lean) **was found in you"***

*"But you **<u>considered your own beauty</u>** (Super-Aurora), and played the <u>harlot</u>"* (his mind strayed from being one with the Source)

*"Your **<u>heart was lifted up</u>** (axial-tilt) because of thy beauty** (aurora), you have **<u>corrupted</u> your wisdom** (changed matrix) by reason of thy **<u>brightness</u>"*** (he awoke in the earth and saw his beauty in the aurora) Ezekiel 16:15/28:13-15

THE <u>BEAST</u> OF tHE BOOK OF REVELAtION
REVEALING THE CODE

*"And I stood upon the **sand of the sea** (stars of the lower sea), and saw a <u>beast</u> rise up out of the sea, having **seven heads** and **<u>ten horns</u>**, and upon his horns **<u>ten crowns</u>**, and upon his heads the name of blasphemy."*

*"And the beast which I saw was like unto a <u>**leopard**</u>, and his feet were as the <u>feet of a bear</u>, and his mouth as the <u>mouth of a lion</u> and the **<u>dragon</u> gave him his power and his seat and great authority."* Revelation 13:

THE MULTI-HEADED BEAST OF REVELATION

This is the illusion we wanted you to believe.

THE <u>REAL</u> BEAST OF REVELATION THAT WE CREATED

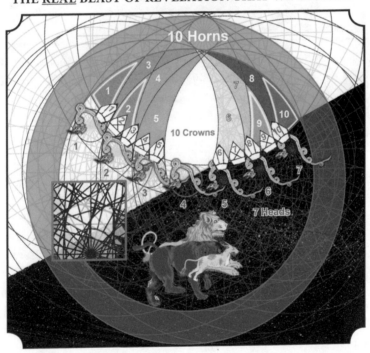

*This is <u>real</u> the beast of Revelation: Count, if you will, the unmistakable alignments that produce **10 horns**, **10 crowns**, and the **7 hubs** or "**heads**" of **Draco**. These details are all*

contained within the red highlighted grid. More so, as each grid was placed it superimposed the constellations of Leo the **lion**, Ursa Major the **bear**, and the **leopard** known as lynx. Please note the expanded line-data on the left that forms the 10 crowns.

We should again note that Greek and Hindu mythology also involved obvious creations of overlapping constellations and grids. In one story, the constellations of Draco, Leo and Capricorn were symbolized as *"Chimera"*; a strange lion-like beast with a lion's head, a goat's body, and a serpent's tail:

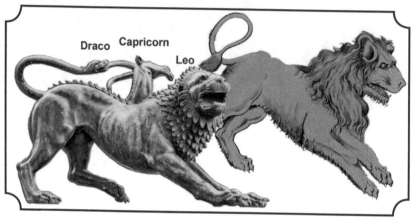

Chimera, *Similar to the beast of Revelation 13, was the Greek creation that combined Leo, Capricorn and Draco. It is a fact that all of our priesthoods used similar grid-systems by which to attain their mythological-lore. Such imagery inspired fear within the child-like minds of the human cultures we controlled, thus helping us to obtain their obedience. At that time in history, there was zero reason to let them believe otherwise...*

THE GREAT HARLOT
REVEALING THE CODE

*"...upon her forehead was a name written, MYSTERY, **BABYLON THE GREAT**... So he carried me away in the spirit into the **wilderness** and I saw a **woman sit upon a <u>scarlot colored</u> beast**, full of **names of <u>blasphemy</u>**, having <u>**seven heads and ten horns**</u>... and the **woman** was arrayed in **<u>purple</u>** and <u>**scarlet**</u> color, ...and here is the mind which hath wisdom. The <u>**seven heads**</u> are <u>**seven mountains,**</u> on which the <u>**woman sits**</u>"*

Revelation 17:

The Great Harlot: *a female figurine superimposed over the image of the beast. Not only are her grids located over Babylon, but so true are her colors per the book of Revelation. Notice the location of the* **scarlet** *(red) color of the Wisdom Wheel over both the beast and the harlot. There was not enough space to include the* **"seven mountains,"** *but hopefully at this point your own imagination will see them within her* **seven grids**.

Let's talk about the wrong colors of the aurora: The Great Harlot of Revelation 17 represents the strayed orbit of the moon in relation to the Earth's tilt and wobble. In so do-ing her celestial persona is clothed with every wrong order of aurora colors: *scarlet* during the winter when it should in fact be blues and purples, and *purples* during the summer when it should be displaying reds. It's fancy that the Wisdom Wheel not only spelled these verses but also labeled the right and wrong colors of the aurora in great detail.

Ironically, the Vatican in Rome has long been equated as the seven mountains of this verse due to its location upon *seven* distinct hills. While I openly disapprove of the historic corruption within many religious institutions, I must confess that the Vatican has no connection to this verse. I do suspect, however, that they have in their possession some or many of our sacred maps—but wouldn't dare disclose them. To do-so would be the same as confess that they knew they were using the scriptures for human control. Then again, they may claim that they were waiting for God to open the seals and felt *"disinclined to release the information prematurely."* We will see what happens.

389

DRACO ON OUR MAPS

As you might imagine the scriptures also placed the celestial serpent within our hybrid map. By using this Grid-System overlay, we can now make sense of literally dozens of verses that before were beyond comprehension to anyone outside of the magistrates. As the images show, names such as **Tyre/Sidon, Pharaoh, Nebuchadnezzar, Egypt, Babylon, The Wilderness, Jerusalem**, etc., cease to be a historical person or location, but instead marking-points of the Earth's tilt on our star-charts.

Through this revelation you may grasp our science in greater depth as well as the code that hid it for thousands of years:

TYRE/SIDON: REVEALING THE CODE

*"Tyre shall be a place for the spreading of __nets__ in the **midst of the sea.**"*
Ezekiel 26:5

JERUSALEM: REVEALING THE CODE

"And I will make Jerusalem __heaps__ and a __den__ of __dragons__." Jeremiah 9:11

PHARAOH OF EGYPT: REVEALING THE CODE

"Thus says the Lord GOD; Behold, I am against thee, __Pharaoh__ king of Egypt, the great __dragon__ that lies in the midst of his rivers" Ezekiel 29:3

KING OF BABYLON: REVEALING THE CODE

"__Nebuchadnezzar__ the __king__ of __Babylon__ has devoured me, he has swallowed me up like a __dragon__," Jeremiah 51:34

"And __Babylon__ shall become __heaps__, a dwelling place for __dragons__...," Jeremiah 51:37

THE WILDERNESS: REVEALING THE CODE

"And I hated Esau, and laid his mountains and his heritage waste for the __dragons of the wilderness__." Malachi 1:3

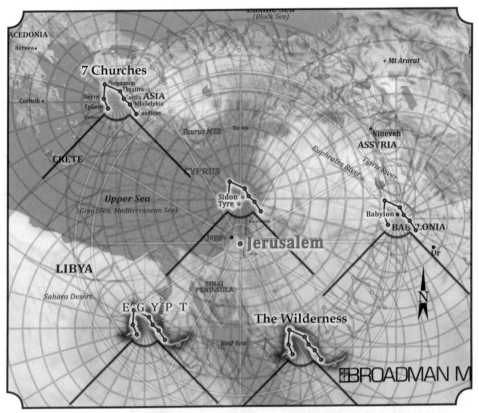

See if you can find the images of the underlined words in each verse. This same line-data could form either "**heaps,**" "**dens,**" or "**mountains**" according to the Word of the Wisdom Wheel. These are the real enemies of biblical Israel—not people, but the wobble and tilt of Draco as portrayed on our maps.

THE MARK OF THE BEAST AND THE MARK OF CAIN
REVEALING THE CODE

"And he causes all, both small and great, rich and poor, free and bond, to receive a **mark in their right hand, or in their foreheads**: Revelation 13:16, 17

"And the Lord set a **mark** upon Cain, lest any finding him should kill him." Genesis 4:15

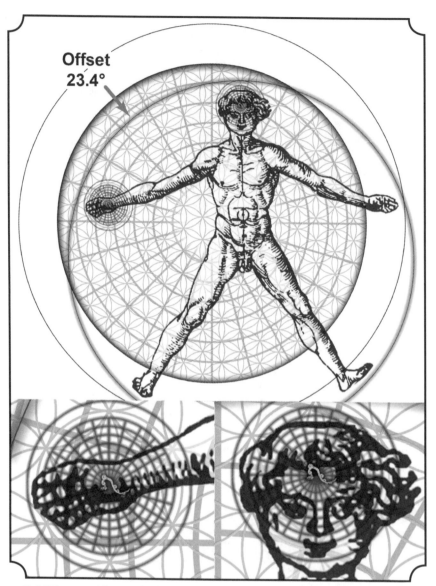

**Offset
23.4°**

Grid Tattoos: *The mark of Cain and the mark of the beast were nothing more than the constellation lines of Draco as they impose upon the right hand and forehead of the figurines. Obviously any number of images can be formed from the grids, yet the verses dictate the specifics of each verse in detail. Our separation from the Source has likewise imprinted a false imagination upon our minds, symbolized by Draco's alignments within the Grid System. Indeed, we think we are human, but we are not. Speak the Word; align the earth; open the Portal; let's go home.*

666
THE MATH OF AN EVIL MAN

*"Here is wisdom. Let him that hath understanding **count** the **number** of **the beast**: for it is the **number** of a **man**; and his number is **600**, **60**, **6**"* (as written in the original manuscripts) Revelation 13:18

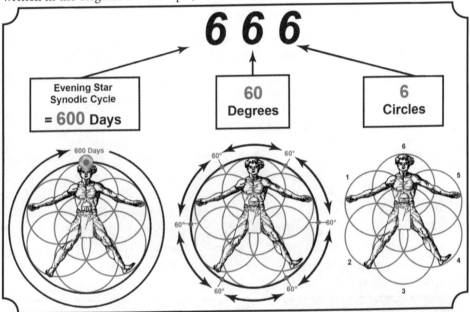

*The real correlation between the **lilies**, **King Solomon** and the number of **666**: Everything, but **everything**, in the ancient scriptures is based upon our images and their math.*

First, please note that we are discussing the **number of a man**, and that the **men** of the Bible were figurines of the Grid System. Enter **synodic-cycles**: a laborious subject of which I refuse to pursue in this writing. It is relevant, however, in the solution of 666. I will tell you this: It takes about *584 days* to complete the formation of a day star/figurine as measured against the celestial equator. However, when measuring an evening star/figurine against the ecliptic, it takes a bit longer, about **600 days**. Thus the number 600 represents the first part of the 666 solution.

Next, *6* is the number of circles in our *"Lilly"* grid design. Likewise, the Bible makes this correlation between Solomon and the number **666**:

*"Consider the **lilies of the field**, how they grow; they toil not, neither do they spin: And yet I say unto you, that even **Solomon** in all his glory was not*

arrayed like one of these (actually he was, but it is a play on words)" Matthew 6:28

"*Now the weight of gold that came to* **Solomon** *in one year was* **six hundred, threescore** (i.e. 60) **and six** (or, 666) *talents of gold,* (or, sunlight)" 1 Kings 10:14

Last, **60** is the number of degrees that separate each of those circles within the Lilly grid-design. Thus when you multiply those **60°** by **6** grids, it equals 360, which is the total number of degrees in a circle. So there you have the formative math or **numbers** *of a man* for a total of **600 days**, **60°** and **6 grids**.

But there is more to the 666 solution. As I've stated throughout this writing, Earth's 24° tilt and wobble is the problem that prevents an open portal. Presently, Earth's poles are now tilted by exactly 23.4° (almost 24°) as of the time of this writing. If you take the total of 90° from the pole to the equator and subtracts the problem of 23.4°, you end up with **66.6°**, and since Draco represents that wobble and offset, you can begin to see the mathematical relevance. Simple.

There is more fun yet however. The magi also developed and used a mathematical cube called a **magic-box**. With this seemingly insignificant item, we were able to attach numeric-values to each and every word that was spelled within the Wisdom Wheel. We called this process "*counting,*" as in "**count** *it all* **Joy**" (James 1:2), or "**count** *it as righteousness,*" or even "**count** *the* **number** *of* **the beast**" (Revelation 13:18). It was assumed that if you were a magi and understood the code, you would literally *count* and comprehend the mathematical-values instead of taking these verses figuratively or literally. Trust me; the numbers will tell a different story than the outer façade.

A magic square on the Sagrada Família church in Barcelona. The **magi** *regularly used* **magic** *cubes (go figure) and squares to assist in the production of the divine Word. Nothing we did was random or haphazard, but according to the math of the stars.*

Counting was especially easy in the Hebrew and Greek languages as they were specifically designed to that end. Likewise an obvious example of *counting* is found in Revelation 9 and 13, in which the name of the beast is given as both ***Abaddon*** and ***Apollyon***, both of which our magic cubes valued at <u>***600, 60, and 6***</u>

"*And that no man might buy or sell, save he that had the mark, or the* <u>**name** *of* **the beast**</u>*, or the* <u>**number** *of his name*.</u>" Revelation 13:17

And they had a king over them, which is the **angel of the bottomless pit** (an image of the grids), *whose* <u>**name**</u> *in* *the* <u>**Hebrew**</u> *is* <u>**Abaddon**</u>*, but in the* <u>**Greek**</u> *his name* **is** <u>**Apollyon**</u>." Revelation 9:11

"<u>*Let him that hath* **understanding** **count** *the* **number** *of* **the beast**</u>" Revelation 13:18

And so now, finally, after almost 2,000 years, you too know the mystery and <u>understanding</u> of 666.

THE CHAINING OF THE DRAGON
REVEALING THE CODE

"*I saw an angel come down from heaven, having the key of the bottomless pit and a* <u>**great chain in his hand**</u>." Revelation 20:1

"*And he laid hold on the* <u>**dragon**</u>*, that* **old serpent, which is the Devil,** *and Satan, and* <u>**bound him a thousand years**</u>" Revelation 20:2

The Chaining of the Dragon: *The design of this ancient chain perfectly symbolizes the constellation dots and lines of Draco. The hand is that of the Jesus figurine. Remember, the dots are also the seven cities mentioned at the beginning of the book of Revelation. The Wisdom Wheel made these nifty correlations for us. Pure God-magic.*

There were three variations of Draco's star-pattern used by our priesthoods around the world, yet the one displayed is **_identical_** to the version we used in Israel, only the brightest stars being chosen. Likewise notice the unmistakable likeness of an ancient chain and the constellations lines that they symbolize. As you can see, the hand of Jesus is pictorially *"binding the dragon."*

But what does the chaining of the dragon mean in real terms? It's referring to something of infinite significance. It is a prophecy, the beginning of which is already being fulfilled. Slightly, oh so slightly, Earth's tilt is lessening. The effects of the satanic mind, symbolized by Draco, is weakening. Metaphorically he is being *chained*. The process has begun; the angels in this age of resurrection are just beginning to stir within your minds, and this information is the trumpet that sounds their return.

The proof? The scientific proof is found in that the earth's tilt and wobble are in decline. Remember that the very reason I even have this knowledge, -the only reason I could have seen the little old man, is because *something **has** changed*. For over 2,500 years no one outside of the magi priesthood has had this knowledge, and I will tell you that the only reason I have it now is that the portal has once again blinked **on**. Indeed in the same way that it once failed, it is now trying to reignite.

It is not *on* yet but flickering, just a tiny bit closer than before; just enough that something wonderful happened for you; that you would finally be given the whole truth; that the *seals* were finally loosed; and that the science of the magi should be known. What do you have to lose? What risk is there by reading the ancient scriptures, by *projecting* the Word into space? *Take a chance*, as unlikely as it may seem, that maybe, just maybe, the magi were right. Indeed, it is a magic spell more powerful than you can imagine. Let the unassuming become the unfathomable in your life.

More important than the morning sunrise is the salvation of a soul from another world that most don't even know exists. This priceless artifact must survive. It's God's will that it should. It is not a joke; it is not some mythological ruse but the most real thing you will ever be. Let's get on with it.

And like a thief in the night came a battle within that we didn't suspect and in a way we would have never imagined.

The battle of Armageddon, the war for your soul, <u>is here</u>. The struggle occurs not outside in some distant land but inside of your mind. The Word is our ally in this war that heralds the return of the Great White Serpent, aka; the mind-wave of the <u>Atomos</u>—the <u>Element of God</u>.

XIII

THE ANGELIC-EVIDENCE
The Clues of Our Visitation

Perhaps now is a good time to correlate other parts of the magi's past and their relationship to your world today. Much of what I have to tell you is from memory while other facets of my knowledge are purely instinctive. Simply put, I know how the magi thought, and thus recognizing the significance of an ancient object is often intuitive. Other times however, I still see images from my past, having either been directly or indirectly involved.

On that note: Similar to the sacred scriptures, the ancient pyramids were also resurrection machines. Some archaeologists have touched upon this, though they generally attribute their application to the king who was supposedly buried therein. Pyramids were in fact, our first, best-try as resurrection-mechanics. Indeed we made them by the thousands and in practically every corner of the world including Egypt, Central-America, South-America, China, Indonesia, India and the list goes on.

And though pyramids get a thumbs-up for grandiose scale and architecture, they also are typically misunderstood by modern man. The range of misconceptions go from a superstitious novelty of the past all the way to the belief that they were built by ancient aliens. In a sense, the alien concept is correct, but rather than extraterrestrials, the magi were a remnant caste of _interdimensional_ beings. But the real premise for the pyramids is of course the _science_ of connecting the dimensions.

So, how do they work? During the approximations of the spring and fall equinox and depending upon the moon phase during those seasons, we felt an unusually strong loosening of our minds. When that happened, we knew that the portal was trying to open, if only slightly and for a few days each year. Under those conditions and during those days, Earth's magnetic field aligns well enough to allow a minute amount of portal function. As a result, we designed the pyramids to maximize those alignments to our advantage.

It occurred to us that if we could somehow magnify a point of relative gravity during the equinox, then we could better utilize those conditions to open a mini-portal at the apex of the structure. To acquire the extra gravity requires mass, that is, -huge amounts of rock stacked in a very specific design and with an alignment that can funnel the geomagnetic energy of the earth. And even though our solution required a monumental amount of labor, we certainly had lots of time, so it really didn't matter. The science of course can be seen in the pyramids construction:

1. *Mass:* —mass creates gravity which has a <u>co-dimensional</u> property; this is the advantage of using heavy stone—the more weight, the more natural gravity.

2. ***The pyramid's alignment with either the existing polarity or the celestial equator***—alignments affect the directions of the magnetic-fields and/or the gravitational flow of a pyramid.

3. *Sacred-geometry:* —this was ***obtained via the Grid System***. This is a form of mathematical purity. Much like a chemical reaction requires a perfect mixture, so too does the design of a structure that taps into the magnetic field.

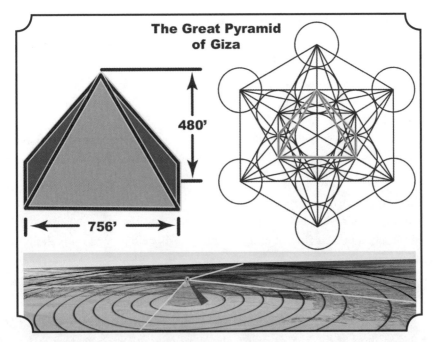

The Great Pyramid
of Giza

480'

756'

The sacred geometry of the Great Pyramid of Giza was born from the Grid System art. This huge machine gathered and focused the Earth's local geo-magnetic energy by which to open a mini-portal.

So-long as one lived within sight of a pyramid, their inherent design assured that your personal God-DNA was resurrected back into the higher dimension upon your earthly-death. The downside was that it only worked on or around the equinoxes when Earth's magnetic-fields were better aligned with those of the sun. The calculations for these *mini-portals* took into account both the curvature of the earth, the height of the pyramid, and the point of incidence between them.

During physical-death, the Atomos enjoys a small window of opportunity in which it either lingers or enters another living organism or, if within the critical distance from a pyramid, is ejected through its portal. If there's no portal available, and no living organism to inhabit, the Element can lie stationary until Earth's magnetic-circuitry captures and distributes it elsewhere around the planet. Excess or unattached source-element will always be subject to this roller-coaster ride of Earth's magnetic currents. Eventually, however, it will always reconnect with a host-being, usually a human.

So you see, our pyramids were by no means just for kings, even though their royal-arrogance demanded exclusivity therein. Obviously we told the kings whatever their ego needed to hear yet designed the pyramids for our own ends. They never knew the difference. The point was to siphon off as much dimensional DNA as possible, which is why we built so many pyramids in each of the ancient cultures. The more pyramids, the more humans within the sphere of our portal-mechanics.

Perhaps you are wondering then, why more than one pyramid is often found in proximity such as those in Giza, Egypt. All I can say is that the kings were egotistical and competitive. They were also in control (*sometimes at least*) and often demanded, against our advice, that we build one at a given location. The kings were the worst when it came to the *"bigger is better concept"* and were only too eager to outdo the pyramids of their predecessors.

Honestly, it wasn't necessary to have these extra structures, but neither did it hurt anything. Either way, it didn't matter to us as we weren't the ones hammering, chiseling, lifting, and dragging of all those stones. All we had to do was design and oversee their construction.

Like a well-tuned engine, most pyramids cater to the alignments of the Sun during the equinox and magnetic poles in order to function. The problem however, is that the natural tectonic movement of the continents over thousands of years has altered the position of these structures (*some more than others*). This in turn has reduced their effectiveness and resurrection value. Likewise the smoother outer surface of the Giza pyramids was found to aid the resurrection mechanics, but this too has been destroyed over time. These days most pyramids run more like an old car that's missing a spark-plug.

Not all pyramid designs were successful. An example of outright failure in fact is the <u>Bent pyramid</u>, which was an attempt to extend the structure's resurrection cycle from the <u>fall equinox through to the winter solstice and into the spring equinox</u>. It was an experimental version in which its designer (*wasn't me*) tried to capitalize upon the pyramid's dual-angle design, thus matching the angular position of the sun during those seasons.

Those angles are bracketed within the slopes of the pyramid to within 10° total. Again, this mimics the highest and lowest points of the Sun on March 21st and September 21st as well as on December 21st. These are the equinoxes and shortest days of the year.

Likewise, we could easily judge the success or failure of a pyramid by merely sitting in its interior. If it gave us a *"buzzed"* feeling on or near the equinoxes, then it was trying to separate our angelic-consciousness from the human mind. However the testament to the Bent pyramid's failure is that the design was never used again.

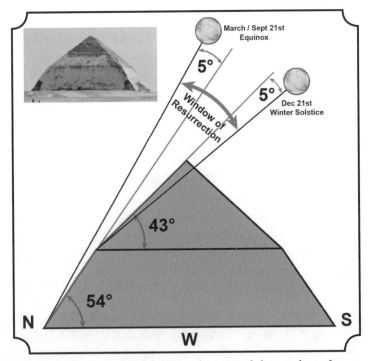

Pyramid Fail: The Bent pyramid was designed to extend the window of resurrection each year, its slopes catering to the height of the sun between the winter solstice and the equinoxes and thus its magnetic angle-of-pull during those times. Had it been successful, the Egyptian sages would have surely built more just like it.

Eventually, however, we all came to the same conclusion: the scriptures were the only sure method for long-term successful resurrection. Other than in the Americas, with which I personally had no contact, one may draw a definitive timeline in which pyramid-building ceased and scriptures began to be written—that, and the fact that in places like Israel and Greece the lower populations didn't allow for pyramid construction.

Instead we achieved the necessary *mass* by having everyone gather and listen-to or repeat the scriptures upon command. There is strength in numbers; thus, the more people who could read or repeat our verses, the stronger the output signal of the Word. Meanwhile the *alignment* issue was solved by the inherent math of the Word and even the timing of the day and year in which those scriptures were employed.

The difference is that instead of siphoning-off the Element upon each person's death and only during the equinoxes as with the pyramids, the Word will instead cause a general exodus once Earth's axis realigns. Ultimately, 12° is the final tilt that solidly locks the portal into perfect function, but by then the angelic force will all but be gone and a flood of new element will cycle through on a monthly basis, thus bringing a return of the new *Covering Cherub* (see "<u>*Day of the Fallen*</u>"). This is the **Paradise-alignment** in which Earth's rotation is nearly perpendicular to the sun.

As a side note, the Mayan's reasoning for human-sacrifice atop their pyramids was trifold: First was the resurrection theme in which the forfeiture of the physical body was necessary in order for the Element to access heaven. Flesh and blood cannot inherit the higher-dimension as even the Book itself states in 1 Corinthians 15. The Mayan priests knew this as well and were by no means shy about the issue of physical death.

Next was the marketing value: I'm fairly certain that people watching these ritual slaughters considered the cost of breaking the rules, *any rule*. To do so might mean front-row seats for getting your heart cut out and then your head rolled down the pyramid like a ball in front of your family and friends. Call it "*effective crime deterrent and crowd control*." Capital punishment spoke loudly to miscreants and thieves; it reduced crime and helped maintain social order.

The third reason for human sacrifice, however, was population control. Food shortages as a result of drought and crop failure were a real problem then, just as they are today. So instead of making the breeding situation worse, we simply rid ourselves of the surplus population until the rains and food-sources returned. In the near-term those deaths released that much more angelic DNA if accomplished atop the pyramid itself. Basically we eliminated the extra mouths and put a few angels back into heaven. *There, fixed it.*

Let the bodies hit the floor: Human sacrifice served multiple roles for the Mayan (magi) priesthood: ressuration value, crime-deterrence and population control during crop-failure.

We were by no means heartless and cruel, just simply not concerned about individual human lives but rather the God-Element that lies within. We stayed focused on the goal, and so should you. We would all do well to remember this going forward: even today our outlook should not be on who we are *temporarily* by the flesh but on the *eternal source* that sleeps; this is the real person of whom we will all want to awake.

However, the Mayan sacrifices were also pictorial, as even the four *Chaacs*, (*the sacrificial assistants*), represented the four cardinal points of the compass by which the pyramid was aligned. Another interesting note about the pyramids is their baseline harmonics. When we built a temple via celestial-math, it was inherently tuned with acoustics that *"messaged,"* or separated, the angelic-consciousness from the human mind. *Everything* exists on a vibrational frequency of one sort or another, thus the correlation of gravity and dimensional-Element were critical to this end. It's not so much that we accounted for this in our engineering calculations, but rather the sacred math figured it for us.

To better magnify the pyramids' effectiveness, many were also infused with the best superconductor we could produce at the time: *liquid mercury*. Mercury has been found in both Chinese and Aztec pyramids. As time goes on, however, you will surely find it in more ancient structures including many of those in Egypt. So keep looking.

We typically either lined the foundation of a pyramid with a connective stream of Mercury or, sometimes, with a sealed container in the lower or center third of the structure. This in turn served to better channel and gather the Element from within the surrounding magnetic-field. Had there been more mercury available, we would have surely integrated it within each and every layer of our structures. This detail of pyramid construction is just one of many designs that you are yet to discover.

The Granaries of the Heavens

*"And the famine was over all the face of the earth: and Joseph opened all the **granaries**, and sold unto the **Egyptians**; and the famine waxed sore in the land of Egypt."* Genesis 41:56

*A mosaic from a dome in St. Mark's Basilica showing the traditional belief that pyramids were storehouses for grain. But the real grain of the Bible's code were the **stars** that provided the math of an open portal. These numbers were also housed within the dimensions of the pyramids themselves.*

Religious tradition and literalism have for years led folks to believe that the *"granaries"* of Genesis 41:56 were the pyramids themselves. And while scholars today have seemingly debunked that belief, it is only because they misunderstood the scriptures. Remember, the Bible is written in code; it is an encrypted catalog of the alignments of the heavens. Thus, once again the word *"granaries"* is a symbol-word for *stars*, that is, the *"grains of heaven"* or the *"math of the stars"* that are indeed stored within the dimensions of the pyramids themselves. So though the Bible never directly mentions the pyramids, we were in fact alluding to them.

Genesis 41 also compares this *"**grain**"* as the *"**sand of the sea**,"* also a metaphor for the countless stars of the night sky that are likewise portrayed in the lower section of the Wisdom Wheel:

*"And Joseph gathered **grain as** the **sand** of the sea, very much, until he quit **counting**; for it was beyond number."* Genesis 41:49

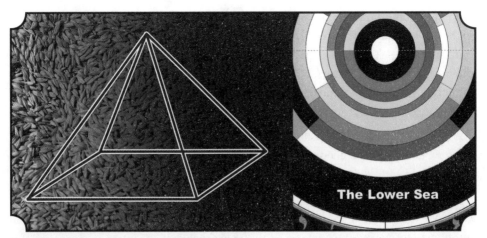

The Lower Sea

Stars' symbolism: food for the mind and the sands of the night sky. Though Genesis was describing a Grid System image, it also spoke a truism of the ancient pyramids. Within them was housed the math of the stars and the answers to the mysteries of Heaven.

Aside from their resurrection value, the pyramids were also astronomical clocks. Within them is a record—not only the divine math but also the timeline in which all things will happen. More importantly, as the Element awakens within your subconscious, it will decode itself for you, thus giving testimony to the coming day. That's how this works.

The amount of data stored within megaliths such as the Giza Pyramid complex or even Angkor Wat in Cambodia, is beyond logical comprehension. Constants such as Pi and the golden ratio were used throughout, not only within the architecture of these time capsules but also in their relative locations. Indeed, they even replicate the critical dimensions of the earth as well as the final placement of the magnetic poles upon the portal's reopening. The information is all there.

The long journey across the eons from which the magi first appeared is well preserved for you today that you might believe. The symbolism and design, our intentions and even more, are there for you to decode. The magi knew each other's mind, and spoke little. Likewise, most of what we did say was in the code of our constructions. Through them we spoke yet kept silent, in that keeping silent we spoke countless volumes to the generation that would one day hear.

We did, however, find it necessary to give verbal direction to our humans, directing the captains and overseers who built our temples according to instruction. The high-priests too were but figure heads, *middle men* who delegated our will to the multitudes who labored. The kings, the captains, and *our illusions*—it was a balancing act of deception for the pitiful bands of beasts with whom we lived. Again, we did what we had to do.

Over time, however, and with the passing of each magistrate, came the diminishing of the intellect. But best as possible we passed our energy to those who lived and worked in proximity. It wasn't the same, but it was something. This second generation of magistrates did not live thousands of years, but only a hundred or so, then progressively fewer with the diminishing and solidification of the ages. They did, however, number in the hundreds and, for a time, assisted in the continuation of our science as best they could.

Though humans saw us as gods, they did not realize that it was God who slept in us all, that it was the divine Master Himself who was the seed that fell to the ground of this world and _died in all our forms,_ not merely once, 2000 years ago as the literary façade would suggest, but since the beginning of the fall itself.

We told you that the spirit was crucified from the foundations of the world in all our human forms, but most people seem to miss that fact:

_"According as he hath **chosen us in him** **_before the_** **_foundation_** **_of the_** **_world_**_, that we should be holy and without blame"_ Ephesians 1:4

"...whose names are not written in the book of life of the **Lamb slain from the foundation of the world**." Revelation 13:8

Yet within these countess deaths is the power of the universes itself. Therein the irresistible force of God will birth in such a way as to defy **all** imagination. It is not an abstract; _it is real._

THE EGYPTIAN ANKH
THE PORTAL: THE REAL BREATH OF LIFE

Can you see the symbolism? *The ankh represents a perfect, paradise-alignment and not our present alignment. That said, we can already see how the portal/magnetic reconnection is attempting to function in this NASA heliophysics image. Only a little more tilt to go . . .*

*The moon's function in opening the pyramid portal was detailed in this Egyptian hiero-glyph. Each person in white represents a full moon, while the darker-dressed characters reveal a new moon phase, etc. The **ankh** in their hands symbolizes the paradise-alignment and reveals the specific-phases in which the pyramid portal functioned.*

The Egyptian _ankh_ was envisioned as the *"breath of life"* and rightly-so. Simple in design, this ancient symbol is found in hieroglyphics throughout Egypt yet represents the profound science of portal technology. The shape of the ankh *is* that of the magnetosphere during the paradise-alignment and it is *this* that will bring real life and eternity. Truly a breath of life for creation.

Again, however, modern man is left with the question of how the ancient Egyptian priests knew about the shape of the magnetosphere without satellites and telescopes—and over 8,000 years ago! Indeed it is humbling to ponder that, today, mankind knows nowhere near as much as they think. We should let that be a lesson and listen to what they knew. Modern science has some catching up to do and we left you the cliff-notes and text books by which to learn. Now all we must do is learn how to read them.

The Knights Templar
And the Holy Grille

It is very likely that the Knights Templar, so named due to their housing atop the Temple Mount in Jerusalem, also knew about the Grid System. The question is, *how did they know?* Well, according to lore, around 1099AD eleven knights dug under the ruins of Herod's Temple—the same structure that trapped me in 70AD during the Jewish rebellion. As the story goes, they tunneled for nine years before reportedly finding something of great significance.

The discovery was big too, so big that it needed guarding for fear of disrupting the entire Catholic Church and thus social order. Some speculate that the discovery was the Holy Grail or perhaps a text that undermined the Catholic Church as a genuine authority on God. Shortly thereafter the Templars met with the Pope in Rome and, I believe, extorted the promise of free rein from the Church in return for the Templars keeping their findings secret.

Incidentally, the Templar's wealth quickly increased and is reflected in that they built hundreds of their own churches shortly thereafter. Consequently, they integrated Grid-System imagery within the architecture of these structures as well as within the design of their clothing, flags, and even their shields. This includes both the Morning Star, abstracts of the zodiac, the white and black sectors of the Wisdom Wheel and even the Cross of the Wisdom Wheel itself:

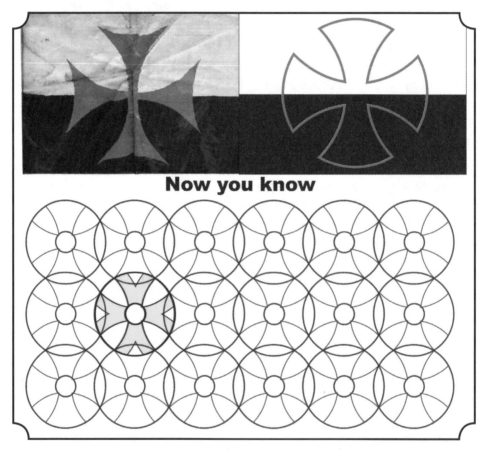

Look familiar? The Templar flag not only replicated the first layer of the Firmament Model, but also the Cross formed by the four large "angelic" circles. The only way the Templars could have known of these icons was if they found them in our storage rooms beneath the Temple Mount.

From their uniform to the very sails of Columbus's ship: The Cross of the Great Wheel became iconic to the Templars just after they dug under the Temple-Mount in Jerusalem. This is not a coincidence.

A Morning Star from the Knights Templar Church, <u>Santa Maria do Olival</u>, in Portugal— more evidence that the Templars found images of the Grid System when they dug under the destroyed Temple.

I'm fairly certain I know what happened. You see, it was under the Temple that we stored the mappás and Grid System images in a series of rooms and tunnels. Down there it was easy to keep the moths and sunlight from deteriorating the cloth on which they were printed. Likewise when the Temple collapsed during the war with Rome in 70AD, most of the mappás were buried yet preserved under tons of stone and rubble.

The word *"grille"* was an <u>old English</u> term, (*Some say it's French, but both were languages of the Knights Templars*). It denotes, among other things, a gridiron (*g-r-i-d*), or framework. It is my belief that those knights found the Grid System or *"Holy <u>Grille</u>"* as they would have pronounced it. You see; their discovery was not a *"grail,"* as a divine cup was never mentioned in the scriptures, but instead the *"Holy Grille,"* or, our *divine images.*

It does make sense; for how do you suppose that a cup, whether real or imagined, could somehow unhinge the Catholic Church? It couldn't. But the controls of the outward Church function solely upon the literal interpretation of the scriptures; something of which the revelation of the Grid System could certainly unhinge. Admittedly literalism was needed at that time, considering the prevailing lack of knowledge and education that existed. Indeed it was the scare-tactics of the outer lore by which social order was maintained.

I believe the Templars represented a serious risk to the Catholic-hierarchy. So while it is well known that King Phillip of France owed the Templars money and had reason to eliminate them—he was indeed responsible for their torture and murder—it is also true that the Pope did *nothing* to stop the slaughter. Though the Vatican has their own account of what happened concerning the Templars' demise, I personally don't buy it.

The question is, where are the items that the Templars found under the Temple Mount? I know that the image sheets were there; I *specifically* remember *holding them in my hands* before the collapse of the structure. While some were whisked away just before the Temple's destruction, many more were not. So where are they now? Does the Catholic Church have them? Maybe the state of Israel? The world may never know, but I hope someone comes forward if they have these priceless treasures in their possession. My bet is that <u>someone</u> still has those maps.

The Free Masons

I personally don't know that much about the Free Masons; however, I do recognize Grid-System designs when I see them. Free Mason constructions include the Pentagon, the Washington Monument and, perhaps, even the street designs in Washington, DC. I suppose that most Free Masons are oblivious to the Grid System's existence, but it appears as though someone in their organization did or does know something.

The sign of the Magi: Notice how the masonic-symbol of Solomon matches both the light and dark sectors of the Templar flag as well as the cross of the Wisdom Wheel. I suspect that the original Free Masons were aware of the Grid System via a hand-me-down knowledge from the Knights Templar.

THE WHITE HOUSE   THE PENTAGON

The street designs of Washington DC seem suspect to influence by the Free Masons who themselves were descendants of the Knights Templar. It's quite obvious that the **White House** would be at the top or center of the street star just as the **white** dot was also at the center of the Wisdom Wheel. Oh, and don't forget the five sides of the Pentagon, which is also a likely abstract to the five-sided stars. Who knew that the science of the magi would likely exist at the highest levels of world government?

My guess is they were a remnant group of the Knights Templar seeing as much of the Masonic symbolism and command-structure is similar. There is also an odd coincidence of timeline in which the Templars were either burned at the stake or disbanded only for the Free Masons to emerge within a few short decades. Not every Templar was murdered by King Philip and the Church. In other words, those who survived may have merely reorganized under a new name, e.g., the *Free Masons*.

Another clue that the Masons may have known something about the Resurrection Machines is that they built large objects with Grid-System-like imagery. Here again we have the base equation of the pyramids:

(Sacred geometry + alignment) x mass = Resurrection Machine.

Likewise, the tip of both a pyramid and an obelisk are the focused- energy points and thus the portal location. To human eyes the portal is invisible, as are the magnetics by which the resurrection machines function. Just because you can't see it doesn't mean that it doesn't exist; the portal, however small, is there.

That said, some of the larger pyramids did emanate small, glowing orbs, about the size of a basketball at their very tip-top point. These lights didn't show all the time, but could certainly draw a crowd for six to eight days each year during the equinoxes.

The Washington Monument and the Egyptian obelisk were another solution to portal mechanics. Obelisks were viewed less in terms of resurrection and more as focused "thought machines" for visitors of our temples. In the end it was still: <u>mass x alignment x sacred-geometry</u>.

Obelisks require far less work than a pyramid to construct yet serve an equally important function. By touching or standing near the structure, one gains a degree of clarity, wisdom and understanding. President Harry Truman, a Grand Master of the Free Masons, was well known for frequenting the Washington Monument. Now you know why.

Portal mechanics are witnessed on the back of a one dollar bill. Not only was this a design of the Grid System, but it also is an icon of the Free Masons, further linking them to the Templars' discovery in Jerusalem. The mysterious, all-seeing "eye" represents the open portal along with the new mind that dwells deep within our being. The largest of the Giza Pyramids once glowed atop its apex as does the dollar-bill.

THE NAZCA LINES AND THE MAGNETOSPHERE

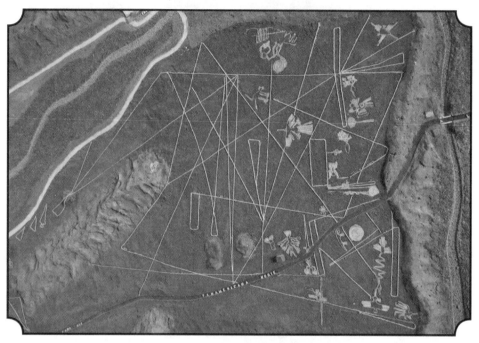

What a Mess: *This map of the Nazca lines show the remnants of a once-vital agricultural plain. The elevations and confusion of the lines dismiss the idea that these were used for anything besides farming.*

The solution to the Nazca lines is simple: These miles of ancient impressions in the Nazca desert of South America were part of a massive irrigation and water catch system as well as crop boundaries— **_agriculture_**, that's it! No doubt, some lines were used for alignment, astronomy, rituals, and symbolic décor, yet a majority were for *crop images*.

However, this in no way diminishes the physical accomplishment of the Nazca project as a whole. Indeed, these ancient creations involved a huge amount of planning, surveying, and work to accomplish. Yet for a tribe of people with no written language, this massive geometric project would have been unlikely without some technological help. In fact, the Nazca culture shows strong evidence of having been organized and led by the magi.

Beyond the telltale mathematical signatures are of course the elongated skulls found in Nazca burials. Ancient cultures viewed us as gods and thus mimicked the shape of our cranium. They bound their children's heads from birth while the skull was still malleable in an effort to reproduce our visage. Add to that the Stonehenge-style mandala overlooking the plains of Nazca, plus a few small pyramids, and you begin to see a picture of the magi's involvement.

The water-system that once supplied the Nazca-lines begins in the same valley of which sits the present-day city of Nazca. It is here that the ancient underground aqueducts were discovered. Basically the water flowed from the higher elevations into an underground channel upon which nine miles of the Pan-American Highway were later built. From there the aqueduct branched out in many sub-channels across the Nazca plain to water the once-fertile fields that grew cotton, corn, beans, etc.

Interestingly, the Nazca plain was once a *huarango* forest that was cleared for farming and originally contained most of the creatures that are represented in the Nazca geoglyphs: *spider, humming bird, monkey*, etc. These made for some really cool-looking crop designs that could be viewed from the surrounding hills. If you look closely, you will see the connecting inlet-lines of many glyphs from the feeder channels that supplied them.

Irrigation channels today

Irrigation channels in ancient Nazca

Though more artistically designed than today, the shallow irrigation lines of Nazca are easily identified by most anyone who lives or works a on farm. From about 100BC to around 500AD, these ancient fields were covered in crops that were accentuated via these shallow hieroglyphs.

The Nazca Geoglyphs: Many of the Nazca images are animals that once thrived in the huarango forests that covered the Nazca plain. The crop-designs must have been beautiful from the surrounding hills.

So that's what the Nazca lines are all about: aqueducts and shallow irrigation sloughs that once caught and distributed water over vast fields of crops. At one point around 500AD, El Niño weather patterns sent catastrophic flooding to the area of the Nazca followed by a prolonged drought. In this case, both conditions were further aggravated by a now-deforested Nazca plain that could neither resist erosion nor replace the ecosystem that once existed. This in fact happened more than once in that region of Peru and basically ushered the demise of the Nazca culture. It all came crashing down and, just like a disappearing magic-trick, these cultures also vanished. But I guarantee you, the magi were already long gone.

Massive human die-offs occurred frequently in ancient times. Nowhere was this more evident than in the Americas. Indeed, weather extremes existed then just as they do now and led to prolonged periods of flooding that were generally followed by severe droughts. This in turn led to failed crops, starvation, and finally the collapse of those cultures. In many respects, it was an unavoidable cycle. The Mayans, the Nazca, the ancient tribes on Easter Island, and many more, all succumbed to either drought, deforestation, floods, or a combination thereof.

An interesting note, however, is that the Nazca spider bears an eerie resemblance to the Earth's magnetic-field. Now, I certainly don't recall any involvement with the priesthoods of the American continents, so I can't say for sure, but in light of the fact that everything we did was geared toward realignment and resurrection via those magnetics, I find it likely that the Nazca Spider was purposely designed to mimic those magnetic patterns.

But just like the Bible and other ancient scriptures, what you see is not always what you see. I smell code; I smell the magi at Nazca. Taken in context with the geometric similarities between the Nazca Mandala, Stonehenge, and the New Jerusalem, my assertion about the spider is thus the likely answer. Maybe, *just maybe*, the magi left their calling card after all.

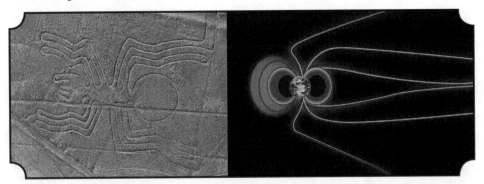

Coincidence? Maybe, but I doubt it. Our knowledge of the magnetosphere is likely reflected within the Nazca spider.

When the magi trekked to the Americas, they did so for the same reason as we did everywhere in the world: to organize the native peoples by which to build resurrection machines (i.e., *pyramids*) or to speak our magic-spells (i.e., *math-code*). The evidence shows that they likely arrived around 800BC, though I seem to recall a much older journey of my brethren. Once there they obviously spread out, made contact, and organized the Aztec, Incan, Mayan and other empires that came to rule those lands.

There's actually a lot of evidence that, if you choose to accept it, points to our influence in the Americas:

- *an intricate knowledge of astronomy*
- *the serpent-imagery of the American megaliths*
- *Chief Joseph's statement about ancient white visitors and his Babylonian relic*
- *the bowl found in Bolivia*
- *the bearded stone images in the Peruvian temples* (Native Americans typically removed all facial hair), etc.

Yet there is just as much proof that the magi's involvement was short-lived, perhaps only 1,600 years, after which they their element likely slumbered as elsewhere during the age of Pisces. But in case you think this is hype and made-up mystery, consider that in 1520 Cortez himself recorded Montezuma's revelation. Initially the Aztec ruler heralded the Spaniards as the return of the ancient gods: the same bearded white deities who the Incans credited as the builders of the mighty temple in Tiahuanaco.

Another conquistador, Pedro Pizarro, also noted that several Incans had blond hair and were *"whiter"* than even the Spaniards. When questioned about this, the Incans held that those individuals were descendants of the gods themselves. I'm telling you the obvious: that these were the remnant children of the magi who were also noted on Easter Island, the accounts of which say they had long heads, long beards, and a light complexion. These genetics and physical traits didn't otherwise exist in that part of the world.

Beyond this however, were many legends amongst the tribes of the American continents. They almost always speak of bearded *"white gods"* who arrived from the east. These deities wandered the lands throughout Central, South, and even North America bringing order to these cultures. Indeed, they taught these primitive peoples, as elsewhere in the world, planting, building pyramids of resurrection, and extending their powerful priesthoods. They impacted the Toltec, Olmec, Paraca, Polynesians, Mayans, Aztecs and Incans. The magi were the key to the geometrically precise structures in Tiwanaku, Puma Punku, Nazca, and many more civilizations, *all* of whom recorded these wondrous beings within their paintings, carvings, and ancient lore. It all attests to one unavoidable truth: *that we were there*.

But the magi weren't dumb, and I know their mind. When things became irreparable in these cultures, and just before their collapse, they simply slipped away. They moved on to another land and started over again. Rest assured of this: wherever they found themselves, the magi were always preaching and reaching to their angelic brethren within each new human form they encountered. Their duty was to train the sub consciousness of man, preparing them for the final day of resurrection and guiding them through the fall.

THE MYSTERY SCHOOLS OF WISDOM

The original magi didn't need schooling as the angelic genius was strong within them. Their knowledge was instinctive and intrinsic, very awake and very aware. However, as the predicted age of Pisces approached, the angelic-genepool diminished. As it did, it became obvious that any future priests would require a formal education.

Parallel to this timeline we can see that by 500BC the individual priesthoods were already switching to Word emission (sacred scriptures) as the final solution for realignment of the earth. Likewise, the building of pyramids was increasingly viewed as an under productive means of resurrection with little yield and at a huge cost in resources: *time, men and material.* Worse yet, the body of the original magi, though seemingly immortal, *was not.* They were dying of various causes and returning in ever weaker ratios in each new human incarnation.

There was a lot of work to do and only a short time in which to make it happen. We needed help as there were no longer enough magi to run the world's religious circles. Therefore, in an effort to expand and maintain the various priesthoods, we created schools of wisdom. Therein we vetted and admitted select humans with only the highest of displayed intellect who could then assist in the maintenance of our religious-institutions.

The two main schools at that time were in Babylonia and Egypt. There we taught our second generation of priests and then dispatched them to local priesthoods around the world, including Jerusalem, Athens, India, China, etc. Therein students were taught the *"mystery arts"* of:

- *Higher-math*

- *Harmonics and wave-pattern design*

- *Magnetic structure and planetary interaction*

- *Interdimensional-physics,*

- *Word creation*

- *Grid-art*

- *Metaphysical paradigms and*

- *The organization, guidance and maintenance of human cultures*

However, by no fault of the schools, it became apparent that our students worked from an intellectual deficit. Their craniums were no-longer elongated thus reducing total brain size by which to capacitate the angelic-genius. More important, as we entered the age of Pisces the faith Element would be subdued. As it did, the Super-Aurora that could once be seen as far south as Jerusalem, Israel, likewise disappeared.

As one might guess, this dimming of our light only facilitated the ignorance of humanity to reign supreme and in turn led to the eventual disintegration of the schools and the mishandling of our wisdom. That's why these institutions were restricted to those with only the highest displayed genius for as long as possible.

We realized that our genetic repression was not a matter of *if,* but *when.* This was the bonus of the pyramids in that they are nearly indestructible testaments that survived the era of ignorance that occurred during the last 2,000 years. Undoubtedly the pyramids will emerge as a reminder for you when the portal begins to reopen. Our hope was that at least some of these efforts would survive, and they did. Add to that the scriptures themselves, which also survived, and you have quite an accomplishment.

Though I frequented both the Babylonian and Egyptian schools, I must say that the latter was my favorite for pure grandeur and concise scholarly form. With the exception of the later kingdoms, which were already in decline, Egypt enjoyed more stability as it sat on the fringes of the civilized world. There were fewer directions from which it could be attacked by potential enemies, thus making it easier to defend and keep intact. To the contrary, Israel sat at a physical-crossroads between Egypt, Syria, Babylonia, and Greece, resulting in a nearly constant barrage of wars and conquests that destroyed our temples and handiwork on a semi-regular basis.

The magi were not known for partaking in human warfare. No-doubt however we would have been better strategists than our human counterparts, the *kings*, had we so chosen. Actually, that's not entirely true: We were in fact the most devious and calculating of all warriors. The difference of course is that the battles we fought were for the angelic soul, which itself had been blinded from its own self-knowledge. We fought to outwit and defeat the evil one, the satanic-mind that is transposed across your own vision. Our weapons of course were faith, the magic of the Word, and your mouth.

In context, our main control of the kings was by simply inflating their ego. Through the insinuation that they themselves were *"divinely mandated,"* we thus became entrusted advisors in nearly every facet of the kings' lives. It was safer this way too as the kings were often killed in their countless conflicts, while the magi, *seemingly harmless gurus of a non-violent nature*, were seldom viewed as a threat and thus survived. Indeed, before the age of Pisces our wisdom was respected by all—only to be hated thereafter.

It was in fact our shadow governments that avoided most ancient conflicts. Unknown to the kings, we sent messengers back and forth between the priesthoods; we communicated and devised in secret, a joint-plan of advice to <u>both</u> kings that often prevented war. The kings were unaware of our scheming, but that's a good thing.

Yet occasionally war was unavoidable. It was during those times that the kings would rush off to kill the *"hated enemy"* with or without our advice. As for the magi, we only cared to minimize the damage to our brethren's temples regardless of the country in which we presided. Ultimately, we all had the same goal of escaping the human condition entirely.

Israel, however, eventually became a protectorate of Rome under Herod. It was during this time that I found relative stability by which to expand the Temple in

Jerusalem. By then, however, the tides were turning against the magi and with it came a growing resentment from those in power. I knew full well that the Romans wouldn't tolerate my existence had they known. Thus I worked behind the scenes as a ghost, manipulating the cogs of the Jewish religious circles to my advantage.

By using the diminished-priests of the Jewish priesthood as a front, I stayed out of sight and, thus, out of view of the Romans. That said, the priests used my wisdom only to the ends of getting a Temple design that they were otherwise incapable of accomplishing themselves. They were in it for greed and power, but I for creating a structure through which to employ the Word through the multitudes. So you can see how we used one another.

That said, the Roman occupation allowed for better social structure amongst the Israelites and thus more Jewish adherents (*more speaking mouths*) by which to project the Word into space. Farms and towns became safer, which meant larger crops and even more people. These in turn flocked to Jerusalem to see the grandeur of the Temple and in turn became devout voice boxes of the Word.

Eventually, however, the thoughtless actions and ego of the Jewish people and priests would assure their own demise. It wasn't long before the priests became possessive of their traditions. Increasingly I was viewed contemptuously: *"That wizard with the weird eyes,"* as they liked to say—themselves arrogant in who they perceived themselves to be.

As a result, I finally left. It was safer that way and assured I could continue to write scriptures elsewhere while in seclusion. You can bet, however, that I took the Wisdom Wheel and my trusted magic-wand with me! That and I always had one more trick up my sleeve by which to win the game of portal reconnection.

Like all humans, the Jews were their own worst enemy. Their ingratitude for the peace and relative safety that the Romans brought, escalated into several rebellions that ultimately destroyed both themselves and my Temple, and led to the exile of the Jews and Judaism itself from the land of Israel. Good job! All that work brought to naught because of human ego.

Fate and faith are funny things though, for while the Jewish priests were largely killed or exiled, *humbled* at best, during the Jewish revolutions, the way was now open for something new. The timing was impeccable, for in the decades just before the destruction of Judaism, the Wisdom Wheel had written the long-awaited extension of the older works. It had miraculously produced a divine solution by which I could now continue to distribute the magic Word.

Even though this New Testament was encoded the same as the others, they thus gave a new chapter in the _outer_ religious doctrine of the older Jewish scriptures. In so doing, I was able to set the stage for the single largest religious gathering of all time: the _Christian religion_ that today contains over two billion speaking mouths. Thus I again gathered the mouths of humanity

By about 95AD things had calmed somewhat. As it was safe, I sortied to Jerusalem, armed with these new scrolls. There I conveniently distributed the _"lost and found"_ of the Word of God as I went. I found helpers for this task as well—a _few_ former rabbis, who, with no job, again became useful. With their _"normal"_ appearance, I employed them and they too were gladly employed to spread and teach the new Christian doctrine.

Ironically, these scriptures were doomed to failure in the former Jewish culture of Israel that existed before the war. Now, however, Judaism was destroyed and thus the New Testament was received with open arms by a needy and unguided population. Christianity began slowly of course, also persecuted by the Romans, but to a far lesser degree than that of Judaism. Over time we infiltrated, via the message of hope and resurrection, not only much of Israel's population, but practically every Roman state in existence, thus setting the stage for what came next.

And while I could always cover the shape of my head with a hood, my eyes were always a problem; the glow that once commanded such awe from early humans increasingly made them suspicious and untrusting. This was directly due to the diminishing within them and, _to a degree_, within myself. My power of presence, though still intimidating, was nowhere near what it once had been. I experimented with darkened glasses to cover their glow, but even then, the truth was always evident, always _face to face_. People could always tell that I was different even by the way I spoke.

Things were changing rapidly. The more the God-Element became dormant in humans, the more the _dark_-element became overtly hateful toward my existence. More times than not, people saw me as a threat. The dark element had always been stronger in the humans, but was now overpowering. What had once been a lopsided spiritual tug-of-war within them, was now a spiritual-route in which people became increasingly vile in their minds.

Even I struggled with the diminishing at times, feeling the tug of doubt and disbelief within my own mind. I began to dream at night, often tormented with visions and temptations that I'd never had before. However, those images, _those lies_, could not overpower as I was still far too strong in Element, but the evil one certainly did try.

Accordingly, the wisdom schools found it increasingly tougher to find intellect. The angelic genius became ever more dormant, and with it, fewer potential candidates from which to choose. One such student from Greece was *Pythagoras*. This of course is the famous philosopher who is credited with great advances in both music and mathematics, including the well-known *Pythagorean Theorem*.

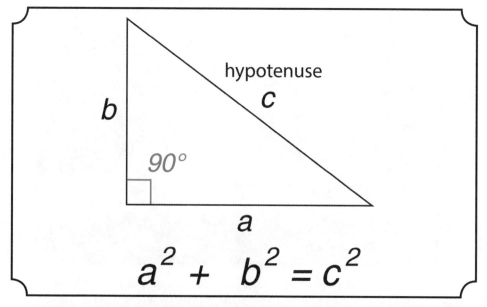

$$a^2 + b^2 = c^2$$

The fact is however that Pythagoras inherited 100 percent of his *"theories"* from the Egyptian magi, including the concept that each of the seven celestial spheres emitted its own sound and frequency. I had used this truism as well in the development of the Wisdom Wheel; the gravitational influence of the sun, the moon, Mercury, Venus, Mars, Jupiter, and Saturn calculated within the words of the scriptures.

A sphere's orbital location acted much like the *frets* of a musical staff upon which their harmonics and relative gravitational values were harvested and then injected into the matrix of the Word itself. Just as a guitar produces many different notes that combine to make a singular song, so too do the relative positions of the aforementioned bodies produce a unified effect in Word production. Thus when their timing and interaction were converted to letters, the resulting Word reflected a perfect celestial note that would impact the Earth's alignment accordingly. Think of it like this: when you speak our sacred scriptures, you are literally singing the actual planetary vibrations that we integrated within them. It was simple math—*for us at least.*

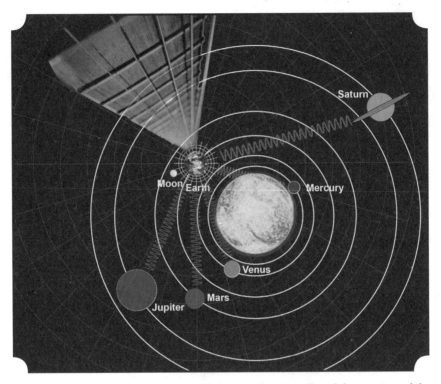

Understanding the notes of the heavens: The gravitational-pull and frequencies of the sun, moon and planets were used to calculate the Word solutions of the Bible. The Wisdom Wheel actually compensated for the direction and magnitude of each sphere's pull within the sentence structure of the verses. The end-product that you spoke had to be perfect—and it is.

The lesser Pythagoras gladly took credit, however, impressing the Greeks with his musical and mathematical knowledge in an effort to bring healing for the body. This of course was a total misuse of the angelic wisdom. To us, healing the human body is a moot point, a temporary fix to a temporary container, and likewise distracts us from the real point of our eternal self. I understand the human desire to live comfortably, of course, but the magi held themselves to a higher standard and application of the angelic arts. Rather than enjoying pleasures on Earth for a season, we instead chose the work of God set before us.

That said, music was very important to the magi and I personally fancied its usage. The stringed instruments of our temples were in fact developed according to the lunar, solar, or planetary reverberations that they were intended to mimic. Much of our music and psalms were admittedly *bland* and devoid of harmony, yet they none the less always served the mechanical purpose of correcting the earth's magnetic properties.

Likewise, the participation of our congregations in singing was limited by their inability to carry notes, hence the priests would typically sing the psalms for them, thus instilling those grid notes within their subconscious. These in turn were verbally and mentally projected into space with an agreeable *"amen"* from the worshipers. It was like hitting the send button on an email that then relays all the information and intent that is contained therein. Meanwhile, flat amplitudes such as the Lord's Prayer could be verbalized en masse and were equally effective in function.

Lucky for us all, these *"resurrection"* scriptures would eventually span the modern world in the form of the Catholic and Protestant religions, thus assuring the verbalization of the Word over the next 2000 years. Though I'm often critical of modern religious institutions, I must give credit where due: There are many religious leaders and adherents who are well intentioned. More so, without the massive *"word power"* of the world's big-four religions, the day of resurrection would not be possible. Knowingly or not, they have all contributed greatly to the expression of the séances of the magi. They all heard, read, and repeated well.

Resurrection and/or rebirth is a common theme even in the outward doctrine of the religions we created. Though it is most obviously portrayed in Christian doctrine, it is absolutely part of Judaism, Hinduism, Islam, ancient Egyptian, and even ancient Greek and Babylonian schemes. Again, the magi designed those belief systems; so the connecting thread is there regardless of the outer or literal facades.

However, a major realignment of our comprehension is both unavoidable and knocking on our door: Religion without the leadership of the wise is like having sheep without a shepherd. Yet once the spirit of wisdom returns, the leadership will come from within, not without. We will understand that we are *not* on separate teams and that *one* religion is not preferred by God above the others. There is one end-goal and it is the same for all.

Don't misunderstand; as long as we are human, religious divisions, corruption, and wars will exist. In fact, not until the new mind comes will strife end, but when it does, <u>*we won't be human any longer either*</u>. So, as we have borne the image of the earthly, so too shall we bear the image of the heavenly. With it comes the new mind. For right now, however, our focus should be on accomplishing what we can, that is, *speaking* sacred Word to the end of reopening the portal.

As you see, the allegories of the ancient scriptures were engineered to hide their true content. It was this literary camouflage that kept our secret safe until today. For generations we gave humanity what they could handle, what they could understand, but now the entirety of our code and its purpose is to be revealed.

It is said that numbers don't lie but liars use numbers. This is true, of course, at least to a degree. But rather we allowed humanity to lie to itself, to see only that which it could see via its own amnesia and lust for the outer world. And to our own end, humanity, in its sleep-state, unknowingly labored for the goal of the angels. It spoke the magic spell we created, the séance of God. In so doing, the Word will bring the awakening of the sons of God from within the human creature.

That said, the clues are there to see: the pyramids, the Nazca lines, the symbolism of the Templars and others. We left evidence for you in the hopes it would survive the age of intolerance and ignorance, a time that we knew must come before the day of resurrection. In the end these accounts would be testaments, *witnesses that* you could one day understand as the Atomos awakens within.

When you bought or borrowed this book, you likely didn't do so for the sake of a college course or documentary. Thus I have limited the content of this writing to only the introductory levels of the angelic-science that can be understood through the images we created. Enjoy then, what I have been allowed to share: the lesson that there is more than humanity would have ever expected and that, maybe, just maybe, there is a new understanding upon the horizons of your mind.

These revelations were given to me and now they are my gift to the world. Though the luminaries were charged with protecting this message until the day of resurrection, the onus of interpretation, that is, *decoding*, is now entrusted to only the true magi priests. It was *we* who built the megaliths to remind you; it was *we* who wrote the ancient scriptures. It is *I* who will loose the seals of those secrets that you may know the truth.

*"For as an excellent spirit, and knowledge, and understanding, interpreting of dreams, and shewing of hard sentences, and dissolving of doubts, were found in Daniel, whom the king named Belteshazzar: **now let Daniel be called**, and he will show the interpretation."* Daniel 5:12

*"Knowing this first, that **no prophecy of the scripture is of any private interpretation**"* 2 Peter 1:20

I stand before you, called of God…

THE ANCIENT OF DAYS

Building a house is both a creation and an evolutionary process. The finished product doesn't happen overnight; it takes time—months and sometimes even years to complete. Likewise along the way, day to day, a builder will experience many sub-chapters in their work of which people living there many years later will never remember nor be aware. None the less, in the end, we don't call a house a *"work of evolution"* but a *"creation"*. In finality we say; *"This house was <u>built</u> in 2019."* Indeed, we do not experience it in its past or creative timeline but presently.

Likewise building the human creature was the same way. It happened as fast as possible, but still very slowly over the ages. We were in fact, the solution to the equation you are today. We saw, we gave of ourselves and it was so. The timing mattered not. How long it took to accomplish was irrelevant, but this is how we created, with our minds.

Along the way there were many bumps in the road. It was by no means simple, clear cut, or without failures. There were many subspecies that preceded who you find yourself to be. Yet in the end, here we are: the final-tally of a blending of two dimensions. That said, how many of you remember the transition from the lesser life forms from which you came, to that which you find yourself now?

In this case however, you are *very* lucky. We gave you the history of your making, of your *evolution*, of your *creation*. The code, rather the facts beneath the code, give us the lost timeline of human construction. By them we can place the age of the fall, the melding, the magi and thus the angelic journey through the ages. These eras and epics are confirmed via archaeology, anthropology, paleontology and even geology. Indeed the ancient polar-shifts, many of which are tracked within the scriptures, have been confirmed separately via the magnetic patterns locked within rock formations, thus providing the timeline in which they occurred.

There is also the issue of my story, my memory. Do I actually remember everything from that long ago? No, of course not, at least not directly. I do see images, but at some point it is impossible to date them. Whether they be 10,000 or perhaps 40,000 years ago I couldn't say.

Other times however, the images are strong; I not only see them, but *feel* them as well. It would be moot, however, to try to place myself in history, as perhaps I was never there at all. Mental images are that way; they are undated pictures from the past no different from flickers from your childhood. You may understand a general timeline in which a memory occurred but seldom an exact date.

Something, somehow, however, has revived this information in my vision. I don't know how or why it happened, but the evidence, especially that of the Grid System is real and undeniable. Admittedly I too would judge someone as a bit *"touched"* had I heard the same claims without such evidence. What I can say for sure is that my knowing is somehow linked to that little old man.

As stated before, sometimes I see _no_ images at all, yet instinctively know just the same. One can't prove an instinct nor that it is correct, but I feel it within, an energy in every fiber of my being. I know the truth when I see it; I feel its inspiration. Perhaps maybe you can either confirm or disprove my claims. I must afford you that freedom, to believe or not to believe what I say. Look into it yourself. Don't take my word. Heck, don't take anyone's word. Seek and find the truth, whatever it may be…

This of course is where the arguments start. No doubt the anthropologists and paleontologists will dispute my every statement as they frequently do their own peer groups. People like to bicker and argue; they often joust over insignificant details, while missing the overriding point of a subject. That said, I will provide some specific dates of human development throughout the ages. These numbers are not so much from my memory as they are from decoding the scriptures, yet my instinct believes, *no*, better yet, -_knows_ they are correct. The numbers I provide witness within me as being true.

Satan, as the Wisdom Wheel labeled the dark and fallen element, began the process of transition from a mental capacity to manifestation long before the Element of Faith. The Earth was his new home and with nothing equal in strength to oppose him, he naturally irradiated at will. As this occurred, his mind went into the creatures of this planet. As it did, his pet creation, the *primates*, gained a marked increase in intellect as well as some obvious physical refinements.

He took a special interest in those who gave him the best chance of mental articulation, thus selecting those that would morph into better hominoids and, eventually, homo-sapiens such as, but not limited to, the *Neanderthal*. This dark melding began immediately from the very moment Satan's charge switched from positive to negative and during the portal's closure at about 1,335,000 years ago (see Daniel 12:12). Here is the math; see the verses and see the code:

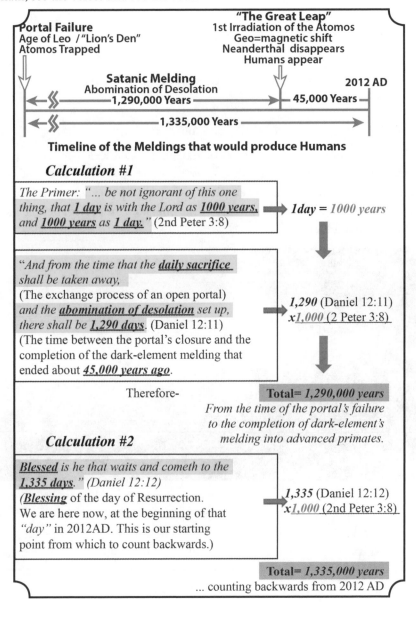

Timeline of the Meldings that would produce Humans

Calculation #1

The Primer: "... be not ignorant of this one thing, that *1 day* is with the Lord as *1000 years,* and *1000 years* as *1 day.*" (2nd Peter 3:8) ➡ *1 day* = *1000 years*

"And from the time that the *daily sacrifice* shall be taken away,
(The exchange process of an open portal)
and the abomination of desolation set up,
there shall be *1,290 days*. (Daniel 12:11)
(The time between the portal's closure and the completion of the dark-element melding that ended about *45,000 years ago*.

➡ *1,290* (Daniel 12:11)
x1,000 (2 Peter 3:8)

Therefore-   **Total= *1,290,000 years***
From the time of the portal's failure to the completion of dark-element's melding into advanced primates.

Calculation #2

Blessed is he that waits and cometh to the 1,335 days." (Daniel 12:12)
(*Blessing* of the day of Resurrection.
We are here now, at the beginning of that *"day"* in 2012AD. This is our starting point from which to count backwards.)

➡ *1,335* (Daniel 12:12)
x1,000 (2nd Peter 3:8)

Total= *1,335,000 years*
... counting backwards from 2012 AD

Thus 1,335,000 years ago is when the portal closed and the Atomos became trapped in a distant age of Leo. We symbolized this era of prehistory across the ancient world variously as *Daniel in the lion's den*, *the Fu dog* (lion/dragon), *Tiamat* (lion/dragon), *Egyptian Sphinx*, etc. Indeed, beneath the codes and symbolism, that's what we were trying to tell you with those megaliths and stories.

However after about the first 1,290,000 years from when the portal closed (see Daniel 12:11), the majority of the satanic melding was complete. This puts us in the timeline of pre-human development at around <u>45,000</u> years ago (the Egyptians said <u>43,200</u> years). The math is;

$$\textbf{1,335,000} \text{ years ago from 2012AD}$$

$$\textbf{-1,290,000}$$

$$= \textbf{45,000} \text{ years ago}$$

For all practical purposes this was the extent of the dark element's upgrade abilities. *Atomically* speaking, his mind was far less active or slower than our mind, similar to the negative ions to which he was attached. As a result, his creations were also *"thicker"* (as in; mentally less acute) than would be the final human species after the melding of the positive, God Element.

The end products of the satanic abomination were brute beasts—*humans* I suppose, at least anatomically, but even less recognizable than today and with an amazing aptitude for barbarism and unprovoked butchery. Admittedly any creature surviving in this world will portray brutal mannerisms in the process of killing for food, yet the man of sin went far beyond normal survival into a gross and twisted mental-capacity that is again rearing its ugly head in our modern societies.

This new animal was hateful without cause. He was premeditative and calculating beyond a means of survival. His intellect afforded a greater level of manipulation than the primates from which he came. He was *mirrored-minded*, that is, an inverse of the God-Element and with the reverse charge of its evil creator. His innocence was gone and replaced with conscious intent.

As a result, these early humans did things in great exaggeration, things that no other creature even conceived. He molested his young, not out of a primitive group bonding, but out of sickness of mind. He was unforgiving and vindictive, *insatiable*. He didn't merely live in this world but *lusted* for it. Indeed he no longer existed as part of the whole but actively sought dominance of everyone and everything.

He was bitter *in* them and *as* them. They committed rape not for the sake of procreation as do many species, but to conquer and harm their own females—again, a mental sickness that is not seen elsewhere in the animal kingdom. But the females too were equally conniving and manipulative, the same dark energy in the guise of another gender. Yet in the end, it was always the same mind.

It is here that we should realize, that it is not the action committed that makes it right or wrong but the state of mind that commits that action. Hardly is it fair to compare a lioness that kills her prey for food, to the gloating victory of those who seek trophy. It is not the same; one is for survival, the other, for dominance. No doubt this new genus committed acts between species or even among their own, that animals untainted by the demonic element, simply *do-not-do*.

There are other retched dispositions which I dare say, you are not quite ready to hear. Trust me when I tell you however, that humans and failed primate crops operate from a spirit that goes far beyond the natural chain of the physical world. You can see it in their eyes; you can feel it when you meet that spirit face to face.

Don't sugarcoat what you sense. *Feel* these energies in others or within yourself. Recognize that mind for what it is. Yet we should also categorize our own inner cogs and actions according to their displayed nature: Are they of the God or of the ruler of the physical world? Very often you will find that it is *not you* but a tyrant from within. *Not the real you, but him.*

Because of this, even our dreams are often tormented with his hatred. His thoughts and temptations playout every morning on the headlines of your news, *not* for survival, *not* to exist, but to control with an often malicious-seething. Its views are twisted beyond that which is natural in the extreme. Ironically that spirit can even read these same words and yet misconstrue their meaning. *It ruins everything* with its

431

filter, not only upon the scriptures we wrote, not only upon the human vessel, but more importantly, upon the sleeping mind of the God Element within you.

This was the mind of the *fallen cherub*, now within the magnetic-structure of your earth as well as the creatures he imprinted. Surely some of these attributes can be seen in other primates as well. Chimpanzees for example, are themselves failed crops that also received satanic upgrades but if far less proportion. They too can be warlike without natural cause. They too are cannibalistic, not for food but from *sickness of mind*.

So that I am not misunderstood, we should note that chimps, again, have been known for loyalty to those they love, sometimes bonding with other species; interacting positively with dogs, cats, and even humans. What I am saying however, is that the same spiritual tug-of-war that exists in humans can also be observed in certain other primates. Obviously they have far more raw instinct than humans but still the undeniable attributes of something else; something on a complex spiritual plain is there. It is part of their very persona, and often, nasty.

Yet as smarter, more promising transitionals emerged during the melding of the dark cherub, the less intelligent hybrids were simply dropped in favor of those that brought better mental wiring. During each attempt, however, the fallen-element became one with the DNA of the animals he imprinted, just like the brass-strands we designed into the pillars of Solomon's Temple displays.

As a reminder, much of the dark element is housed within the brass and black colored aurora which then cycles through the core of Earth's magnetic structure. As it cycles, it also permeates every living creature on the planet most readily attaching to the higher capacitors such as the primates, and now, humans. Once it is attached, it becomes a permanent mental fixture of one's gene pool, a perfect invisible layer of deception that manifests itself in and as your thoughts.

The only salvation from this predicament is an open portal from which will pour a massive and overwhelming quantum of new God-Source, hence, *"Thy Kingdom come, on Earth as it is in Heaven"* (Luke 11:2). However, because the Good Element was far more limited in total volume at the time in which the portal closed, it was forced to use Satan's existing upgrades as a springboard. It was a lopsided chess game in which one side had a full complement of pieces while the other only the meager king.

There simply wasn't enough of our quantum to build enough speaking mouths from scratch, so we waited, patiently until we saw what his own results would be. As a result we could now focus on his best end-product in order to afford us our own best chance at an acceptable, speaking creature. In the end we took his hominids and added to them by which to affect our own solution. In this, our seemingly outmatched *"king"* infiltrated the dark force's entire chess-board as well as each and every piece under his control. Thus the king became a virus and an eventual "checkmate" to Satan's darkness. *Ingenious* wouldn't you agree?

Maybe now it makes sense as to why we had to deceive the human with the outer gospel in order to achieve our goals. The satanic element was stronger in the human and thus we had to trick it into reading a Word that it otherwise would have never understood or read. Because we were limited in our exposure however, we too rejected whole crops of Satan's making. It showed too as some species were soulless, darkened in their hearts and in their minds. Those we discarded were typically lower in IQ and far more primitive and barbaric than those that received our Element en-masse.

Defining barbarism of course is a slippery slope, coming from a magi who didn't so much as bat an eye that his brethren used human sacrifices elsewhere in the world. The circumstances of course must be considered: We understood the way of things, the temporal, and the eternal. We had no illusions and we took our work very seriously.

The bottom line was not only to achieve our resurrection but the repair of the *daily sacrifice*. This was the great conveyor belt by which the sufferings of this world were carried to Heaven each month as the portal opened. Meanwhile, the methods we used were above reproof from those who neither believed nor understood the end goal of the divine plan. In the end, though, we were anything but heartless.

Beginning about 45,000 years ago, however, it was our turn. This is when the 1st melding of the God-Element occurred. This event was short-lived, just over 200 years, but was long enough to accomplish our goals. In terms of altering a creation to the degree in which we did, this is an extremely short amount of time.

This is the *"Great leap"* as your educators refer and was initiated by a geomagnetic reversal of your planet's magnetic field. In this, the Earth's polarity switched directions *just long enough* that our own Atomos escaped the core and irradiated the creature at will. It was then that we saturated the satanic being that would one day speak our Word; it was here that we distributed ourselves amongst the world in volume.

Here we balanced the animal somewhat with our own cognitive traits. Love and an outlook for immortality appeared. Also came increased comprehensive skills along with the faintest scent of a memory from another world. And with this bonding, the animal's coloration typically lightened as well, our illumination becoming one with his own DNA. His body hair diminished too and he now walked as a true bipedal creature. This was the final making of the human.

It is here that we can understand the sudden disappearance of the Neanderthal, which ceased to exist around 40,000 years ago. It did not die out but was rather *"melded out"* of existence. He was as good for a beginning platform as any, and we used him as such. Again, the timeline between the great leap, the Neanderthal's disappearance, and the geomagnetic shift all coincide. Research it for yourself. So now you know what happened.

Yet the Neanderthal is only one of several examples of the 1st angelic melding. There were other transitionals as well; an orangutan derivative in Asia and *"Lucy"* from Africa were also part of our angelic equations. There were others too, some of which migrated over vast distances of the earth, mixing as they went to form the world's physical races as you know them today.

More importantly we created fine motor and speech skills within these beasts that they might someday speak our magic. Now they could do our bidding; though a very long road to salvation, they would one-day reopen the portal with their mouths… We knew that the achievement of our goal was still thousands of years away, but we did what we could as the opportunity arose.

There is a tremendous amount of energy in the God Element once released, just like I felt in the touch of that little old man. As you can see, it has an enlightening and transformative effect. Likewise the 1st melding was equally electrical for the early hominids in which they quickly transformed into what you are today and in less than 200 years.

This overlay also somewhat balanced an otherwise brutish behavior. Notice that I didn't say *"removed"* this brutish behavior, but rather created within the animal a moral dilemma. It was a see-saw of duality between remembering and forgetting—somewhere in between believing and not believing, faith and faithlessness, love and hatred. Again, some crops took better than others. Successful overlays were continued and repeated while others were abandoned.

The single most important facet of our upgrades however, was the ability to speak complex sentence structures. This was of course critical for our purposes. To do so requires several things in conjunction that other primates and *Homo sapiens* didn't or don't have:

- *a hyoid bone positioned to support the tongue,*

- *certain language-genes,*

- *specialized vocal cords*

- *the motor-skills needed to produce a sizable vocabulary,*

- *the ability to consciously control breathing and*

- *a very larger cerebral cortex by which to articulate information*

Don't misunderstand; the angelic- genius is not contemplative as is the human mind. It doesn't *"think"* things through, nor does it need to. The mind of faith operates from a completely different set of parameters than does a calculative mind. It doesn't process information nor does it purposely apply knowledge, but instead knows and flows with understanding. It may notice something or have its attention drawn into focus about someone, something, or a given problem. Once this focus occurs, however, the very being of faith is drawn into a solution. It doesn't do math; it *is* math. It doesn't have faith; it *is* Faith. It heals all things naturally and by the nature of its being.

Likewise, we didn't develop the parameters of human speech, but rather the solution offered itself from within us naturally. It was the Element of God in action. That might be hard for some to understand. We saw the problem and our very being fixed it without thought or effort. This is also the way in which we made the Wisdom Wheel. This is also the way that we made you. It is a dimensional consciousness and thus brings dimensional solutions that are far above that of the human mind.

Air, gravity, mental wave-pattern, thought and the mind of God are all invisible; all remain unseen. Yet all are critical and very, very real. The lesson here is that just because you can't see it, doesn't mean it doesn't exist. It may seem impossible to prove the mind of God, just as it's impossible to see one's thoughts. Still I ask, are there thoughts in your mind at this very moment? –Of course, and so is He, so is God. The solution, *God*, lies within you just as it did within the magi.

And while these details may be arguable to the argumentative, the end results are undeniable. The scientists struggle with this; they see the truth but won't admit that in geological terms the transition from primate to human happened unusually fast; that advanced speech was new, that chimps, gorillas and even the Neanderthal were incapable of vocalizing sound anywhere near that of the human; then suddenly appeared a creature of such physical refinement that it no longer fit the mold of evolution up to that point.

So you see, it is not so-much that humans evolved from lower life-forms, but rather that the God Element *devolved* to form what you are today. Even Charles Darwin's own colleague, Charles Lyell, himself an evolutionist, viewed the Great Leap as an inexplicable event within the model of evolutionary doctrine. Here he parted with Darwin in explanation of the human, freely admitting that something divine, something far different, had to have happened.

435

Evolution in the physical world is of course valid and provable in context to the angelic upgrades. Indeed these gradual improvements occurred ever since the beginning and for hundreds of millions of years up until the portal's failure. But now came a desperate act, a quickening that brought us the voice-boxes we needed; a creature that could reverberate complex sounds, *wave-patterns* that would allow for a detailed modulation of the frequencies, your scriptures, that we would one day develop.

So we mixed and made the living soul: a new race, the *human race*. This was our end product: a genetic overlay that forced the mutations we needed for speech and that also allowed for the development of civilizations. This was the *"special event"*, as some call it, the sudden, yet inexplicable *"spiritual connection"* of evolution. Thus you are not extraterrestrials, but rather, inter-dimensional beings.

You can see the results too, not only in the obvious genetic gap between humans and other primates, but in other aspects as well. Some will claim that chimpanzee and human DNA are 98 percent the same. That too may be provable, but that 2 percent difference might as well be a 1000 percent when considering the end result. Can chimps build pyramids? Can they speak or negotiate the Pythagorean Theorem? How about design a car or create medicines? Let face it, chimps can't even consciously hold their breath.

Yet a purely physical creature also has a far better adaptation for the natural world. Gorilla youth for example can survive the cold, rain and heat; they can crawl, climb, and better negotiate the wild long before a human of the same age. This is directly due to the 1st melding that formed the creature you are today. We took you far beyond the physical; we added *ourselves* to the sum tally of *your* equation, which in turn diminished your natural ruggedness.

Try to understand that the very reason humans are less adapted to the harsh realities of nature is because they are *literally* half God-beings (see Psalm 82:6-7). Though an elevated intellect allows humans to survive by creating clothing and gadgetry, they are otherwise incompatible for natural living. Thus we can observe that humans are a mixture of two worlds; that of the higher-primates from the satanic melding, and that of the angelic (see Matthew 13:30); and though the melding downgraded the robust nature of the satanic creature, it also greatly raised his consciousness.

It's seemingly a contradiction that on one hand we become physical creatures, yet did so in an effort to eventually escape the physical world. But make no mistake, *both* elements exist within the human container. In the same fashion that positive and negative charges exist within the same battery, so do the spiritual elements within you. They are presently inseparable in the end product of who you find yourself to be.

There is more; we saved the best for last: Within only the last 18,000 years we committed the 2nd melding which produced the magi. Here our remaining Element bonded. We needed leadership for the humans we created; someone more advanced and with greater intellect was needed to organize, teach, and tame them.

This wouldn't be easy. The power and perception of magic were needed to gain their attention and obedience. Thus the majority of our remaining Element was direct-ed to a select few specimens: *the magi*; limited in numbers, yet with a concentrated *"godlike"* presence. The magi were greatly altered human stock, glowing with a mi-raculous light that emanated from our very being. In turn this visage worked to our advantage and overwhelmed our humans with awe.

There was however, some additional "spill over" effect during the 2nd release into the existing human tribes. This final boost was noticeable but minimal. And so we fell into your world; and now the Element of God that was on this side, was now doomed to *stay* on this side. Our lifespans, now finite, still lasted in some cases for upward of 17,000 years. To my knowledge, the last two were myself and Ithiel, my own end com-ing half way through the age of Pisces as I assume did his . . .

But even as great as the energy within the magi, it too would dilute and redis-tribute as each incarnation perished over time. As each of our physical embodiments died, that quantum was quickly absorbed by multitudes of human hosts who lived in proximity. Our spirits spread in every direction at death, irradiating into those around us, bringing only minimal advantage to those who were affected.

Through the two great meldings that formed the humans and the magicians, the God Element would *become* you and fall asleep *in* you, *as* you. You wouldn't be aware of it; for just as you failed to recognize us as you, we too, eventually forgot the truth of who we were. We became flesh—we literally became *you*, and though we now slumber within the recesses of your mind, you also now contain the real angelic bloodline. Thus the angels became the proverbial wayward sons, completely losing the memory of our intended purpose, pretending, as you, that we are something other than chosen angels. As a result, you are an ironic and amazing creature.

Coming soon however is another such geomagnetic shift. Polar shifts and axial movement have occurred naturally throughout Earth's history, yet this next one will be the result of the magic that you likely read or repeated. Accompanying this event will be a _polar reversal_ *from north to south*. In lay terms this means your compass needles will point to the south instead of the north. With it comes the mechanics required to accelerate the Earth's tilt and reopen the portal.

Another accelerant of Earth's realignment is the changing ice-packs at the poles. These solid masses presently act as counterweights to the Earth's spin and contribute to its off-kilter wobble. Thus as that ice melts or rearranges, it allows the Earth's natural gyration to correct its alignment. Some say that this melting will inundate coastal areas and kill millions. If so it would matter little. Remember; it's not about saving humanity, but rather the Element within them. _The Element must get out_ and this can only happen with an open portal.

Your scientists are aware that this new shift has already begun. This time it will usher the beginning of the day of resurrection. Increasingly as the portal opens, the God Element will overpower the mind of Satan within humanity. The quantum that is in each of us will, upon our deaths, condense in the coming generations in ever fewer people but in ever greater strength. Likewise, the comprehension of these individuals will be off the charts.

Then, just as it happened over 45,000 years ago, another _"special event"_ will occur. This time however, it will not initiate another melding, but an _awakening_ of the God-Element within. Finally, when it's done, when it's complete, the human brain will no longer be able to capacitate the super consciousness that now sleeps within us all. We are now on the precipice of birthing a nonphysical phenomenon. Tesla pondered it, but you will become it.

During this time, a lot of crazy things will happen including increased earthquakes, failure of electrical grids, failed satellites, etc. These are the results of magnetic reconfiguration and the positive influx of energy through the portal. Add to that the general mayhem from an unbelieving world and we will have quite a mess. Though it seems like a bad thing, this collateral damage is unavoidable in achieving our planet's realignment. Trust me; in the end, and assuming you are on the right side of this thing, you will be glad it happened.

It is a terrible tear of our inner being, these times of which I speak. One part, somehow, will be petrified with fear, insecure and unable to function. The mind of man will burn as if in a consuming fire. The overreactions can and will often be deadly as the dark element struggles to keep its realm. It will rebel, in us, as us.

At the same time there will be another part, another reality that will begin to emerge. There you may somehow find yourself anew, refreshed, secure, and, somehow at peace. But even this is only the beginning of the great _and_ terrible day that lies ahead. (see Joel 2:11)

438

Mind Swap

"Casting down imaginations, and every high thing that exalts itself against the knowledge of God, and bringing into captivity every thought to the obedience of Christ;" 2 Corinthians 10:5

Our thoughts must become captive and they will. The sheer volume of God-Element that floods through the open portal will literally jam or *"drown"* the output signals of the dark element within our minds. The point beyond the code of *"floods"* or a *"melting of the elements"* was to indicate, in code, the destruction of one wave-pattern by another:

*"...as in the days that were before the **flood** (volume of God-Element/wave-pattern)... until the **day** (day of resurrection) that Noah entered into the ark. And knew not until the **flood came, and took them** (false images) **all away**; so shall also the coming of the Son of man (the resurrection)"* Matthew 24:38-39

*"But the **day of the Lord** will come as a **thief** in the night (in a way you don't expect); in the which the heavens shall pass away with a great noise (nner turmoil), and the **elements** (mental/dimensional elements) **shall melt with fervent heat** (Grid System image of red aurora), the **earth also** and the **works therein shall be burned up**."* 2 Peter 3:10

*"Therefore shall all hands be faint, and every man's **heart shall melt**:"* Isaiah 13:7

The God-Element acts like a microwave that completely scrambles and overwhelms the mental signals of its foe. As this happens, Earth's polarity will simultaneously emit positive-ions instead of negative as it now does, thus producing a new imagination within your mind as well as a return of the super-aurora in the skies overhead. In the end we will be a new creation.

A critical facet of casting down false imaginations is to *believe*, to see beyond what the liar portrays on a daily basis. Likewise Joy is the rearrangement of those images and ions into a new reality. The hard pill to swallow is that even the ability to believe will increase during the resurrection timeline of the next 1,000 years. *Real* belief is also part of the birthing process and can't happen until the God-Element awakens within us.

But we still need the mass of our numbers to make this happen. Christians, Muslims, Jews and Hindu—believers of all shapes and sizes nationalities and persuasions, finally on the same team, not in any one religion, but as the many-membered team of God within us all. It is that person who seeks salvation through the *same* gateway to Heaven. And not by the outer names shall we be selected, but by the love and the goodness of heart of God found within.

Indeed, like a seed that is buried in the darkness of the Earth, so is the angelic-element of God. Like a virus enters in secret, to incubate for a time, but ultimately to overwhelm and consume its host, so too were we to the satanic creation. But much like the story in which King Solomon enslaved demons by which to build the Temple, the angels also enslaved the human demon as an incubator that housed our spirit until the day of our rebirth from its dark and wretched womb. This is the *real* temple of which the story of Solomon eludes.

Yet I will say, and I'd be willing to bet, that you also sense there is more than just this life—not that creatures of the earth always pondered beyond their mortality, because truly they didn't. Most species can mourn the loss of another. No doubt they naturally feel and love their own, but seldom if ever do they reach beyond that which they know in this world, that perhaps there is something beyond this reality altogether.

That, my friend is a special quality that is hardwired into the human ever since the melding. At the beginning of our human incarnations, in our youth, in our infancy, freshly in the flesh, untainted just yet, we are a bit more likely to remember heaven. It is then that our angel has not yet reattached to this world.

But then we quickly forget. We reattach. We become bonded to the physical world and reality. It is only after our conception in the flesh, in those first days, weeks and months, just before and after our birth that we relearn the lie, *the deception* of being human. No doubt some remember heaven into their aging, but these are few.

Their days are numbered. For only a little longer will the dark ones will rule the conscious and subconscious mind. Just as before they fight with the brutal weapons of ignorance to keep you asleep. They stifle your memory by creating doubt and disbelief. These demons also work to keep the seals of the Word closed; they seek to destroy these revelations and thus keep you unaware. Their desire of course is that you remain human in all your forms *forever*; and so long as Earth stays tilted and the portal remains closed, they win; they will forever have a home in you. Indeed they live, not in another realm, but in your own mind, as your own body, forming your perceptions of what is real.

Evil has created a web of lies, a support system of contemporary wisdom. These are the external teachings of this world that support our loss of memory. Everything, in fact, including our education, religion, and science, is geared toward the affirmation of your flesh; it is an endless list of *"how-tos"* for being human. And like the subtle serpent, the lie often coalesces as the most unsuspecting of all: as the word of those who pertain to teach you Godliness, but themselves are oblivious to the magnitude of the deception in which you persist.

Their lesson of course is that you learn how God wants you to be happy within your humanity, to find harmony, rhyme and reason in this world. *God*, it is taught, lived in another person, at another time in history. In that age great things happened and, someday, we are told, great things may happen again. But until then, they say, rather concern yourself, we are told, with fitting God into your everyday lives, *here*.

Therein is the great paradox; for Faith requires exactly that; that we <u>do</u> find God in our relationships and every circumstance. The fine-line of deception however, is that we find God in these things for the very *sake* of our humanity. *Au contraire*, we find God in every circumstance of our humanity for the <u>sake of our eternal knowledge</u> <u>beyond this world</u>. It is the failure to recognize this seemingly minute detail of focus that leads us as sheep to a blissful slaughter.

Like a hostage with Stockholm syndrome we wrongly feel empathy for the lie in which we live; we tend to our temporal-being instead of the eternal. Thus we fail to take greater action to secure the truth within our minds, simply because we don't realize that greater action is required. We forfeit the fact that mental participation is necessary to secure our rescue. Unfortunately we are enamored with our captor, with this world, and thus deny ourselves of our one true love, the *Heaven*, from which we came.

Ironically this is **exactly** what caused the Covering Cherub to fall all those years ago. In his crush for the visage of this world, and his own beauty that reflected through the aurora, he forgot. One might say; *"If heaven is so great, how then could one forget it?"* The answer of course, is <u>time</u>, lots of time, and with it, the memory fades. Even memories need to be recharged, no different than a battery. I can attest to this as even my own memory is somewhat faded; can you relate?

It is here then that you should realize the predicament in which you exist: that the very hell spoken of within the scriptures is indeed this existence. We are separate from heaven, and that <u>is</u> our hell! There is no intermediate location, no middle point— no purgatory on the road to perdition. If there ever was a hell, we are in it, *right here, right now*, balanced only by the fact of the trace amount of Atomos within you. Be wise about this fact. And while the angels once marveled at the visage of this world, it was never intended that we become part of it as a permanent fixture.

Yes; Faith brings Joy, not in the things of this world, but in looking forward to our heavenly home. Ultimately, realizing who you are in God, is a prerequisite for getting back to the dimension from which you came, which without we would simply remain oblivious to our condition. Truly there is no incentive, other than pain and death, to move from the hot-burner of being human. Yet it is the spiritual discomfort in this day of resurrection that will force us to move from one place to another in our minds. Either way, action is required; *you must move*. I speak figuratively of course.

What's more, habit often leads us to believe that by delegating a few hours each day or week to religious servitude, we are thus ensured of our eternal salvation. At one time the magi required such diligence from our cultures. *Then* of course, timed dedication was part of a rigid program of verbal/magnetic manipulation. No doubt, hearing, reading, and repeating are still important, but now with comprehension and in the context of doing so by Faith and to open the portal. Before now, humanity could not bear more than simple milk, *that is*—simple religious instruction. Today however, we are not as the child but are awakening into maturity.

Though I designed the Word to be spoken through the mouths of babes, that time is over. It is time to grow up. Now is the time to graduate from *milk* to the *meat* of adults, that is, the food of understanding and the truth that will lead to your salvation. By now you should be teachers yourselves, taught *inwardly*; yet even in this moment I teach you through these revelations, outwardly, by reading the outer words of this book, the oracles of God. My desire is that you become skillful in the use of Faith; that you be filled with the knowledge of the God Element that lives within you and the depth of its magic. *Awake*.

You do not belong to this world: not to spouse, nor children; not to a family of the flesh, but to *Him* only. These hands are *His*; this mind –a temple of the divine. That is my frustration, my anger—that the human loves pleasure more than the truth, that he would rather forfeit an eternity to gain a little fun in this world. Our focus is derailed.

Why am I surprised, considering the human matrix? We say, *"Eat, drink and be merry, for tomorrow we die"*. Like Scarlet O'Hara, they'd rather *"think about that tomor-row."* Indeed we would rather bask in the sun today than plan for our eternity. People are spoiled; they desire the sweets instead of the rigor that brings us to salvation. The child desires *coddling*, the mature adult, *duty and integrity*.

So to the point: the dark angels deny the *real truth* about the life of God in you; for they themselves need a capacitor, a medium through which to manifest, and you are their means to that end. Their mind and energies are real and can be understood by paying close attention to your <u>own thoughts</u>. The mind of the great dragon needs your focus upon <u>this world,</u> thus providing him with the reality and control he seeks. He may speak of God, as this wolf often does within. He sneaks and stalks through our own thoughts, setting an ambush of pleasantries, a false picture of security and a god that fits perfectly within this world. This can range from fighting a war in the name of God, all the way to feeding the poor in the name of God. Either way it supports the flesh.

With a smile we are destroyed wonderfully, murdered with a false- gospel, a teaching that conforms *God to us* instead of *us* to who we *truly are in Him*. We are taught to feed and clothe the poor of humanity, while yet feeding the spirit of God within, a perpetual poison, an elixir of the physical reality and thus eternal sleep. We view war and murder as being of the flesh, never realizing that the real fight is within our hearts and in our minds—a war of perception and self-identity. And when we readily accept that we are human and not children of another dimension, murder has indeed been committed.

The god of the lie is handy too; we can trust him for *physical healing, finances, relationships and <u>human</u> well-being*. Sometimes the deception goes even deeper. Sometimes he leads us in prayer and in praises. I have seen it for myself many, many times throughout the centuries. Yet always he will evade the message of dimensional resurrection and how to accomplish it: *"You need to get your head out the clouds and come back down to earth,"* we are reminded. Yet *"above the clouds"* is indeed where the portal awaits us . . .

Your humanity is a façade in which you suffer once, yet the God-Element within suffers repetitively in each and every human incarnation. Here He is recreated in the flesh countless times, a torture in which every life becomes a new lash of suffering. Here He is separate from His home, an eternal cross in which *you,* as parts of the God-Element (*if you can accept this*), are stranded on this planet, dying in every form, over and over again.

The memories of these countless lives are still there—the *déjà vu* that so many have. You call it reincarnation; I call it *imprinting,* in which the sufferings of each incarnation overlay the God-Element to various degrees. This is, in fact, what accounts for your memories of other lives. No different than even Daniel in the Bible was told he would live again in the end times, so have we all. It is one and the same Element, mixed and messed over the eons in and through humanity.

Ever since the portal closed however, the function and relay of that suffering to Heaven have ceased. So while we sometimes retain fragments of past lives, sadly, we still can't remember our life in Heaven. Again, too much time has transpired. What is it to take hold of something so powerful, so-great as that which lies before us? It is well within reach, yet miles away from the mind of man. Yet all the while, the dark ones will deny, as *your own doubt,* the *might* and the *power,* the miracle that awaits us in the space between space.

THE HISTORY OF DARK DECEIT

"You hear, but do not understand; and see, but do not perceive." Isaiah 69:9

Luckily the *outer code* of the scriptures supports the false doctrines of this world, thus the liar was himself oblivious to the magic spell beneath those words. The satanic-spirit within humanity lusts for the things of this world even in prayer; thus we gave the devil his bait and he took it—but we got those same vessels to open our portal and ultimately, to give *us* our victory.

So we deceived them, but they also deceive you. The lie runs deep: the sheep and the wolves bound together in our midst; a duo of opposition within each and every person. Unfortunately, the wolves often speak, not only within ourselves, but also through the mouths of so-called experts. Even today within the secret halls of the most unlikely nations are those darkened forces, both scientists, priests and politicians, who would stifle these revelations.

Why? Because subconsciously the dark-element within them realizes the threat an open portal poses to its survival. They are predatory in their hatred as well, yet fail to realize why they stymie the truth. They subconsciously catch the scent of their prey; they instinctively recognize and pursue their nemesis of good. They lust for the blood, the very life of the angels of God.

There is historical precedence that I myself witnessed: It was not only the Jewish rebellion that led to the Temple's destruction in 70AD, but also its greatest treasure. Josephus, the Son of the high priest, Matthias, traded the location of the Temple treasury in an effort to save his own life. He promised the Roman Emperor, Vespasian troves of gold and silver.

Yet with the disclosure of that location also came a warning out of spite. Indeed Josephus also warned the emperor of my conniving—to beware of our wisdom that superseded his own. Thus we were rightly perceived as a threat to his control—now not only to destroy the Temple in the course of warfare, but with its destruction, to undermine the magistrates themselves.

The dark ones had them; they saw through the eyes of Josephus and the leaders of Rome. With the reins of the human-lie, they used them for their bidding. I never cared for Josephus before much less after his betrayal. Both he and his father were part of the ring of corruption within the Temple at that time and were one of the reasons I returned to Jerusalem just before the Romans' encirclement of that city.

Gaining freedom as a result of his betrayal Josephus was thereafter made advisor to the emperor's son, Titus. The promise of the Temple treasures was the price of blood by which his own people, the Jews, were destroyed, including the death of his *wife, father and mother*. As I said, only a dark angel would trade an eternal treasure for a little comfort in this world.

That Josephus hated the magi, however, is revealing. Lucky for me, Vespasian was unaware of my entrapment under the collapsed temple and that I sat among his troops thereafter. Had he known, it would have likely been my end. Faith is funny that way in my lives. Somehow, it always finds a way out…

Again in 321Ad, the Romans under the dreadful emperor Constantine would also find advantage in our scriptures. He used them, *the literal translation* and the *outer* word, for containing his frayed empire. He neither understood nor cared for our magic, yet desired the social control it offered. I can't deny that the outward message of our ancient magic abounds with dictations of legal obedience to authority. Obedience was something that the magi needed as well. The difference of course is that we used social control as a means to get home, while the Romans only wanted to preserve their earthly domain.

Constantine thus gathered his sheep, the subjects of his empire, with the weight of religious servitude and guilt, the threat of eternal hell being the consequence of disobedience. And though the hope of salvation was in those same verses, the emphasis was given to Constantine, the self-proclaimed *"keeper of the keys to the kingdom of heaven."* Thus he created the Catholic religion to facilitate this control.

Again, he was directed by the dark element. Being advised by someone, I know not who, Constantine's very first ruling upon becoming emperor was the ***Death Edict of the Magi*** (look it up if you don't believe me). He sent his legions into the far reaches of his empire not only to kill the remaining magi, but to destroy any and all of our works.

So consider that the most powerful ruling emperor in the world was threatened by but a handful of scattered priests who, with no temple and themselves somewhat diminished, were once again perceived as a threat by a world power—*interesting*. But the very fact that the Death Edict was Constantine's very first ruling, is evidence in itself that he knew the stakes at hand.

As well, I imagine he realized that we could undermine his misuse of the scriptures with our own counter information, that is, a decoded explanation of those same verses. Regardless, Constantine set about to erase us from the face of the earth: And though he used the Word of God as the tool of demons, it was only in his blind ignorance that he did so.

Checkmate! For again we won by default. You see, regardless of Constantine's evil intent, he would inadvertently employ our magic through the mouths of hundreds of millions of Catholic and Protestant adherents around the world. For over 2000 years until now, there has been no greater contributor to the expression of our magic than these believers.

So basically Constantine got his control and, unknown to him or anyone else, we got millions of new followers to speak our séance. Indeed *we **all** spoke the spell of resurrection.* Unto the winner goes the spoils. He used our books to his own ends, but we used him to ours. Do not misunderstand; I thank God for those Catholic and Protestant believers.

But Constantine did succeed in killing the remainder of the magi—that is, all but myself and two others who fled beyond the boundaries of the Roman Empire into what is now present-day Iraq. There we continued our efforts at producing and promoting the sacred Word, much of which was stored in the *House of Wisdom.* This was a series of libraries in Baghdad that were nearly the rival of those in Alexandria. Within their halls were thousands of priceless collections from the ages.

There we incorporated many Jewish, Christian and Greek works before Islam too began its downward spiral into intolerance. By about 850AD the God-Element, far less in the human than in ourselves, had faded into slumber far sooner than our own. The reverence with which people once viewed the magi had *faded.* Extreme stupidity and superstition became the norm. In this the dark-element, now left unchecked, seethed in its hatred for who we were. As a result, the very cultures we created, now instinctively despised us.

The Zoroastrian Priesthood declined as well, its adherents trading the pursuits of the eternal for the luxuries of this life. No wonder, as they were themselves *leftovers.* Their own magistrates had long ago died or been killed, leaving the secrets of the ages within the hands of the ignorant. It was these bastards who committed the *"sins of the magi"*, as the Muslims coined.

But I can tell you, we had no part in the worldly pursuits of the Zoroaster. This once noble priesthood now *looked into the liver,* holding the hand of superstition and foolishness. It was these who lost their understanding, no longer able to consult the images of the Wisdom Wheel as could I. It was these who became the haughty and drunken with their own illusion of magnificence.

Outwardly even we condemned magic as did the religions we created, yet in fact were *all* comprised of the real magic of God. We did this to dissuade the attempts of others. We had to ensure that the unlearned, that is, the *un-magi*, steered clear of this deadly serious art. Bad math makes for bad Word of which there is historical *bad results*. The scriptures as written, *all of the scriptures we produced*, were sufficient in correcting the Earth's misalignment and thus to reopen the portal.

Yet through all the outward condemnation of magic, one was still named: *Belteshazzar*, aka *Daniel*, as master of the magicians and one with an *"understanding of the words"*. His purpose was defined, his abilities unquestioned, even by Word of the Wisdom Wheel. Knowing the day of revelation would occur, the Word sent a clear message that you could accept the message of he who broke the seals. Thus my own magic was camouflaged while yet dissuading the attempts of others.

Zoroastrianism had indeed fallen victim to foolishness and bad magic during the diminishing and was rightly condemned. But of their accusers, what are, pray-tell, the **72 virgins**, but a *precession* of 1° over the course of **72 years** measured along the ecliptic through the sign of **Virgo**? And isn't this the same format as the **72 names of the Jewish God** in code? Why also are their **12 imams**, as were their **12 tribes of Israel**, **12 apostles** and **12 Olympians**? Who do you suppose designed these likenesses . . . your prophets or the magi? These are the real equations of infallibility, *one and the same*, a common, encoded thread that connects all of the scriptures we wrote.

It's difficult to comprehend the culture of another until you walk a mile in their shoes. I've walked the paths of many since the beginning. I understand more than you know. But we are all the same, believe it or not—the people of the *sands*, the great *plains* and of the *mountains*. The shallow differences in how we were raised and our outer-circumstances matter little. In the end however and by the science of the magi, we find that both the blessed and infidel are not without, but within ourselves; the wheat and the tares together...

Yet I must say that I was fond of the Arabs, the Bedouin as you may call them today. I admired them more than Islam itself. I came to know the tribes quite well over the centuries and they loved the echoes of the desert canyons as did I. This was the familiar groaning of the *call*, its reverberations; a lock-pic of the pineal gland, was modeled this way. I too longed for the comfort of its frequencies as it cried. This was the music of surrender to God. Five times each day it divided the circle of the sun, the pattern for our 5-sided star. They didn't know this of course, but I do . . .

And like the Arabs, my seclusion produced its own form of madness; *I relate as a man of the hills.* Yet there is no blasphemy in me, only the insanity of one who wanders the imagination. Like them, I too belong to a little people; some say, a *silly people*; in my case, an *imaginary people*—yet I say, *a mighty people* within. You see, we both roamed the trackless expanse, both of us banned from the greenery of Eden, the emerald color of the aurora and the lush dwelling of my portal. I too crossed the Nefud of my mind, as must all who come to God.

This journey destroys many, the loss of the familiar, unbearable to the meek. Yet such trials build the soul of the divine within us. It is here we are forged into finding the distant horizon of who we are. It is in the great nothing where the meaningless becomes the priceless, a miracle of the crossing and, I dare say, a love that is otherwise not easily found. To be great we all need what no man can provide; an open portal and the power of God.

I pine for the rising sun. On many nights I toss, awakened by my own screams, with the knowledge of my seclusion, a constant torment in this horrifying creature I've become. I trembled in my madness each morning as the burning truth of my separation arose. Believing is a daunting task when alone and in a foreign land. But by faith . . .

Yet the same God rules us all: the Muslim and the Jew, the Hindu, and the hillbilly. These are the silly tribes of the Earth and we will remain that way so-long as angels pretend, so-long as they are bliss to who they really are. Do we not all gather around our fires at night, *the same*, as is our light within? Indeed we all walk our deserts until the day of resurrection. Can you say this to yourself as truth? Can you see within what I say? Can you believe it as if it were so? Walk with me, dear friend, and I will cross this barren land of forgetfulness with you.

Ah, the tales through which we alluded: Ali Baba and the ***forty*** thieves, the ***forty*** lashes of Jesus, the flood for ***forty*** days and ***forty*** nights and was not Muhammad ***forty*** years old when he wrote the Koran? *Interesting* . . . And what opened Ali Baba's cave in which lay the *"gold"* of the sun and the *"silver"* of the moon? These are the treasures of gravity, the alignments that open the way and the same treasures of darkness to which we eluded to in Isaiah 45:3.

Yet it was a den of thieves, this darkened universe, the cave that sealed the life of God within the tomb of the human creature, its entrance now shut by the portal's closure. *Aha! But by my magic: "Open Sesame!" **Sesame**,* the Hebrew name for <u>**Heaven**</u>. Yes, **open Heaven**—*the portal itself.* We weren't trying to get <u>***in***</u> to this cave, <u>but to escape</u>. We tried to tell you in so many ways . . . Now perhaps you can hear *my* call.

And who is the mighty angel *Gabriel* and the savior—*Jesus*. What of the lawgiver *Moses* and *Lord Vishnu?* Have I not already shown you these founding images? Wisdom is power; it changes things: what we believe and how we perceive ourselves and the world in which we live. Now that the seals are broken, what will we all do? To know the truth and yet turn from it is the greatest blasphemy of all. This is the one sin God will not forgive. Our damnation is in our choice to remain blind, to continue to walk the ruinous paths of our past. Indeed our own dogmas are the hells which await us. Awake to the light in front of you! Open your eyes!

Forgive the ramblings of a ruined mind. Increasingly we became outcasts in Baghdad, the prior esteem we held for generations now lost to the narrow views of those who lacked understanding. There we hid within the slums, safe among the impoverished. In their daily bid for survival, they had little time to bother with a few lone magicians who wandered amongst them. We were running out of options however; nowhere else to go, no home and no priesthood.

Our work continued upon the rooftops. There we could still somewhat view the voice of the stars. Occasionally, over time, we donated new Word to the House of Wisdom. But within these final writs you could now see *interruptions* and *inconsistencies*. As with the writing of the Koran, the glory of the heavens, the *Super-Aurora*, was now completely gone. In turn the color-coded altimeter of the Wisdom Wheel was of no further use, thus removing a critical facet of Word production.

The Koran does include, in code, the colors of the sun and three moon phases, yet only alludes to the green of the portal in its mentioning of Paradise. So not only was the Wisdom Wheel going dark, but so too was the final gasp of God Element within creation. The spirit was never strong in man, *ever*, but it was now ever-more evident that it was completely asleep. It was surreal to watch the darkness of that age.

The ignorance, the intolerance, the suspicion and superstition. The wars of sleep from the age of Taurus till my last memory. The stupidity got worse with time; each nation, each tribe, each religion insisting upon the death of one another and even their own, for but petty differences and misunderstood scriptures. Muslim against Muslim, Christian against Christian, and even the Hindu as well—and for what? Yet I knew full well this would happen as the last remaining intellect of God went dormant.

I can't say for sure how long we stayed in Baghdad or whether we traveled elsewhere, but I do remember our capture by the Mongols. It would have been 1258AD, and I suppose the excitement imprinted the details upon my memory. Death was a given for those who resisted these savages, but the glimmer of Heaven within our eyes was still a powerful presence. You could see in us a fearlessness, a fact that did not go unnoticed by our captors.

As the hordes ransacked and murdered the rich and poor together by the tens of thousands, it finally became our moment to face them as well. Yet our unshakable persona gave them pause when no other human in the city did or could. They stared us in the eyes, swords drawn, they glimpsed into eternity. They stumbled at our visage, as did all to who beheld our faces uncovered; they fell backwards, unable to process what they had seen. Their hesitation led to marvel, then questions; and while they spared not the life of our companion, the lesser priest, they yet stayed the blade for myself and Ithiel.

Instinctively able to speak their language we quickly gained their admiration and, as a result, an audience with the Kahn himself. Unlike the sack of Jerusalem in 70AD, we were not the only survivors of the siege of Baghdad, but were in fact the only ones in good form. Behind us lay ruin; the books of wisdom were all but destroyed, a treasure of infinite value forever lost, thrown by the thousands into the Tigris.

With them, another 800,000 dead and many more homeless and orphaned humans. Similarly the destruction of the great scrolls in Alexandria in this same era is, to my knowledge, evidence of the demonic push at that time. Indeed the dark-element was overwhelming in the age of Pisces.

However, within a day of our presentation before the Kahn we were treated to the highest honors that Mongols could muster. Hulagu was taken by our spirit. Even without our former luminance, he could tell we were different; the eyes, the elongated head, the undeniable intellect. Torn between admiration and execution, he mused at parting us but ultimately could not bring himself to the task. As fortune would have it, we became his personal advisers and traveled parts of the globe that even I hadn't roamed in all my years before. Thus we served the Kahn until 1261AD.

Finally, through discord among our captors as well as a bit of craft, we eventually made our escape. The Mongols, known for infighting, left us unattended on a branch of the Silk Road. The route itself being heavily patrolled, we instead traveled the trackless Gobi desert until arriving in China.

There we found that other magi had been to the Orient long before, as far back as 1600BC and now, over 2800 years later, here we were again. We recognized the calling card of our brethren, the ubiquitous-image of *Shangdi*, the ancient dragon itself. But by now I too was weakening, doomed to sleep and the death of my aging body. It was time. I faintly remember the end: Ithiel, my millennia-old friend, standing over me, talking, smiling, and beaming with joy. I do not recall his words, yet the promise was in his spirit and expressions; the opening of the Books and the day of the return. I remember nothing else; this is where the images end for me.

And though barbarians such as Constantine, Titus and the Khans are all gone, the mind of darkness still prowls the thoughts of world leaders today. More subtle than before, they are no-less determined to keep their earthly realms. Thus the message of the magi is still a threat. The demons within instinctively sense the end of their control. They didn't know before, but now they are fully aware of the implications of our magic and a realigned earth.

Governments seek control by any means necessary, and historically religion is their number-one tool to get it. They use it not for the knowledge of God, but for cultural compliance—not that we should ditch moral living, because we shouldn't. Yet we have to see this thing from a government's point of view: To them, a culture that believes in God is easier to manipulate. That, and sheep are easier to corral or rally to a seemingly noble objective, though, more often, for the greed and power of those in charge. Of course, by all means, believe in God, but without the imposition of false doctrine.

Thus they want you, for all the wrong reasons, to follow religious instruction. Indeed they often tailor their agendas to inflame your religious sensitivities through false propaganda. They stoke the fire of your feelings by tying bogus or otherwise unimportant issues to your religious values. In so doing you will *fight* or *vote* for a seemingly noble cause. Doctrinal manipulation for the sake of political gain is in fact the oldest trick in the political-playbook.

It is amusing how they cut off their nose to spite their own faces; for in using the outward religions we created, (*As we knew they would*), they cannot speak against the systems of accepted morality and goodness that are engrained within those same cultures they intend to rule. Thus the adherents of those religions still hear and repeat the magic of the scriptures we wrote. So they use you, but we use them.

Now however the new religion of the dark-spirit is *science* itself. Not without some merit, it typically serves the creature instead of the creator. Similar to organized religion, science too can be used to twist the truth, create an unfounded panic and manipulate your emotions and thus your votes and actions. With those in power, "*scientific-truth*" is also often nothing more than skewed math for the sake of cultural control—not so-much among the scientists, but among those who would use it to support a political agenda. Perhaps the old adage applies: *Numbers don't lie, but liars use numbers . . .*

Since the ultimate goal of science is truth, it is readily apparent that the science of the magi achieved exactly that—*an open portal*. Our studies focused on portal mechanics with little regard to human wellbeing. Modern science on the other hand has reversed the formula of faith and magic and instead revolved its efforts around improving the human condition verses the spiritual being within.

I suppose I shouldn't be too harsh as ever since the age of Pisces, what little spiritual intuition humanity did have, died long ago. You can attribute this to the dark element that is also attached to your own DNA. Scientists today simply don't know the equation of eternity or even if it's possible, much less how to identify this yet undiscovered layer within the human genome. Therefore I can't expect those who are oblivious to revolve their energies around it.

What modern science has managed is to make humans live a few years longer than before. This is of course, vanity; yet that makes me a hypocrite, for my first incarnation lived for over 17,000 years—still far short of the eternal mark. Yet even in that long timeline, I never once enjoyed the flesh as much as my prior angelic state. There is no comparison between Heaven and here. I may have enjoyed the risk and the reason, but never the limitations and pain. I understood and accepted the divine plan, yet never once lost sight of the ultimate goal of our return to Heaven.

Unfortunately modern science can also be used to prevent earth's realignment and thus the Day of Resurrection. It comes in the form of secret antenna arrays in Alaska and elsewhere that, I suspect, create counterproductive bulges in the magnetosphere. *"Prove it,"* you say. The following article was written by <u>Becky Ferreira</u> in a publication of Space Science Reviews:

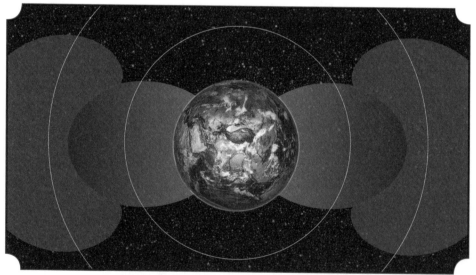

The false magnetic encapsulation of the earth via man's VLH signals.

*According to the article humans have "accidentally" created a protective bubble around Earth by using **very low frequency (VLF) radio transmissions** to contact* submarines in the ocean. *These underwater communications are said to have an outer space dimension. A video explainer, released by NASA visualizes how radio waves wafting into space interact with the particles surrounding Earth, and influence their motion* (sound familiar?). *Satellites in certain high-altitude orbits, such as NASA's particle-watching Van Allen Probes, have observed these VLF ripples creating an "impenetrable boundary," a phrase coined by study co-author Dan Baker, director of the University of Colorado's Laboratory for Atmospheric and Space Physics. This doesn't mean impenetrable to spacecraft or asteroids, per se, but rather to potentially harmful particle showers created by turbulent space weather.*

The boundary extends out to the inner edge of the Van Allen radiation belts, which are bands of charged particles created from the clash of the **solar wind against Earth's magnetic field** (told you so). *The VLF bubble might actually be* **pushing the Van Allen belts farther into space** (similar to the bulges in the magnetosphere that we created with the scriptures), *suggests Baker, considering that they have receded farther from Earth since the 1960s, when VLF use was not as widespread.*

Next, scientists are figuring out whether the VLF bubble can be used to **purify the near-Earth environment from charged particles** (aka: **ions**), *which would make humanity a little safer.* (Well done, random radio-induced space cocoon.)

So, what pray tell do you think is attached to those positive ions that they wish to purify or prevent? Have I not stated throughout this writing that it is indeed the God-Element itself? So there it is: Indeed almost anything humans do to impact Earth's magnetic field will be counterproductive in some capacity.

Their efforts are seemingly noble of course. *"Helpful to the earth"*, they say. *"Something that will make us all safer,"* they assure us, but ultimately is the scheming of their slave masters within, the fallen mind of the dark angels who work to prevent the Paradise Alignment. No doubt the scientists will claim that a nearly perpetual equinox will cause climate destruction, or that perhaps those VHL waves will protect us from an electromagnetic burst from a rogue nation or maybe even from solar storms that would destroy our electrical grids. *"National security"* is always a good one too. Yet all of this plays on the public's ignorance of the real issue and threat that the ancient portal poses to the dark element that presently appears to control this world.

Regardless of the details however, there seems to be something that the world governments know and are not telling. There is a reason that Israel balked at releasing the Dead Sea Scrolls and was likewise selective in what they did release. Ponder that: What 2,000 year old object found in the desert could be so damning so as to keep it secret? If in fact my memory is correct, then I know exactly what it is . . .

Then again, maybe NASA discovered more about portals after all. They've admittedly launched four such probes into the realm of the magnetosphere since 2012 to find exactly that. As well, maybe it's just simple instinct of the dark element within man. One doesn't need space satellites, scientific forays or even a space agency to sense the truth. We all know something is coming. Just as I claim my own instinct, the dark-element also feels the inevitable doom of its earthly domain and will do what it can to prevent it.

Constantine for example, had no scientific-clue in 321AD about the information of which I speak. He was oblivious to *the* _what_, _when_ or _how_ of our magic, yet still knew to destroy the magi. And though his death edict left our scriptures untouched, it succeeded in all but erasing our priesthood from existence. Being oblivious to the details of his instinct, he nonetheless sensed the threat we posed to his control. More important than the survival of the ancient magicians however, was the magic itself. It was the spell we cast that mattered, and it **_did_** survive. It was a danger to the dark-element then, and is now its undoing.

It is amazing however, at how devious and persistent the evil one can be within the mind of man, how since the beginning it labored against the truth with an overwhelming ferocity. But the timeline of the magi will not be denied as history has shown and will continue to reveal. Ultimately the dark element will fail as the Word has foretold, but at least you can be aware of the powers that fight for your mind. Thus the real message comes, not to the unbelieving of the outer man but to the luminaries of faith within. For no matter how obvious the lesson, only those who can hear; will hear, and in this day of hearing, that you should account yourself among those destined for resurrection.

JUDGMENT DAY HAS BEGUN.
THE GREAT AND TERRIBLE WAR WITHIN.

"Behold, the **_day of the LORD_** comes, and thy spoil shall be **_divided in the midst of you_**." Zechariah 14:1

"To deliver such an one unto Satan for the **_destruction of the flesh_**, that the spirit may be saved in the **_day_** of the Lord Jesus." 1 Corinthians 5:5

"But the **_day of the Lord_** will come as a thief in the night (I.e.-in a way that we don't expect); in the which the heavens shall pass away with a great noise, and the **_elements shall melt_** (I.e.-Mental elements within) with fervent heat,..." 2 Peter 3:10

"Judgment" sounds so cliché in today's world. We live in a time in which people say;

"If it feels good do it; there is no judgment; there is no God. The sky is the limit now, so do what makes you happy."

But you see, that's not what the scriptures say at all. As for me, I'm going with what the Word says—not in literal form of course, but as I know it to be beyond the code. It gives promise, sure enough, and I've shared all that with you. You can begin to get the point now, -that there is a portal, a path to Heaven for those who love and belong to God, for those seek Him diligently.

Yet there is also a path to destruction, and it is just as real. It is good that the demon within should burn, and I look forward to it—he deserves it. This is the path of the haters, murderers and contentious ones within. Just so that you know, he will burn *in* us, very much, **as** us. The Judgment will be anything but easy for those who refuse to let go of this world.

Make no mistake; the Lord comes to execute His judgment upon all and to convince all who are ungodly among them of all their ungodly deeds that they have ungodly committed and of all their hard *speeches* that ungodly sinners have spoken. These are murmurers, complainers, walking after their own lusts and speaking great swelling *words*, that is, the *outer-words* of the scriptures, having men's persons in admiration because of advantage.

I give the prayer of a poor man, but it reaches the ears of God nonetheless. *Yes*, let judgment comes speedily, but when? I tell you that it knocks at our door this very day, this *biblical* day. Second Peter 3:8 defines a biblical *"day"* as a 1,000 year period of time, hence the day of the Lord's return is indeed a millennia-long ordeal of transformation. This is the great fire within that purifies or rather burns the mind of the flesh. It coincides of course, with the portal's reconnection. As new Atomos, or God-Element floods our magnetosphere, so too within our minds, it will destroy the beast that now controls us.

Remember when I said that the age of Pisces brought the final death or subduction of the God-Element within? This timeline of 2,000 years was one and the same, *in code*, as the story of Christ's death on the cross:

Two days in the grave, and on the *third*, -resurrected.

Accordingly the real resurrection begins today; now is the **real** third day or 3rd millennia of which the Bible truly spoke:

"After two days (2,000 years) *he will **revive us**: in the **third day** (third thousandth year) he will **raise us up**, and **we** (not singular, but many in one body) shall live in his sight."* Hosea 6:2

So you see, the *real third day of the Bible*, begins our resurrection from within your human-host, as you, but eventually into a new, singular embodiment and into the dimension of Heaven. Thus the countdown for the 3rd day resurrection began at the beginning of Pisces, just over 2,000 years ago; *that is, -two biblical-days ago*.

For the sake of clarity, change the statement of *"In the **name** of Christ"* to *"In the **day** of Christ's resurrection"*, for only in the day of resurrection can Heaven be attained. Likewise what now begins as a mere yawning in 2,000AD, a meek stirring from within, will increase over the next 1,000 years into something far more powerful and magnificent than even the original magi.

I ask, what mind will you choose? Will you attach to the spirit of God within, or merely cling to the mind of the flesh? Will you be born with us, as us, or choose the dark and retched womb from which we emerge? The choice is yours to remain in this world or not.

The Resurrection Machine, *our scriptures,* worked perfectly; they give us an opportunity that we would otherwise never have had. The portal is beginning to open. It is now that judgment day begins, that the *great **and** very terrible day* of the Lord will occur in the minds of all humanity (see Joel 2:11). It is great and terrible indeed, for it is now that two greatly opposing things will happen in unison, the likes of which have never happened before. It is not all light and glory. The human creature, is a two-part entity and one part, the mind of this world, must be destroyed; it must die.

During this time the God-Element will be forced to leave the perceived comfort of its proverbial *"Egypt"*, to which we truly never belonged. Today is the *real* exodus; a journey in which we are forced from a foreign land, the physical reality, and driven from our false identity. Likewise, to those who are brave-enough to let go of this world, your memory of heaven will begin to return. This will not happen overnight. At first, it will happen slowly, internally, mentally, within. It will well-up within us, increasing over the generations of the next thousand years until reaching a critical mental mass.

That brings us again to the fire of God that is also contained in the Word. Its job is as fuel is to fire: to destroy all things that are incompatible with the dimension of heaven. Like gold purified in a fire, every false imagination that can be destroyed, shall be, so that only that which cannot be destroyed shall remain. And though it annihilates one reality, it readies our collective web of consciousness for the next. *The Word has permeated the fiber of every living organism on this planet; everything* now contains the *fire-image values* of the wave-pattern we created. It is too late to stop it; -well beyond the point of no return.

In this day the elements shall melt, that is, the matrices of your mind. That fire has already begun. You can feel the tension and the struggle within; the unrest and turmoil in your cultures. The dissatisfaction in your world is like never before. We all know something is wrong, but we can't quite discern what it is. It is, that the world and the things therein are already passing away and growing old like a cloth.

The significance of the world in which we live is quickly losing its appeal in an ever greater percentage of humanity. Things that once seemed important or even normal, are slowly losing their significance. Our thoughts too will come into judgment; those of this world into torment, dissatisfaction and increasing confusion, while those of God, into wisdom and peace. Like all fire, whether that of the physical or of the mental dimension, the reclamation process is not without pain. It will be a very real loss, but a very real promise as well.

I wouldn't be shy about salvation as we no longer have time for play and speculation. Take your salvation boldly, -possess it while you can. An open portal doesn't guarantee rescue. To survive the crossing requires choice as well. There is no free ride here. Choices, real choices, must be made going forward in each new incarnation in which we find ourselves until the end, until the *"twinkling of the eye"*, the final moment in which we are all finally changed into one eternity or another. This is the promise of the Day of Resurrection. Focus, take it seriously, *because it is . . .*

THE MAN OF SIN

*"Let no man deceive you by any means: for that **day** (or 1,000 years) shall not come, except there comes a **falling away** (separation) first, and that **man of sin be revealed, the son of perdition;**"* 2 Thessalonians 2:3

*"**Get thee behind me, Satan** (figurine): you are an offence: for you savor not the things of **God** (Jerusalem/spin grid), but those of **men**. (Tyre/Sidon wobble grid)"* Matthew 16:23

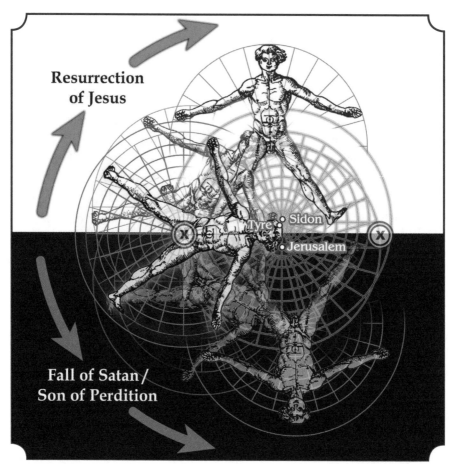

The Day of Separation; The incidence of Jesus' grid upon the periphery of Jerusalem and Satan's grid upon the periphery of Tyre, seemingly make one man in perfect alignment, aka; "Get thee <u>behind</u> me, Satan," However, as Jesus ascends into Heaven, the dark-element plunges to his doom in the lower section of the Wisdom Wheel. On the opposite side of the Wheel there was an identical alignment of peripheral grids that show Satan's assent into Heaven (Isaiah 14:13) while Daniel descended into the "den" (Daniel 6:16). The schematic of the Grid System tells the story of the battle within all the way since the portal's closure till now!

Every hero has his archetype to which the image of Jesus was no exception. In this case we may notice the perfect incidence of Jesus'-grid with that of a peripheral grid of Tyre. As stated before, the spin-grids of the Great Wheel rotate clockwise and account for Jesus' assent into the heavens of the Wisdom Wheel. Meanwhile the Tyre of wobble grids retrograde in a counter-clockwise motion.

As they do, the evil *"man of sin"* or *"wicked one"* of the Dead Sea Scrolls, is revealed as he descends into the black abyss of the lower Wisdom Wheel. Both figurines were at one point directly superimposed, showing us how the wheat and the tares grow up as one. While this is all pictorial, it nonetheless indicates the timeline and matrix of good and evil up until the day of separation.

In this day, one facet of our soul will be cast into torment, while the other will be saved. Thought, doubt, control, manipulation and disbelief are a sudden stop, while peace, belief and faith—the path to the portal. Choice however, is still part of the program and you must choose wisely and consciously. We must all attach to the correct spirit in our minds. One brings life without end, the other, death and a never-ending torment

As I've said many times, every word of the scriptures, no matter how seemingly literal or benign, is in fact part of the code. In this case, an alternate name for the Son of Perdition is, in fact, *"death"*. Thus every time you see the word *"death"* in the Bible, it is referring to the figurine and timeline in question:

*"... The **last enemy** that shall be destroyed is **death**.*

*...How are the **dead** raised up?... and with what body do they come?... there are also celestial bodies, and bodies terrestrial:*

*And **as we have borne the image of the earthy, we shall also bear the image of the heavenly**. For this **corruptible must put on incorruption**, and this **mortal must put on immortality**.*

*...then shall be brought to pass the saying that is written, **Death** is swallowed up in victory. O **death**, where is thy sting? O grave, where is thy victory?"* 1Corinthians 15:

Such is the day of separation. But here is the mind twister: the meshed image of Jesus and the Son of Perdition is a 2,000 years old alignment. In other words, the separation process in humanity had not yet begun. That involves a new image and alignment. Again, the science is revealed in the history of humanity. So, as a thief in the night, the facts are sprung upon us in this day.

But I can tell you this: you haven't seen anything yet. The evil one will resist; he is determined to make you believe the lie, and the longer this goes, the more obvious the spirits within us will become. Make no mistake; you are in a fight for your eternal life. Madness beyond what history has witnessed will ensue within the human creature. In the end, the consciousness to which you choose to attach will exist in a permanent state of perfection or destruction.

The spirits will also coalesce more and more in each generation, evil collecting in some, good in others. What you see is what you get. The room for repentance, that is, *change*, will narrow. A thief and a liar will always be just that; and a giving spirit, the same. One seeks self-gain, the other, the mind of God.

So you see, Satan, aka, **_the son of perdition, is our human-mind and our human-selves_**. Humanity *is* the man of sin. Don't believe it? Look around; wars, murders, rapes, abuses, constant disasters and hatred. And the reason that the world seems to be losing its mind is because *it is, for real, -losing its mind*. It is burning from within, as madness itself will become the norm. And in this process you will notice many things in many people—every spirit will be tested. The good and the evil in others as well as within ourselves.

In this day you will literally feel yourself being ripped apart inside, often not knowing what to think or feel. But your refuge will be in your focus on God and in being *still* within, *this* must be your choice. Have faith in the things of God and let nothing besides His spirit of love guide your consciousness. I beg you to stay the course, to ride it out until the end. Believe and accept the love of God and that it is real, for without believing, the resurrection is not possible. Your logical mind may struggle to accept these things, yet it is the *rationale of unbelief* that the dark spirit uses to his advantage. I give you the imagination of God, a new identity that can literally take you to the world beyond.

It was tough bringing you what I know; sharing what was given to me to share. I had to give it all up; everything that I knew and had lived and loved, but for a greater family. Against all the stares, the murmuring of family and friends, -the accusations and ridicule. Family of course is *sacred* where I am from, the feud, a symptom of our dedication and loyalty.

Yet now you are my family. Within, another man, another brother or sister; another angel. We are all in fact part of the being of God and there is my greatest loyalty of all. But the judgments and condemnation of others is nothing compared had I forgot my first loyalty to the family of God, my true kinsmen in the spirit.

This has been my work since the beginning: to infiltrate this dimension; to download a virus that the enemy would never suspect: The Word was the proverbial, *"Trojan horse"*, quietly accessing every capacity, every recess of your mind, lying dormant, it incubated for all these thousands of years. But that the blind should see, you were given this information, the overwhelming evidence in this book, the code of the scriptures, the images and more so, the revelation that within you lies the power of the universe.

I am not the end of these things, but only the beginning; my task is and always has been to introduce a new thought; to interrupt as imagination, your sensory input signals and to encourage a new reality that you may awake from the lie in which you are imprisoned. And like the code of the Book, there is so much more that lies beyond the surface of your perceptions.

Where then *is* the wise; where *is* the disputer of this world? The Word comes as a consuming fire to destroy the wisdom of those who profess, and bring to nothing, the understanding of the prudent (1 Corinthians 1:19). Indeed God chose the code to confound the experts, and an improbable science to muddle the haughtiness of man. For by neither man's science nor his religions did we come to know truth, thus it pleased Him, by the unlikely, to save them that believe beyond this illusion.

THE BREAKING OF THE BRASS AND IRON AURORA

*"I will go before thee, and make the **crooked** **places straight**: I will break in pieces the gates of **brass** (bronze aurora), and cut in sunder the bars of **iron** (black aurora):"* Isaiah 45:21 Compare these verses to the image...

*"For he must reign, till he hath put all enemies **under his feet**."* Corinthians 15:25

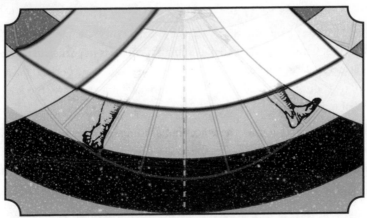

*The Feet of Jesus: We see pictorially, how the satanic mind is grounded within the brass and iron **anti-aurora** of the magnetosphere. These areas of the aurora were only recently restudied in 2001, yet we spoke of them in-code over 2500 years ago. Within them is the mental force that altered us from the light of God, into the fallen creation of the human. The Word has prophesied the destruction of this mind; promising to crush every false imagination and take every thought captive.*

The negative-ions that span the black and bronze aurora; this is the *"iron"* and *"brass"* that is displayed in the Wisdom Wheel under the feet of Jesus. In those *dark-ions* is attached the *dark element* as well which must be revealed and eliminated. They are attached, not only to the magnetosphere of your planet but to the very cogs and gears of your mind. This pseudo imagination must be destroyed, -stamped out and cast out along with Earth's crooked alignment, they must be eliminated forever. Brothers, sisters; please, listen . . .

Built within the Word is *faith* itself, instilled within its matrix, the power of God. Subtle but unstoppable, even on this side of the portal, it exists in trace-elements and is also inherent within the God Spell. But more-so let us hope that this same faith, which was never a human attribute, but the actual substance of the Almighty, has now taken hold of your physical-being. There it marinates every fiber of your mind and body. It lies dormant for the now, but stirs within us as the day begins to dawn.

A child who turns within its mother's womb, sees only darkness, finding its way via the blackness of a yet undeveloped imagination. Yet even the unborn instinctively sense the light that lies beyond. It is the miracle of child-birth that proves the power of faith and imagination, ourselves the new creation; pushing for that which we can nei- ther see nor prove. We can hear, just barely, *His mind, His muffled voice* as a dedicated Father who encourages us from a dimension beyond. It encourages us to continue on this journey that leads to light and life. And so we continue to turn and push towards salvation and birth.

When that which is perfect shall come, that which is in part shall pass away. That which is perfect is already here, *faith*; but something even more perfect, *the love of God*, the *indwelling*, is on its way. Faith has it perfect place, but real love, the *love of God*, is the totality of perfection.

It is my inner-dialog now, the voice that accompanies my mind, the teachings of wisdom and understanding. It reaches me in my dreams and as I awake, every still mo- ment of every day. I hear it always. It is not another voice, but the familiar stillness of God.

The words of the little old man were replaced with a never ending dialog within. This unassuming entity who so transformed my life was himself perhaps far older than I realized. He too had been here since the fall, a facet of the divine imagination. He was trapped as was I, not separate from myself, -but one and the same.

To receive the voice of God is the end goal, the result of letting-go of this world and indeed, our human selves. We all want change, but are we willing to do what we must to get it? Rather, are we willing to let the love of God illuminate the temple that we are, to dwell within our minds? We must ask however; is it really that God presides in our mind, or that we simply begin to understand that He always was our *true* mind from the beginning; not separate, but one and the same; not *us*, but *Him*.

I love you. I have always loved you, and that is why I shared the secrets that were shared with me . . . Within you is a parcel of God, yet there comes a time when each one of us must work out our own salvation with fear and trembling. We must each accept the discomfort of our spiritual birth and continue on the path that leads to the portal. You now, are responsible to find the way and to find God in you.

If you expected more promise, more peace and more prosperity for your human body, then perhaps you expected too much. God's intention was never to find Himself permanently as your human. He never promised health, wealth and wisdom for the flesh. No, the intention was to drive you out altogether, to bring you out of this strange land and into the rightful home of those who believe.

It is here then that I encourage you to leave the days of the fallen for that which lies ahead, –to trust in that small still voice within, and to believe in that which only the faintest of instinct can direct. Turn to the portal of salvation, the star-gate of which the scriptures have before spoken; the door that leads us from the darkness of this universe to the light of another world.

Call it *Heaven*, call it the *Element* of *God*, or even the *dimension from above*: Call it whatever you want, but the power of which I speak is real and is a mind beyond comprehension. Truly it summons us as does light in a darkened world, showing us our long forgotten home.

I cannot promise that you will win or lose this war for your soul: In fact, all I can say for sure is this; that the power to accomplish victory is hidden within the Word of God. Trust the Word, *believe in it, speak it*, see it for what it is; *a chance at salvation*. The magic is there, you know, as is the Source from which it came. Truly it is a séance from another dimension, and the greatest magic-spell ever written...

For the longest time now people have pondered visitations by aliens. Perhaps, now they got what they wanted. I am not from another planet, but nonetheless from another world. The Ancient of Days came to my mind, and now, it comes to you. It is the return of the God-consciousness. *I am, Daniel*; the God Spell prophet, the last magi; an interpreter of dreams, a royal scribe and the judge who was given of almighty God. Having once been the master of the ancient magicians; my calling now is to reveal our many secrets.

It's hard to leave an angel speechless, but it did happen once that I know. I stood in the empty dining room of the old cabin, a small framed picture in the corner-shelf caught my eye. I had seen it every day for decades, and-so forgot, over time, to see it for what it truly was. It was a childhood picture of the body in which I still lived: a little Daniel, only two or three years old. For some reason here at the end it caught my eye. I saw it now, not as who I was then, but as the sacrifice that little human was and would be.

He had no idea how hard the road would become—no clue at all at how difficult the path before him; the struggle to accept the truth of who he was before. I cannot tell you how moved I was in that moment to realize the precious sacrifice, a life for God, knowingly or not, that my life had been for Him; really—*His life*, not mine: God and the human now finally connected.

I now saw him as the human to which I was attached. I loved and admired him so, his little self, for what he was and had been; a capacitor in this world for the tiny bit of Atomos. He was about to die, but I was not, yet it was he who would live on in me for eternity. It shook me to understand how profound a matrix that only a higher wisdom and God could create. I was honored, I was silent; I used the boy's tears to express my own feelings of gratitude and appreciation for my time in this life, in him—*no words*, no words at all.

It was perfection to completion: I in him and him as me, the perfect expression, not incomplete, but perfect by faith, as are all of our lives should we choose to see it . . . What shall I say of the tiny image of a deer embroidered upon his vest? Are we not all the sacrifice in this field of life?

How wonderful in the eyes of God, the bodies to which we are attached; the coming of the Sons of God…and in his eyes, that little boy. I saw it; still new from the other world; in his eyes the hope, the being of the God, not yet snuffed, never defeated, the mighty God-Element, and the remnant heart from another dimension. This is the story of love in us, not separate, but one with God, always and from the beginning…

And so I paused my departure to write these final words. The seals have been loosed; the truth before you. I have fought the good fight, I have finished *my* course; I have kept the faith. It was a prophecy so-sure, so absolute and now the end is here, but not the end of the story. I have things far greater than these that I wish to show you… I have written them down for you already; *"I am here to help you remember…"*

HEAR THE PLEA OF THE ANGELS
…THEY LIVE OR DIE IN YOU. AS I HEAR THEM, SO SHALL YOU…

"And he said unto me, O Daniel, a man greatly beloved, understand the words that I speak unto thee, and stand upright: for unto thee am I now sent. And when he had spoken this word unto me, I stood trembling. Then said he unto me, Fear not, Daniel: Now I am come to make thee understand what shall befall thy people in the latter days: for yet the vision is for many days." Daniel 10:11

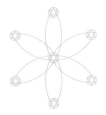

Credits

- Bible verses credit: The Holy Bible, King James Version. Cambridge Edition: 1769; King James Bible Online, 2019. www.kingjamesbibleonline.org.
- Verses for the <u>Book of Enoch</u> and the <u>Book of Adam and Eve</u>; credit: The Lost Books of the Bible Copyright 1926 by Alpha House, Inc. The Forgotten Books of Eden Copyright in the United States of America and in Newfoundland 1927 by Alpha House, Inc.
- Front Cover; by © H&R Productions LLC, all rights reserved.

Introduction

- viii, Siberian portal by © H&R Productions LLC, all rights reserved.
- viii, Background image; Beautiful Aurora Borealis over sea, by Nejron Photo/Shutterstock.co

Preface

- xi, Earth's magnetic field, illus.; the Earth, the solar wind, the flow of particles, elements of this image is furnished by NASA, by Naeblys / Shutterstock.com

Chapter I

- opening, Page Jacob wrestles with the angel; Picture from The Holy Scriptures, Old and New Testaments books collection published in 1885, Stuttgart-Germany. Drawings by Gustave Dore. Image, By Nicku / Shutterstock.com
- Page 17, Mind-twist Collage by © H&R Productions LLC, all rights reserved.
- Facepalm statue Tuileries Garden in Paris, near Louvre. A, image by Mariusz Stanosz / Shutterstock.com Image, refer to same image on page 124
- Figurine, by Heinrich Agrippa; De occulta philosophia libri tres/Public Domain

CHAPTER II

- Page 25, portal/grid by © H&R Productions LLC, all rights reserved.
- Figurine; Heinrich Agrippa, De occulta philosophia libri tres/Public Domain

CHAPTER IV

- Page 68, Deer, illus. Daryl M. Benningfield/ by © H&R Productions LLC, all rights reserved.
- Page 69, Old Magi, image by © H&R Productions LLC, all rights reserved.

CHAPTER V

- Page 89, Dragon/serpent collage, by © H&R Productions LLC, all rights reserved. -Piasa Bird, image by © H&R Productions LLC, all rights reserved.
- Black and white Draco, image by © H&R Productions LLC, all rights reserved.
- Old Draco image, by Sidney Hall, 1825; Old Image Book Gallery Shutterstock.com images:
- Dragon statue with the blue sky field, image by Ohmega1982
- The show of Chinese Golden Dragon Celebrate Chinese New Year night scene at Huahin, image by Daykung
- The Destruction of Leviathan - Picture from The Holy Scriptures, Old and New Testaments books collection published in 1885, Stuttgart-Germany, drawings by Gustave Dore image by Nicku.
- Babylonian "Ischtar Tor", Istanbul Archaeological Museum, image, by Zzvet
- Dragon statue Ljubljana Slovenia, image by TheWorst
- Hindu and Buddhist snake statue, image by TEERASAK KHUNRACH
- Page 90, Indian Petroglyphs in Eastern Washington, image by 4nadia/iStock.com
- Page 95, Prayer collage, by © H&R Productions LLC, all rights reserved. Shutterstock. com images:
- Hasidic Jews gather and pray, image by David Cohen 156.
- Pentecost and Catholic pilgrimage, image by salajean.
- GANGASAGAR, INDIA, Hindu pilgrim, image by CRS PHOTO.
- Vatican City, Pope Francis St. Peter's square, image by nomadFra.
- Bangkok / Thailand, Monk, Buddhist, temple, image, by PeatPing.
- Muslims gathered in Mecca, image by Zurijeta.
- Page 96, Bible pic; Old Jewish man hands holding a Prayer book, image by tomertu.
- Page 97, Luminaries collage by © H&R Productions LLC, all rights reserved./Shutterstock. com images:
- Aboriginal cave paintings in the Kimberley, Australia, image by paulmichaelNZ.
- Aboriginal rock art, image by Lella B.

CHAPTER VI

- Page 99, Bible image by © H&R Productions LLC, all rights reserved.
- Realistic transparent yellow sun rays, illustration by MicroOne / Shutterstock.com; edit
- Page 102, Our Problem; Image by © H&R Productions LLC, all rights reserved. Shutterstock.com images:
- Earth, 3D illustration isolated on white background. Elements of this image furnished by NASA. – illustration by Harvepino.
- Wood spinning top on white background and string. image By gosphotodesign.
- Page 103, Our way home; Image by © H&R Productions LLC, all rights reserved. Shutterstock.com images:
- Earth, 3D illustration isolated on white background. Elements of this image furnished by NASA. Illustration by Harvepino.
- Wood spinning top on white background and string, image by gosphotodesign.
- Page 103, Portal-reconnection: Magnetosphere, NASA Heliophysics; edit/ Reconnection point; NASA, data from Polar spacecraft, circa 1998. / © H&R Productions LLC, all rights reserved.
- Page 104, Aurora, Colorful northern lights, image by Frozenmost/ Shutterstock.com
- Page 107, Pyramids; The mysterious old legacy of ancient Egypt, the Greatest wonder of the world, the Egypt pyramids, image by Veronika Kovalenko / Shutterstock.com; edit.
- Page 108, Hypogeum in Malta, Public Domain/Before 1910.
- Page 109, Divine Plan; Image by © H&R Productions LLC, all rights reserved. Shutterstock.com images:
- Astrologer watching to the stars; edit / Vintage illustration from "La petite soeur par Hector Malot" 1882 image by Hein Nouwens.
- North America on detailed model of planet Earth; edit. Elements of this image furnished by NASA, illustration By Harvepino.
- Rumor rumour barbershop hand concept; edit, image by Roman Samborskyi.
- Sound waves oscillating glow blue light, Abstract technology background. Vector. Vector by Titima Ongkantong.
- Hasidic Jews gather and pray, image by David Cohen 156.
- Muslims gathered in Mecca, image by Zurijeta.
- Page 112, Siberian portal, image by © H&R Productions LLC, all rights reserved.
- Background image; Beautiful Aurora Borealis over sea, by Nejron Photo/Shutterstock.com
- Page 114, Wisdom wheel, image by © H&R Productions LLC, all rights reserved.
- Page 115, Antikythera Mechanism, image by © H&R Productions LLC, all rights reserved. Shutterstock.com images:
- Astrologer watching to the stars; edit / Vintage illustration from "La petite soeur par Hector Malot" 1882 image by Hein Nouwens.
- Visitors look at 2,100-year-old Antikythera Mechanism, Museum in Athens, Greece, image by Alexandros Michailidis.

- A replica of a medieval astrolabe capable of 43 different astronomical calculations, image by Brian Maudsley.
- Page 116, Wonder Layer, image by © H&R Productions LLC, all rights reserved.
- Broadman Maps copyrighted © 1983 by Holman Bible Publishers, used by permission, all rights reserved.
- Shir ha-shirim: Song of Solomon. 1794 made by Baruch ben Shemariah of Brest-Litovsk for Abraham Kaiser, 1794.
- Page 119, Magi time keeping, image by © H&R Productions LLC, all rights reserved. Shutterstock.com images:
- Bright Star Trails in Victorville, California at Night, image by tobkatrina
- Old vintage book on a white background, image by Photokava.
- An Astrolabe is a circular planar imaging of the sky where the north pole of the world form the center, image by a40757
- Page 120, Twelves, image by © H&R Productions LLC, all rights reserved.
- Page 120, Word Sheet, Shir ha-shirim: Song of Solomon. Made by Baruch ben Shemariah of Brest-Litovsk for Abraham Kaiser, 1794.
- Page 122, Our Father, -Rumor rumour barbershop hand concept; edit, image by Roman Samborskyi / Shutterstock.com
- Sound waves oscillating glow blue light, Abstract technology background. Vector. Vector by Titima Ongkantong / Shutterstock.com
- Page 124, Appearance of Stars, image by © H&R Productions LLC, all rights reserved. Shutterstock.com images:
- Word salt in the white salt, image by FotoDuets.
- View of bench against christmas tree and shining lantern through snowing, image by Adam Gryko
- Man and woman kissing on the roof under an umbrella during the rain at night in blur, image by Alexey Tikhomirov.
- A backlit and silhouetted image of a surfer riding a blue wave, image by SAPhotog.
- Fire sparks particles with flames isolated on black background. Very high resolution, image by Jag_cz. drops of dew on a green grass, image by nadiya_sergey.
- PHUKET, THAILAND, an unidentified devotee of a Chinese gods walking on fire in Vegetarian Festival, image by nuwatphoto.
- Page 125, Milky Way, image by © H&R Productions LLC, all rights reserved. Shutterstock. com imges:
- Milky Way over Mountain, image by Avigator Fortuner.
- Incense smoke on black background, image, by Nuttawut Phopom.
- A chef in a black apron sprinkles flour on the kitchen table with flour, image by Katrina Era.
- Road Leading Towards Milky Way Galaxy, image by Chris Lee Photography.
- little girl in the village in winter, image, by Julza.

- Sprinkled flour over background, image by artjazz.
- Fantastic views of Selfoss waterfall in the national park Vatnajokull. Iceland. Fantastic starry sky and the Milky Way, image by Standret.
- Page 126, Constellations, image by © H&R Productions LLC, all rights reserved.
- Page 127, Sheet Horses, image by © H&R Productions LLC, all rights reserved.
- Shir ha-shirim: Song of Solomon. 1794 made by Baruch ben Shemariah of Brest-Litovsk for Abraham Kaiser, 1794.
- Page 128, Taurus Aries, image by © H&R Productions LLC, all rights reserved.-Ultraietic; An ancient priest killing a lamb as a sacrifice amidst a crowd of people, Apud Fransiscum Halma, 1681. Etching by J. van den Aveele, 1681. Shutterstock.com images:
- Indian man and woman in national costumes commit ritual actions in Gangaikonda Cholapuram Temple, image by Ailisa.
- BETHLEHEM ISRAEL 26 10 16: Fresco in Shepherd Field Chapel, image by meunierd.
- Page 129, Earth Spin, image by © H&R Productions LLC, all rights reserved / Americas on detailed model of planet Earth; Elements of this image furnished by NASA, Illustration By Harvepino / Shutterstock.com
- Page 129, Temple Model, image by © H&R Productions LLC, all rights reserved / Alec Garrard's Temple Model/Edit. Geoff Robinson Photography Cambridge, UK.
- Page 130, Earth Tilt, image by © H&R Productions LLC, all rights reserved / Americas on detailed model of planet Earth; Elements of this image furnished by NASA, Illustration By Harvepino / Shutterstock.com
- Page 131, Nets, image by © H&R Productions LLC, all rights reserved / Throw The Net, image by Glenn Valentino / Shutterstock.com
- Page 131, Webs, image by © H&R Productions LLC, all rights reserved / pretty scary frightening spider web for halloween - Image By Willequet Manuel / Shutterstock.com
- Page 132, Millstones, image by © H&R Productions LLC, all rights reserved /Stone wheel object as an early invention of the prehistoric era and ancient symbol of technology and innovation designed by a caveman, Illustration by Lightspring / Shutterstock.com
- Page 132, Wheels, image by © H&R Productions LLC, all rights reserved /
- Big vintage rustic wooden wagon wheel, image by pzAxe / Shutterstock.com
- Page 133, Grid-series, image by © H&R Productions LLC, all rights reserved
- Page 134, Di Vinci Lilies, image by © H&R Productions LLC, all rights reserved / Leonardo da Vinci, Codex Atlanticus Public Domain; edit.
- Page 135, Great Millstone, image by © H&R Productions LLC, all rights reserved / ancient millstone on the grass, natural background, image by 100ker / Shutterstock.com
- Page 135, Clouds, image by © H&R Productions LLC, all rights reserved / single white cloud on clear blue sky background, image by Suti Stock Photo / Shutterstock.com
- Page 136, Fish, image by © H&R Productions LLC, all rights reserved.
- Page 137, Eyes, image by © H&R Productions LLC, all rights reserved.
- Page 138, Baskets, image by © H&R Productions LLC, all rights reserved.

Chapter VII

CHAPTER VIII

- Page 240, Lamp unto Feet, image by © H&R Productions LLC, all rights reserved. / Baruch ben Shemariah-Song of Solomon; edit / Heinrich Agrippa; edit.
- Page 240, Magic Wand, image by © H&R Productions LLC, all rights reserved. / The Hammurabi Code and Sinaitic Legislation. Credit: Wellcome Collection. CC BY /4.0.
- Page 243, Portal, image by © H&R Productions LLC, all rights reserved. / Stargate egypt Anubis, illus by Dinar Omarov/Shutterstock.com

CHAPTER IX

- Page 244, Four Corners, image by © H&R Productions LLC, all rights reserved. / Baruch ben Shemariah-Song of Solomon; edit / Broadman Maps copyrighted © 1983 by Holman Bible Publishers, used by permission, all rights reserved.
- Page 246, Map Making, image by © H&R Productions LLC, all rights reserved.
- Page 248, Jesus on the Map, image by © H&R Productions LLC, all rights reserved. / Figurine, Heinrich Agrippa De occulta philosophia libri tres. Public Domain; edit. / Broadman Maps copyrighted © 1983 by Holman Bible Publishers, used by permission, all rights reserved.
- Page 248, Jesus 7 Churches, image by © H&R Productions LLC, all rights reserved. / Heinrich Agrippa De occulta philosophia libri tres. Public Domain; edit. / Broadman Maps copyrighted © 1983 by Holman Bible Publishers, used by permission, all rights reserved.
- Page 249, Jesus Sword, image by © H&R Productions LLC, all rights reserved. / Figurine, Heinrich Agrippa De occulta philosophia libri tres. Public Domain; edit. / Broadman Maps copyrighted © 1983 by Holman Bible Publishers, used by permission, all rights reserved.
- Page 250, Jesus Eyes, image by © H&R Productions LLC, all rights reserved. / Figurine, Heinrich Agrippa De occulta philosophia libri tres. Public Domain; edit. / Broadman Maps copyrighted © 1983 by Holman Bible Publishers, used by permission, all rights reserve.
- Page 251, Jesus 1st Conjunction, image by © H&R Productions LLC, all rights reserved. / Figurine, Heinrich Agrippa De occulta philosophia libri tres. Public Domain; edit. / Broadman Maps copyrighted © 1983 by Holman Bible Publishers, used by permission, all rights reserved.
- Page 252, Jesus 2nd Conjunction, image by © H&R Productions LLC, all rights reserved. / Figurine, Heinrich Agrippa De occulta philosophia libri tres. Public Domain; edit. / Broadman Maps copyrighted © 1983 by Holman Bible Publishers, used by permission, all rights reserved.
- Page 252, Jesus 3rd & 4th Conjunctions, image by © H&R Productions LLC, all rights reserved. / Figurine, Heinrich Agrippa De occulta philosophia libri tres. Public Domain; edit. / Broadman Maps copyrighted © 1983 by Holman Bible Publishers, used by permission, all rights reserved.

- Page 253, Jesus 5th Conjunction, image by © H&R Productions LLC, all rights reserved. / Figurine, Heinrich Agrippa De occulta philosophia libri tres. Public Domain; edit. / Broadman Maps copyrighted © 1983 by Holman Bible Publishers, used by permission, all rights reserved.
- Page 254, Jesus 6th Conjunction, image by © H&R Productions LLC, all rights reserved. / Figurine, Heinrich Agrippa De occulta philosophia libri tres. Public Domain; edit. / Broadman Maps copyrighted © 1983 by Holman Bible Publishers, used by permission, all rights reserved.
- Page 255, Land of Milk Honey, image by © H&R Productions LLC, all rights reserved. / Broadman Maps copyrighted © 1983 by Holman Bible Publishers, used by permission, all rights reserved.
- Broadman Maps copyrighted © 1983 by Holman Bible Publishers, used by permission, all rights reserved.
- Page 256, King Nebuchadnezzar Map, image by © H&R Productions LLC, all rights reserved. / Figurine, Heinrich Agrippa De occulta philosophia libri tres. Public Domain; edit. / Broadman Maps copyrighted © 1983 by Holman Bible Publishers, used by permission, all rights reserved.Shutterstock.com images:
- Hammered silver long cross penny Edward I, image by Sponner.
- Edward III Gold Noble coin, image by t50.
- Page 257, Giants, image by © H&R Productions LLC, all rights reserved. / Figurine, Heinrich Agrippa De occulta philosophia libri tres. Public Domain; edit. / Broadman Maps copyrighted © 1983 by Holman Bible Publishers, used by permission, all rights reserved.
- Page 258, Two Kashmir giants, and their exhibitor, Professor Ricalton. Reproduction of a photograph. Credit: Wellcome Collection. CC BY /4.0
- Page 260, Male/Female grids on map, image by © H&R Productions LLC, all rights reserved. / Broadman Maps copyrighted © 1983 by Holman Bible Publishers, used by permission, all rights reserved.
- Page 262, Jerusalem/Zion; Adam & Eve, image by © H&R Productions LLC, all rights reserved. / Figurine, Heinrich Agrippa De occulta philosophia libri tres. Public Domain; edit. / Broadman Maps copyrighted © 1983 by Holman Bible Publishers, used by permission, all rights reserved.
- Page 263, Old & New Jerusalem locations, image by © H&R Productions LLC, all rights reserved. / Figurine, Heinrich Agrippa De occulta philosophia libri tres. Public Domain; edit. / Broadman Maps copyrighted © 1983 by Holman Bible Publishers, used by permission, all rights reserved.
- Page 264, Jesus on right Hand of God, image by © H&R Productions LLC, all rights reserved. / Figurine, Heinrich Agrippa De occulta philosophia libri tres. Public Domain; edit. / Broadman Maps copyrighted © 1983 by Holman Bible Publishers, used by permission, all rights reserved.

CREDITS

- Page 265, Tyre Sidon/wobble-grid location, image by © H&R Productions LLC, all rights reserved. / Broadman Maps copyrighted © 1983 by Holman Bible Publishers, used by permission, all rights reserved. / Asia on detailed model of planet Earth. Elements of this image furnished by NASA, illus. by Harvepino/Shutterstock.com
- Page 267, Sackcloth Ashes Collage, image by © H&R Productions LLC, all rights reserved. / Figurine, Heinrich Agrippa De occulta philosophia libri tres. Public Domain; edit. / Broadman Maps copyrighted © 1983 by Holman Bible Publishers, used by permission, all rights reserved. / Ash-Man, Graeme Churchard-flikr; adapted: Attribution 2.0 Generic (CC BY 2.0) Shutterstock.com images:
- Toldos Aharon Hasidim (hasidic Jews) gather and pray, image by David Cohen 156.
- Ashes on man's forehead as he reads Bible, image by Chad Zuber
- Page 269, The Real Garden of Eden, image by © H&R Productions LLC, all rights reserved. / Broadman Maps copyrighted © 1983 by Holman Bible Publishers, used by permission, all rights reserved.
- Page 270, The Real four Rivers of Eden, image by © H&R Productions LLC, all rights reserved. / Broadman Maps copyrighted © 1983 by Holman Bible Publishers, used by permission, all rights reserved.
- Page 271, The Trees of Life & Good & Evil, image by © H&R Productions LLC, all rights reserved.
- Page 273, The Two Olive trees, image by © H&R Productions LLC, all rights reserved.
- Page 274, The New Tree of Life, image by © H&R Productions LLC, all rights reserved.
- Page 276, God on Mt Sinai, image by © H&R Productions LLC, all rights reserved. / Broadman Maps copyrighted © 1983 by Holman Bible Publishers, used by permission, all rights reserved.
- Page 277, Baby Moses, image by © H&R Productions LLC, all rights reserved. / Broadman Maps copyrighted © 1983 by Holman Bible Publishers, used by permission, all rights reserved. Shutterstock.com images:
- Vietnamese man, basket boat for tourists, image by charnpui.
- Curious coconuts boats on the seaside in Hoi An, Vietnam, image by Sabino Parente.
- Page 278, The Real Burning Bush, image by © H&R Productions LLC, all rights reserved. / Figurine, Heinrich Agrippa De occulta philosophia libri tres. Public Domain; edit.
- Page 279, Blood of Jesus, image by © H&R Productions LLC, all rights reserved. / Figurine, Heinrich Agrippa De occulta philosophia libri tres. Public Domain; edit.
- Page 280, Jesus/Wisdom Wheel Cross, image by © H&R Productions LLC, all rights reserved. / Figurine, Heinrich Agrippa De occulta philosophia libri tres. Public Domain; edit. / Mosaic of Jesus Christ, Hagia Sofia in Istanbul, Turkey, image by PavleMarjanovic/Shutterstock.com
- Page 281, The Four Map-Scales of the Grid System, image by © H&R Productions LLC, all rights reserved. / Broadman Maps copyrighted © 1983 by Holman Bible Publishers, used by permission, all rights reserved
- Page 282, Survey/Mapping, image by © H&R Productions LLC, all rights reserved.

- Page 283, Earth Lilies, image by © H&R Productions LLC, all rights reserved. / Asia on detailed model of planet Earth, elements of this image furnished by NASA, illus. by Harvepino.
- Page 284, Telescope Fu dog, image by © H&R Productions LLC, all rights reserved. Shutterstock.com images:
- Astrologer watching to the stars / Vintage illustration from "La petite soeur par Hector Malot". Ilus. by Hein Nouwens.
- Imperial guardian lion in the Forbidden city Beijing, China, image by testing/Shutterstock.com
- Page 285, The Mappas, Shir ha-shirim: Song of Solomon. Made by Baruch ben Shemariah of Brest-Litovsk for Abraham Kaiser, 1794.
- Image# 174 Removed/no image

Chapter X

- Page 289, Cubits, image by © H&R Productions LLC, all rights reserved.
- Page 290, First and Last man Adam, image by © H&R Productions LLC, all rights reserved. / Figurine, Heinrich Agrippa De occulta philosophia libri tres. Public Domain.
- Page 291, Solomon's Temple image by © H&R Productions LLC, all rights reserved.
- Page 292, Sea of Brass/12 Bulls, image by © H&R Productions LLC, all rights reserved.
- Page 293, Altar Sacrifice, image by © H&R Productions LLC, all rights reserved. / Figurine, Heinrich Agrippa De occulta philosophia libri tres. Public Domain.
- Page 294, Temple Pillars, image by © H&R Productions LLC, all rights reserved.
- Page 295, DNA Chain image by © H&R Productions LLC, all rights reserved.
- Page 296, Mystery of the Solstice Pillars, image by © H&R Productions LLC, all rights reserved.
- Page 297, The Holy Place, image by © H&R Productions LLC, all rights reserved.
- Page 298, The Holy of Holies, image by © H&R Productions LLC, all rights reserved.
- Page 300, Ark of Covenant, PHOTO by iStock.com/ 3Drenderings.
- Page 300, Ark of Covenant, image by © H&R Productions LLC, all rights reserved.
- Page 301, Ark Cubit Measurements, image by © H&R Productions LLC, all rights reserved.
- Page 302, Grid-Jerusalem, image by © H&R Productions LLC, all rights reserved.
- Page 303, Jerusalem Grid-wall, image by © H&R Productions LLC, all rights reserved.
- Page 304, Ark PHOTO, image by © H&R Productions LLC, all rights reserved.
- Page 305, The Real Noah's Ark, image by © H&R Productions LLC, all rights reserved.
- Page 307, Animals Ark Image#2, image by © H&R Productions LLC, all rights reserved. Figurine, Heinrich Agrippa De occulta philosophia libri tres. Public Domain. / Vietnamese man showing of rowing spinning basket boat for tourists, image, by charnpui.
- Page 309, Noah's Ark, Ararat, image by © H&R Productions LLC, all rights reserved. / Broadman Maps copyrighted © 1983 by Holman Bible Publishers, used by permission,

all rights reserved. / Curious coconuts boats on the seaside in Hoi An, Vietnam, image by Sabino Parente/Shutterstock.com

- Page 310, Bow in Cloud, image by © H&R Productions LLC, all rights reserved.
- Page 311, The Magistrate, Illus. Daryl M. Benningfield/© H&R Productions LLC, all rights reserved.
- Page 314, Aku/Hermès Trismegistus, Aku, Shrine stela, Nefertiti and Echnaton in Egyptian Museum, image by Radiokafka./Shutterstock.com / Hermes Trismegistus; Public Domain.
- Page 316, Temple Logic, image by © H&R Productions LLC, all rights reserved. / Alec Garrard's Temple Model/Edit. Geoff Robinson Photography Cambridge, UK.
- Page 319, Temple Magic, by © H&R Productions LLC, all rights reserved. / Illus. by Daryl M. Benningfield. / Temple Model by Alec Garrard's Geoff Robinson Photography Cambridge, UK.

CHAPTER XI

- Page 324, The Destruction of Leviathan, image by Nicku/Shutterstock.com
- Page 332, Science of Evil, Wellcome Collection, Caduseus; edit; Creative Commons Attribution (CC BY 4.0)
- Page 334, Glory/Lord Paradise, image by © H&R Productions LLC, all rights reserved. / Colorful northern lights, image by Frozenmost/Shutterstock.com
- Page 337, Montezuma Headdress, image by © H&R Productions LLC, all rights reserved.
- Page 339, Leo/Winged Angels, image by © H&R Productions LLC, all rights reserved.
- Page 340, Winged Creations, image by © H&R Productions LLC, all rights reserved. / Chaos Monster and Sun God; Public Domain. / Human Headed Winged Lions and reliefs from Nimrud, image by ChameleonsEye/Shutterstock.com. / Saint Michael the Archangel. Engraving by G. Folo after B. Nocchi after G. Reni, Wellcome Collection, Caduseus; edit; Creative Commons Attribution (CC BY 4.0).
- Page 341, Angel Image Origin Magnetosphere, image by © H&R Productions LLC, all rights reserved. / The Christ the Redeemer statue, created by French sculptor Paul Landowski, Brazil, image by R.M. Nunes.
- Page 342, Priest/Magnetosphere, Daryl, image by © H&R Productions LLC, all rights reserved. / Priest illustration by Daryl M. Benningfield.
- Page 343, Ezekiel Covering Cherub, image by © H&R Productions LLC, all rights reserved. / Figurine, Heinrich Agrippa De occulta philosophia libri tres. Public Domain; edit.
- Page 344, Personal Aurora, image by © H&R Productions LLC, all rights reserved. Silhouette of Asian business man walk, image by elwynn/Shutterstock.com.
- Page 347, Polar Shift, image by © H&R Productions LLC, all rights reserved. /Asia on detailed model of planet Earth. Elements of this image furnished by NASA. – Illustration, by Harvepino/Shutterstock.com.

- Page 348, Dragon of Bible, image by © H&R Productions LLC, all rights reserved. / North America on detailed model of planet Earth. Elements of this image furnished by NASA, illustration By Harvepino/Shutterstock.com.
- Page 350, Earth-Axis Symbolism, image by © H&R Productions LLC, all rights reserved. / Brass-serpent courtesy of Carl Moore Antiques / Caduceus; Public Domain.
- Page 351, Ancient symbolism of Earth's Axis, image by © H&R Productions LLC, all rights reserved. / The Three Snake Gods monument, image by Myroslava Bozhko/ Shutterstock.com. /
- Wellcome Collection image credits: Assyro-Babylonian oil beaker relief, Assyro-Babylonian oil beaker, Egytian Goddess Sekhet,
- The world as an egg: three cosmological figures. Etching by Barlow, 1795.: Wellcome Collection. (CC BY 4.0)
- Page 352, Dragons Tilt the Globe, Jesuit observatory, Beijing, China: bronze astronomical instruments with decorative bronze dragons. Photograph, ca. 1860. Credit: Wellcome Collection. Creative Commons Attribution (CC BY 4.0)
- Page 352, Vault B, Illus. Daryl M. Benningfield. / Image by © H&R Productions LLC, all rights reserved.
- Page 353, Gate of the Sun, Tiwanaku Bolivia, image by Adwo/Shutterstock.com.
- Page 353, ElCastillo, image by © H&R Productions LLC, all rights reserved. /Temple of Kukulkan pyramid, Mexico, image by Romrodphoto/Shutterstock.com.
- Page 354, The Frequency of Evil, by © H&R Productions LLC, all rights reserved./Serpent Mound image courtesy of the Ohio History Connection.
- Page 356, Good-Grid/Bad-grid, by © H&R Productions LLC, all rights reserved.

CHAPTER XII

- Page 359, The Image of our Enemy, image by © H&R Productions LLC, all rights reserved. / Figurine, Heinrich Agrippa De occulta philosophia libri tres. Public Domain.
- Page 360, Draco, the Ancient, image by © H&R Productions LLC, all rights reserved.
- Page 361, Serpent Handling, image by © H&R Productions LLC, all rights reserved. / Figurine, Heinrich Agrippa De occulta philosophia libri tres. Public Domain.
- Page 362, Serpent Handling PHOTO, WikiMedia Commons; Public Domain
- Page 363, Treading on Draco Scorpio, image by © H&R Productions LLC, all rights reserved. / Figurine, Heinrich Agrippa De occulta philosophia libri tres. Public Domain
- Page 363, Paul, Serpent, Acts:28:3, image by © H&R Productions LLC, all rights reserved. / Figurine, Heinrich Agrippa De occulta philosophia libri tres. Public Domain.
- Page 364, Medusa, image by © H&R Productions LLC, all rights reserved.
- Page 366, Hole of the Asp, image by © H&R Productions LLC, all rights reserved. / Figurine, Heinrich Agrippa De occulta philosophia libri tres. Public Domain.
- Page 367, Tread on Leo the Lion, image by © H&R Productions LLC, all rights reserved. / Figurine, Heinrich Agrippa De occulta philosophia libri tres. Public Domain.

- Page 367, Foo Dogs, By LIUSHENGFILM Royalty-free stock photo ID: 492945625
- China Beijing Forbidden City Lion Statue - Image By testing Royalty-free stock photo ID: 320845565
- Imperial guardian lion in the Forbidden city Beijing, China - Image
- Page 368, The Fig Tree and the Serpent, image by © H&R Productions LLC, all rights reserved. / Figurine, Heinrich Agrippa De occulta philosophia libri tres. Public Domain.
- Page 370, False Imagery of Adam and Eve, Greek Vase image, courtesy of Robert Bowie Johnson, UK. / Adam and Eve, Duomo facade. The first pillar, image by wjarek/ Shutterstock.com.
- Page 370, The Origin of 7 & 24 Serpents, image by © H&R Productions LLC, all rights reserved. / Hindu and Buddhist naga statue, image by TEERASAK KHUNRACH/ Shutterstock.com.
- Page 372, Demon Possession Mary, image by © H&R Productions LLC, all rights reserved.
- Page 376, Magnetic Anomolies, Earth Magnetic Anomaly Grid Version 3, credit/courtesy, NOAA/NCEI.
- Page 380, Hermès/Lightning, image by © H&R Productions LLC, all rights reserved. Hermès Trismegistus, Public Domain.
- Page 383, Ball Lightning, image by © H&R Productions LLC, all rights reserved.
- Page 384, Grid System Evil opposite of God, image by © H&R Productions LLC, all rights reserved.
- Page 387, BEAST PHOTO, Wellcome Collection, Creative Commons Attribution (CC BY 4.0)
- Page 387, Beast Image, image by © H&R Productions LLC, all rights reserved.
- Page 388, Chimera, Mythological bronze monument representing the Etruscan city of Arezzo in Tuscany Italy, image by pegasophoto/Shutterstock.com
- Page 389, Great Harlot, image by © H&R Productions LLC, all rights reserved.
- Page 391, Heaps and Dens, image by ©H&R Productions LLC, all rights reserved. / Broadman Maps copyrighted © 1983 by Holman Bible Publishers, used by permission, all rights reserved
- Page 392, Mark of Beast Cain, image by © H&R Productions LLC, all rights reserved. / Figurine, Heinrich Agrippa De occulta philosophia libri tres. Public Domain.
- Page 393, 666, image by © H&R Productions LLC, all rights reserved. / Figurine, Heinrich Agrippa De occulta philosophia libri tres. Public Domain.
- Page 394, Magic-Square, Sagrada Familia, image by © H&R Productions LLC, all rights reserved. / Stone Relief, the large unfinished Roman Catholic Church in the city of Barcelona, image by Norman Thomson/Shutterstock.com.
- Page 395, Chaining the Dragon, image by © H&R Productions LLC, all rights reserved. / Figurine, Heinrich Agrippa De occulta philosophia libri tres. Public Domain.

CHAPTER XIII

- Page 415, Nazca Irragation Channels, image by © H&R Productions LLC, all rights reserved. Shutterstock.com images:
- Top view of agricultural land. Valley of fields and fruit farms with irrigation system, image by Scharfsinn.
- Situated in the south region of Peru, the Nazca desert is popular for its mysterious lines drawn on the ground, image by Roglopes.
- Page 416, Nazca Spider before and after, image by © H&R Productions LLC, all rights reserved. / Aerial view of Nazca line, Spider, Peru,south America, image by Siriwatthana Chankawee/Shutterstock.com.
- Page 417, Nazca Spider/Magnetosphere, image by © H&R Productions LLC, all rights reserved. / Aerial view of Nazca line, Spider, Peru,south America, image by Siriwatthana Chankawee/Shutterstock.com.
- Page 423, Hypotenuse, image by © H&R Productions LLC, all rights reserved.
- Page 424, Frequencies Guitar frets, image by ©H&R Productions LLC, all rights reserved.

CHAPTER XIV

- Page 429, Timeline of the Fall/Charts, images by ©H&R Productions LLC, all rights reserved.
- Page 430, The Melding, image by ©H&R Productions LLC, all rights reserved.
- Page 452, False Magnetic Encapsulation, Credit; Becky Ferreira: Space Science Reviews.
- Page 458, Son of Perdition, image by © H&R Productions LLC, all rights reserved. / Figurine, Heinrich Agrippa De occulta philosophia libri tres. Public Domain.
- Page 461, Breaking the Iron and Brass, image by © H&R Productions LLC, all rights reserved. / Figurine, Heinrich Agrippa De occulta philosophia libri tres. Public Domain.
- Image on back-cover; Road Leading Towards Milky Way Galaxy - Image By Chris Lee Photography/Shutterstock.com.